Level 1

Repair and Servicing of Road Vehicles

College

Student's Name

Home Address

Name of Employing
Firm/Managing Agent

383 Repair and Servicing of Road Vehicles Series

Level 1

Repair and Servicing of Road Vehicles

Editor   Roy Brooks
Formerly Senior Lecturer in Motor Vehicle Subjects
Bolton Institute of Higher Education

Authors   Jack Hirst
Lecturer in Motor Vehicle Subjects
Burnley College

John Whipp
Senior Lecturer in Motor Vehicle Subjects
North Manchester College

MACMILLAN

First published in 1989 by
THE MACMILLAN PRESS LTD
Houndmills, Basingstoke, Hampshire RG21 2XS
and London
Companies and representatives
throughout the world

ISBN 0–333–51008–9

A catalogue record for this book is available
from the British Library.

Printed in Hong Kong

10   9   8   7
00   99   98   97   96   95   94   93

Contents

Preface

This book is presented in a very similar style to the previously highly successful books in the Macmillan Vehicle Engineering Series. Its specific aim is to make easier and more rewarding the task of students, instructors and teachers working through the City and Guilds 383 Repair and Servicing of Road Vehicles, Level 1 Course and comparable courses.

The form of presentation relieves both teacher and student of much of the chore of preparation and note taking. As such it enables considerably more of that most valuable ingredient — time — to be devoted to 'real' teaching and learning. Marking and checking is simple, and numerous sections could easily form the basis of guided discovery and project work.

Great care has been taken with the blank spaces that need to be filled in, and the drawings requiring completion, so as to allow users of the book as much freedom as possible within the confines of the syllabus. However, for anyone requiring precise guidance as to how the spaces may be completed a 'Lecturer's Guide' or 'Answer Book' is published as a companion to this volume. This can, of course, be a most valuable aid to teachers in respect of both lesson preparation and presentation.

Anyone completing this book conscientiously should be confident in his or her possession of a sound basic knowledge in the repair and servicing of road vehicles. They should also be thoroughly equipped to succeed in their end-of-course examinations.

The objectives set out in Level 1 of the City and Guilds 383 Course are carefully interpreted and properly covered, without any attempt to 'overteach'. In a very few instances the editorial team considered that a small amount of back-up learning would be helpful, and this has been included as an aid to student progress. Similarly, the addition of Section 12 dealing with basic workshop calculations provides students with the opportunity to become familiar with the everyday type of motor-vehicle numerical problems encountered at work and leisure.

As a further aid to those new to motor vehicle work, a Glossary of terms explains the meaning of commonly used technical words and abbreviations.

The work is presented with appropriate syllabus references. It is realised that this is very unlikely to be the teaching order, but it does maintain an internationally recognisable uniformity.

The editor and authors wish success to everyone who uses this book. If you have any constructive suggestions that you would care to make about it we should be most pleased to hear from you via Macmillan Education Ltd., Basingstoke.

Roy Brooks
Editor

Industrial Studies

Since the 1989 edition of this book, Industrial Studies has been regraded to a Level Two Unit (Element 30, Unit 22).

Because of this regrading, the previous contents pages 193 to 212 have been placed with the other Level Two Units and are now to be found in the Level 2/3 book **Transmissions, Chassis and Related Systems** by John Whipp.

Acknowledgements

The editor, authors and publishers would like to thank all who helped so generously with information, assistance, illustrations and inspiration. In particular the book's principal illustrator, Harvey Dearden (previously principal lecturer in Motor Vehicle Subjects, Moston College of Further Eduction); colleagues of the Burnley College and the North Manchester College; and the persons, firms and organisations listed below. Should there be any ommissions, they are completely unintentional.

A-C Delco Division of General Motors Ltd.
Austin Rover Group Ltd.
Autodata Ltd.
Automobile Association
Automotive Products plc
Avon Rubber Co. Ltd.
BBA Group plc
Robert Bosch Ltd.
R. Boughton Esq.
British Standards Institution
Castrol UK Ltd.
CAV Ltd.
Champion Sparking Plug Co. Ltd.
Citroën UK Ltd.
City & Guilds of London Institute
Clayton Dewandre Ltd.
Dunlop (SP Tyres UK Ltd.)
Fiat Auto (UK) Ltd.
Firestone UK Ltd.
Ford Motor Co. Ltd.
Girling Ltd.
Hepworth & Grandage Ltd.
HMSO
Holset Engineering Co. Ltd.
Honda UK Ltd.

T.F. Keller & Sons Ltd.
Land Rover Ltd.
Lotus Group of Companies
Lucas Industries plc
Luminetion Ltd.
MAN-Volkswagen
Metalistic Ltd.
Mitsubishi Motors
Mobelec Ltd.
Mobil Oil Co. Ltd.
Peugeot Talbot Motor Co. Ltd.
Pirelli Ltd.
Renault UK Ltd.
Ripaults Ltd.
Sherrat Ltd.
Sykes Pickavant Ltd.
Telehoist Ltd.
Unipart Group of Companies
VAG (United Kingdom) Ltd.
Vauxhall Motor Co. Ltd.
Weber Concessionaires Ltd.
Westinghouse CVB Ltd.
Zenith Carburettor Co. Ltd.

UNIT 01

VEHICLE SYSTEMS SKILLS

INCLUDES

Chapter 1

Road Vehicle Systems and Layouts

1.1 TYPES OF VEHICLE BODY

A vehicle body is designed according to the purpose for which the vehicle is intended. One of the most popular types of vehicle body is that shown below.

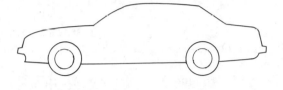

Body type ....

Name the type of body illustrated above and make simple sketches opposite to show the four body types named.

State below examples of current vehicle makes and models which are of the types listed.

Type	Make	Model
Saloon	....	....
Convertible	....	....
Estate	....	....
Hatchback	....	....
Coupé	....	....
Sports	....	....
Grand Tourer	....	....

List what you consider to be the most important body features of one of the body styles listed above.

Make .... Model .... Engine Capacity ....

Features

....

....

....

Hatchback

Coupé

Convertible

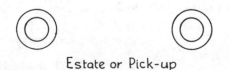

Estate or Pick-up

VEHICLE BODIES — PURPOSE AND FUNCTIONAL REQUIREMENTS

The main purpose of the vehicle body is to accommodate driver, passengers and luggage, or in the case of a goods vehicle to carry various forms of goods, e.g. solids, liquids, bulky, heavy, etc.

What other factors must be taken into account with regard to the design and structure of a car body?

....

....

....

....

....

....

....

....

....

....

The car body must also provide mounting points for the main mechanical and electrical components, e.g. engine, transmission, suspension, steering, exhaust systems, wiring and lighting, seat belts and seating.

In recent years designers have paid considerable attention to the aerodynamic aspect of body shape. Why is this?

....

....

....

GOODS VEHICLE BODIES

Many goods vehicles consist basically of:

A CHASSIS on to which all the running gear, engine and transmission are mounted.

A CAB which provides comfortable, safe accommodation for driver and passengers.

A BODY which is designed according to the type of loads to be carried.

The main body types for goods vehicles are

....

....

....

....

....

....

....

....

....

....

In a RIGID type of goods vehicle, the body is mounted on the chassis immediately behind the cab. With an ARTICULATED type of goods vehicle, the body is mounted on a separate semi-trailer chassis.

Many vans have a combined (one piece) cab and body mounted on a separate chassis; small vans are often of integral construction with body and floor (i.e. 'chassis') in one unit.

1.1 A popular type of light goods vehicle based on a car layout is illustrated below. Name this type of vehicle and give a reason for using it as opposed to a van or estate derivative of a car.

An 'integral' type of van body is shown at A below. Complete the illustrations at B & C by sketching on the chassis shown, the types of van body named.

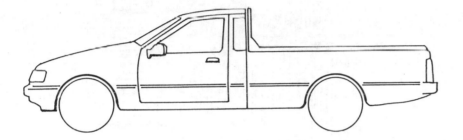

Type ....

Typical make .... Model ....

Reason for use

....

....

....

An optional extra with this type of vehicle is a glass fibre van top (Truckman Top) which can be easily attached to the load deck to give weather protection when required.

Add such a top to the drawing above.

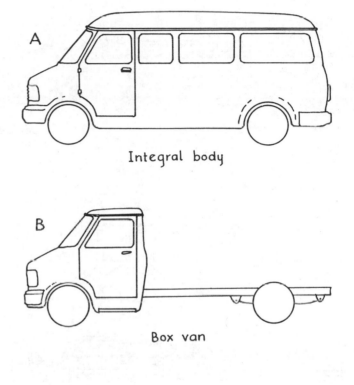

A

Integral body

B

Box van

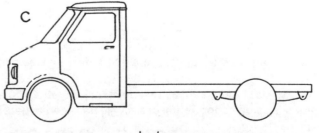

C

Luton van

5

1. Name the types of bodies shown below and give one advantage of each.

....

....

On some integral van bodies there is no 'bulkhead' between the payload area and the forward driving compartment. The driver can therefore step from the driving seat into the rear load space and then out through the nearside door to make a delivery. What is the name given to this type of van?

....

HEAVY GOODS VEHICLES (HGVs)

The main difference between HGVs and light goods vehicles is that the HGV, apart from being longer and heavier, usually has more than two axles.

Name the types of HGV below and add the labelling to the drawing at (c).

(a)

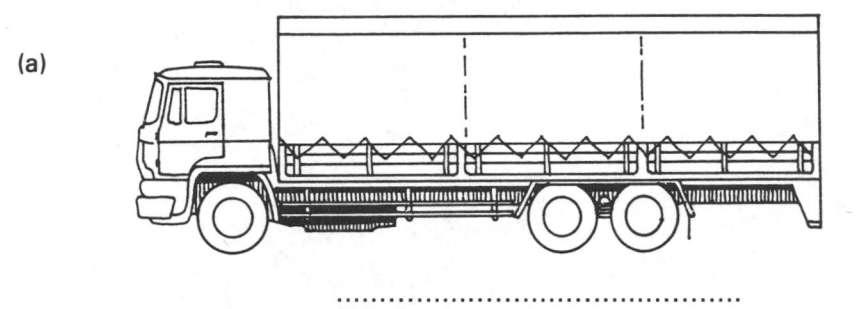

....

(b)

....

(c)

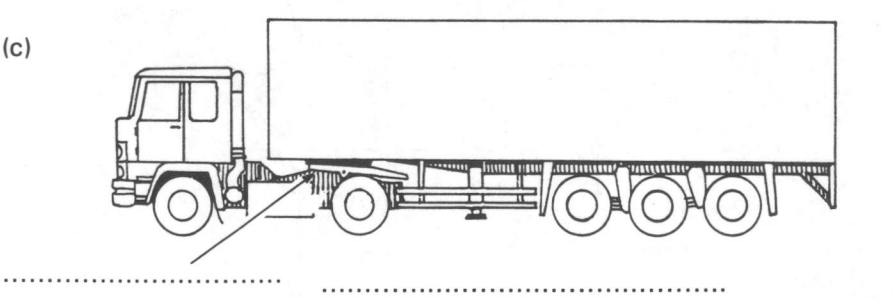

....

....

The fifth wheel coupling is the connecting mechanism for the semi-trailer. During cornering or manoeuvring, the semi-trailer pivots (articulates) about the fifth wheel coupling.

FORWARD AND NORMAL CONTROL

Goods vehicles can be classified as NORMAL CONTROL or FORWARD CONTROL according to the layout of the vehicle. This refers to the driving position in relation to the steered wheels. The drawing at (a) below shows a forward control type vehicle. With this arrangement the driver sits slightly forward of the front wheel centre.

(a)

Make a sketch above to illustrate the layout of a normal control type vehicle.

PASSENGER TRANSPORT VEHICLES

As with goods vehicles, passenger vehicle bodies are designed and constructed according to the type of work in which the vehicle will be engaged.

A coach body is shown at (b) below.

How does this body differ from the omnibus body as used for in-town multi-stop work?

(b)

....
....
....
....
....
....
....

Sketch one other form of passenger vehicle body.

VEHICLE LAYOUT

The 'layout' of the motor vehicle is concerned with the arrangement of main mechanical components.

List the names of the main components.

1. ....

2. ....

3. ....

4. ....

5. ....

Two popular layouts (A and B) are shown opposite: Give a name to each layout and label the drawings.

State TWO advantages of layout A.

1. ....

2. ....

State TWO advantages of layout B.

1. ....

2. ....

Engines can be mounted longitudinally or transversely.

State TWO disadvantages of a transversely mounted engine over a longitudinally mounted engine.

1. ....

2. ....

Show an alternative vehicle layout by completing drawing C opposite. Label the parts you add. Give a name to the layout and state two advantages of the layout.

1. ....

2. ....

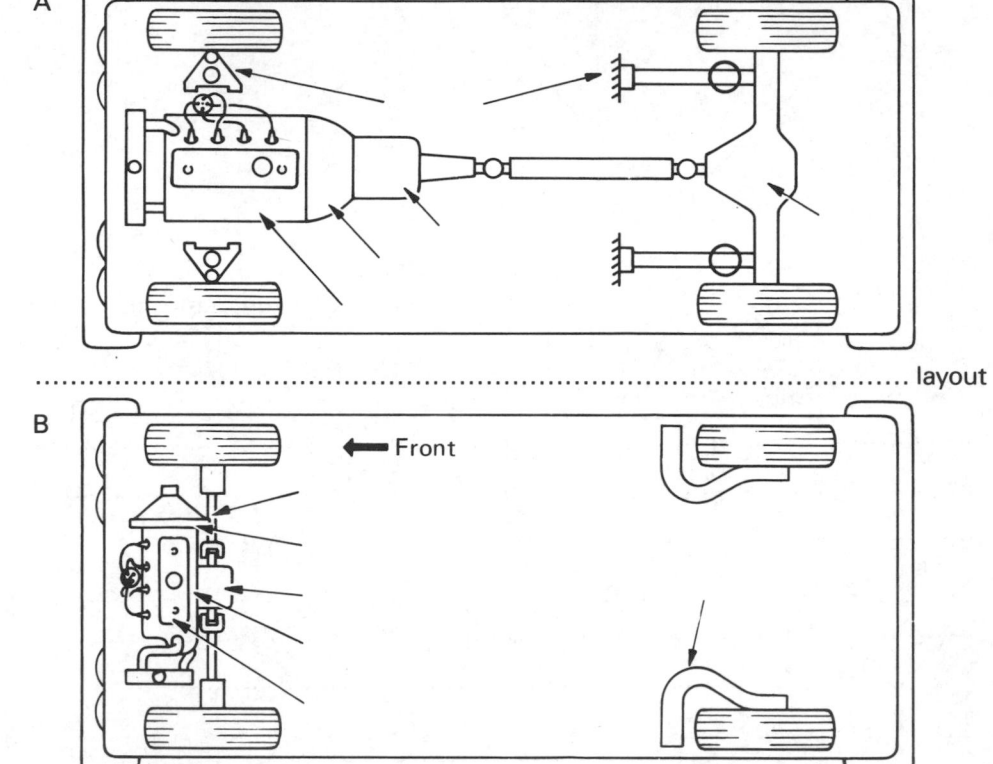

A

.... layout

B

Front

.... layout

C

.... layout

1.1 In the sports car shown below, the engine is transversely mounted immediately behind the seating compartment driving the rear wheels. Many high-performance cars and almost all single-seat racing cars employ this arrangement, although the engine in single-seat racing cars is usually mounted longitudinally. Name this arrangement.

....

4 × 4 Transmission Layout4 × 4 Transmission Layout

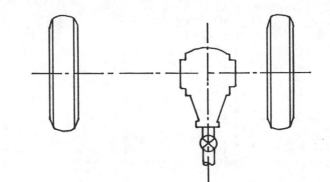

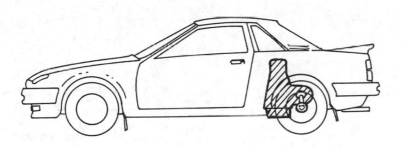

FOUR WHEEL DRIVE

As the name implies, four wheel drive (4WD) or (4 × 4) is where all the four road wheels are driven. In the past 4WD was used mainly on vehicles operating off the normal roads, on uneven, slippery or soft surfaces.

Two examples of such use are

1. ....

2. ....

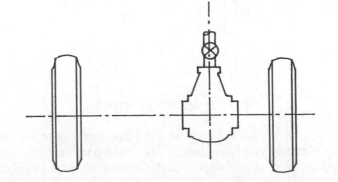

In recent years, owing to the refinements in 4WD systems, many new cars employ the system. It offers improved traction and control. Complete the layout opposite to show the main components in a 4WD system.

9

CHASSIS

The chassis is the framework of a vehicle on to which all the main components of a vehicle are attached. It may be a relatively heavy rigid structure which is separate from the body of the vehicle (as in goods vehicles) or, as illustrated below, a single body/chassis structure as adopted for most cars.

Name and label the structure below and explain briefly how rigidity and strength are achieved within the structure.

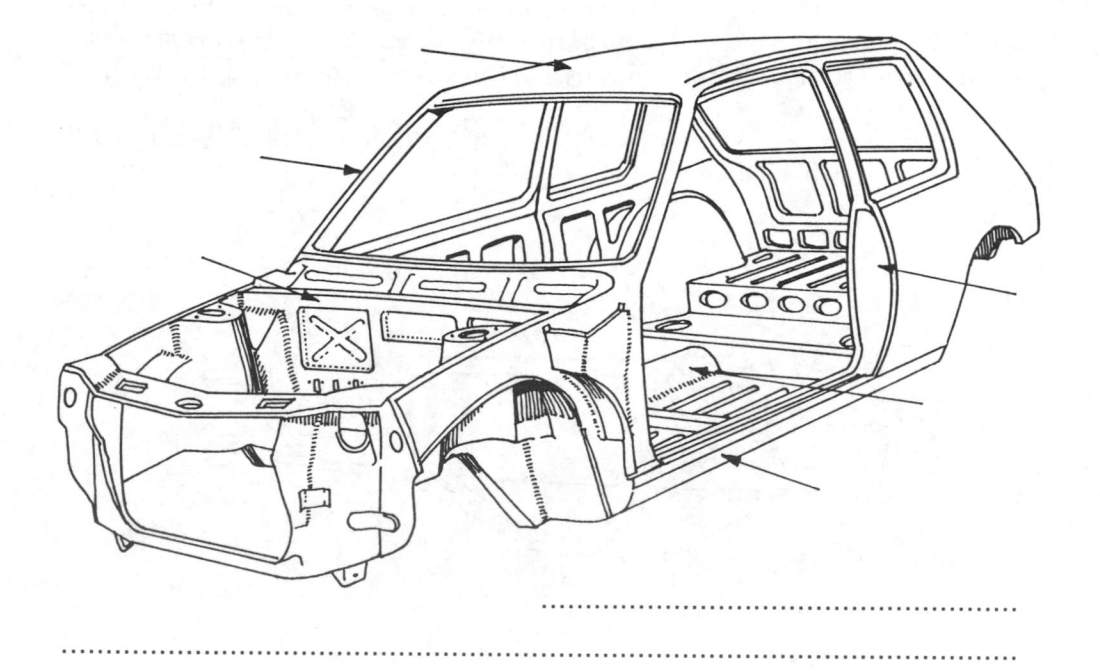

....

....

....

....

....

....

Make a sketch below to illustrate a separate chassis frame as used on a heavy goods vehicle. Indicate on the drawing where the main components, i.e. engine, transmission and suspension would be attached to the frame.

Ladder Frame Type Chassis

Longitudinal members

SUBFRAMES AND MOUNTINGS

On a car the major components such as engine, transmission and suspension are sometimes not directly attached to the main integral body/chassis. The loads and stresses imposed on the car body by such components can be somewhat isolated from it by attaching the components to a rigid frame known as

a ....

Investigation

Examine a car fitted with front and rear subframes and make a simple outline sketch below to illustrate the shape of a typical rear subframe.

Indicate on the sketch the subframe/chassis mounting points and the suspension/subframe mounting points.

Vehicle Make .... Model ....

A typical front subframe assembly is shown below with the various mounting points lettered, which are

(a) ....

(b) ....

(c) ....

(d) ....

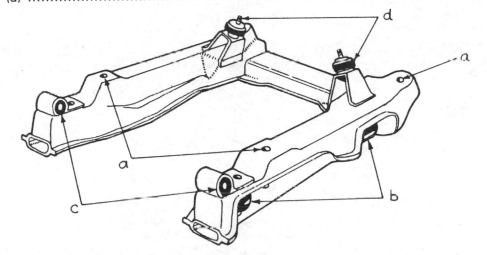

FLEXIBLE MOUNTINGS

The major units on a vehicle are usually attached to the chassis or body structure through flexible rubber mountings. Sketch and label mountings for engine/transmission and suspension. Give reasons for using these mountings.

....

....

....

1.3 CAB MOUNTING

The cab of a goods vehicle is mounted on the chassis via flexible or sprung mountings. It may be fixed permanently in position or, as is the case with many forward control vehicles, the cab is hinged at the front to allow it to tilt when required. A fixed rubber-type cab mounting and a modern rubber-spring, leading arm, front tilt cab mounting are shown below; complete the labelling on the drawings.

A modern tilt cab mounting arrangement is shown below. The system acts rather like a vehicle suspension system using springs and dampers to isolate the driver further from road shocks and vibration.

Label the drawing.

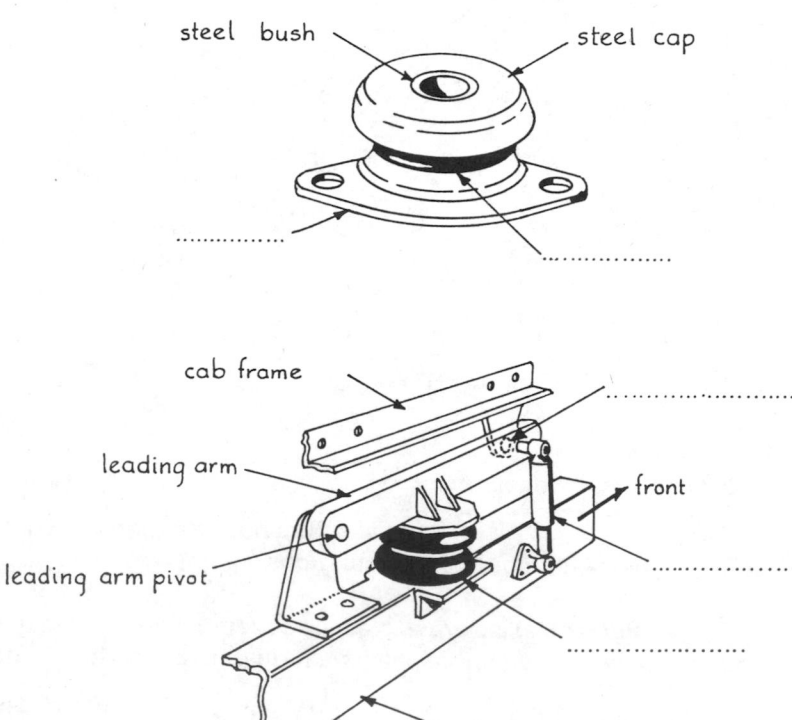

steel bush   steel cap

cab frame

leading arm

leading arm pivot

front

chassis frame

What benefits are to be obtained by allowing a cab to tilt forward?

....

....

....

....

....

....

....

1.3 LOAD PLATFORM ATTACHMENT

One method of securing the load platform or body of a goods vehicle to the chassis is shown at (a) below. Examine a goods vehicle similar to the one shown below and sketch an alternative method of body attachment at (b). Indicate on the vehicle drawing below the number and position of these attachments.

(a)   (b)

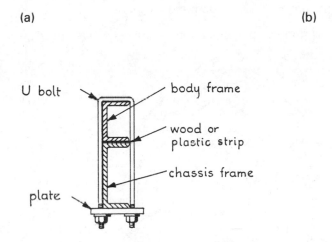

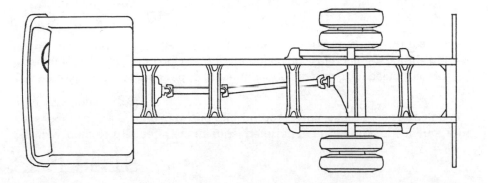

The doors on most cars and goods vehicles are hinged at their forward ends. The van shown below has a side sliding door.

Give reasons for using this arrangement in preference to hinged doors on many vehicles of this type.

1. ....
....
2. ....
....
....

Give examples of places on a vehicle body where access HATCHES and FLAPS are used.

HATCHES ....

FLAPS ....

13

SEAT BELTS

The law requires that safety belts must be fitted to protect the driver and front passengers on all private cars and dual purpose vehicles first registered on or after 1st January 1965.

The restraining force required to prevent car occupants from being thrown forward when a collision occurs is extremely high. Seat belt anchorage points on the vehicle body must therefore be sufficiently strong to withstand the loads involved.

Add to the above sketch, a seat belt and its mountings.

The seat belt is normally wound on a spring-loaded reel when it is not in use. An amount of belt is drawn off the reel according to the seat position and the size of the driver when it is secured in place. This is known as the INERTIA REEL system. What advantage does this system offer over the fixed length belt?

....

....

....

JACKING POINTS

The jacking points are the places on a vehicle body at which the jack is applied in order to lift a wheel (or wheels) clear of the ground. The body structure at the jacking points is made sufficiently strong to withstand the concentrated load imposed when the vehicle is jacked up.

How many jacking points are usually built into the vehicle body?

....

....

Investigation

Examine a vehicle and complete the drawing below to show the vehicle body outline. Indicate on the drawing the location of the jacking points and show by simple line outlines the position of the engine and transmission.

Make .... Model ....

Give two reasons why a vehicle's own jacking points are not normally used during servicing by a garage.

1. ....

....

2. ....

....

1.3 BODY EXTERIOR

The illustration below shows some of the panels which are attached to the basic integral structure of a car.

Name the panels shown.

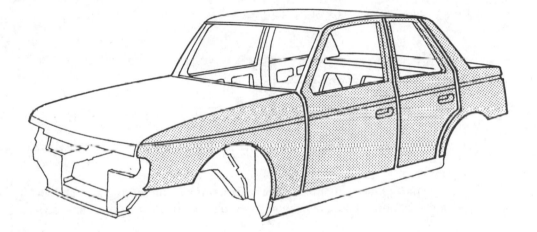

How are these panels usually attached to the vehicle framework?

....

EXTERNAL TRIM

The external trim on modern cars is usually made up of a number of plastic mouldings or chromium-plated strips which are bolted or clipped on to the body panels.

Investigation

Examine a modern car and name the parts that constitute external trim.

Car make .... Model ....

Component   Secured by

....

....

....

....

....

Examine the bumper assembly and make a sketch to show how it is attached to the vehicle frame.

VEHICLE WINDOWS

The windows on a vehicle may be HINGED, DROP, FIXED or SLIDING. Give examples of places on a vehicle where each type of window is used.

HINGED ....

DROP ....

FIXED ....

SLIDING ....

The illustration below shows the weather sealing arrangement of a car door. Examine a car boot and sketch the sealing arrangement employed.

Door Seal

Boot Seal

INTERIOR TRIM

The interior trim of a vehicle can be extremely basic, as on lower priced models, or quite lavish as on some models (e.g. Ghia) or expensive vehicles.

Name the items which make up the interior trim on a car.

....

....

....

....

....

SEATS

What are the important features of front seats in a modern car?

....

....

....

....

....

How do the front seats in expensive sporty saloon cars differ from standard type seats?

....

....

....

....

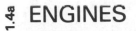

ENGINES

The engine of a motor vehicle provides the POWER to propel the vehicle and to operate the various ancillaries, such as the alternator, water pump, vacuum-assisted brakes, air conditioning and such like. However, when the accelerator is released and the road wheels are made to turn the engine, it provides a useful amount of vehicle RETARDATION without the use of the brakes.

ENGINE TYPES

Engines used in motor vehicles may be referred to as FOUR-STROKE or TWO-STROKE engines.

The term stroke refers to ....

A four-stroke engine is one in which ....

A two-stroke engine is one in which ....

The number of revolutions completed during a working cycle on a four-stroke

engine is ....

The number of revolutions completed during a working cycle on a two-stroke

engine is ....

Investigation

Complete the tables below to identify different types of engines used in motor vehicles.

Four-stroke engines

Vehicle	No. of cylinders	Type of fuel	Engine capacity

Two-stroke engines

Vehicle	No. of cylinders	Type of fuel	Engine capacity

Identify the engines shown in terms of two and four stroke.

State two reasons why each engine can be so identified.

Name the arrowed parts.

Type ....

Reasons for identification

(a) ....

....

....

(b) ....

....

....

Type ....

Reasons for identification

(a) ....

....

....

(b) ....

....

....

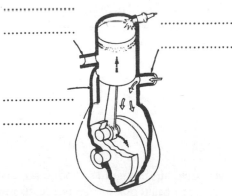

THE OTTO (OR FOUR-STROKE) CYCLE

The four-stroke cycle is completed in four movements of the piston during which the crankshaft rotates twice.

Complete the line diagrams to show the positions of the valves and piston crown at the commencement of each stroke. Indicate the direction in which the piston is moving in each case.

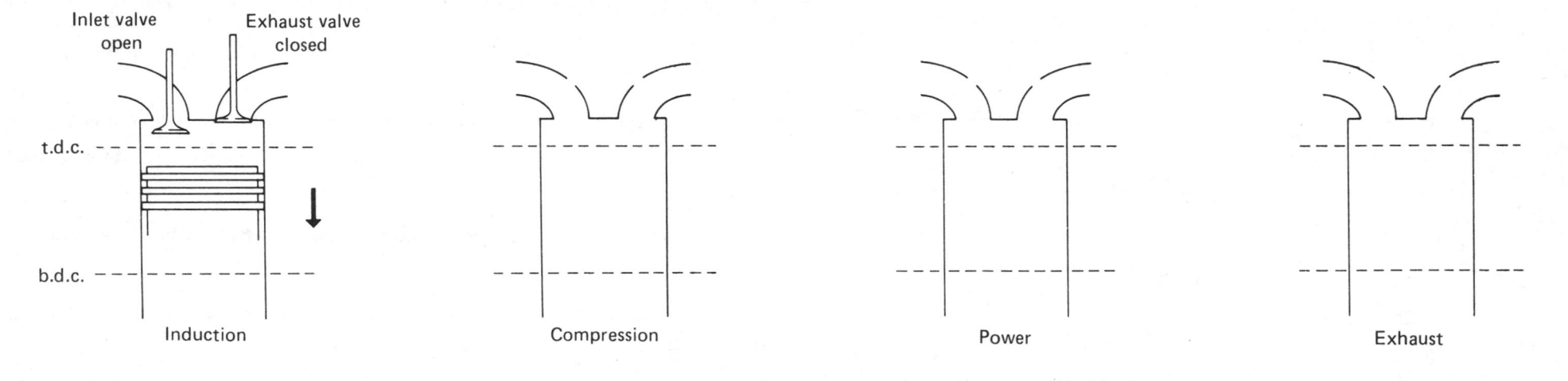

Investigation

By use of a sectioned four-stroke spark-ignition engine, note the sequence of operations of the piston, valves and spark when the engine is rotated, and describe what happens on each stroke when the engine is running.

Induction	Compression	Power	Exhaust

TWO-STROKE CYCLE
(Crank-case compression type)

By making use of both sides of the piston, the four phases, induction, compression, power, exhaust, are completed in two strokes of the piston or one crankshaft revolution.

No valves are used, the piston itself acts as a valve covering and uncovering ports in the cylinder wall.

....
....
....
....
....
....
....
....
....
....
....
....
....
....
....
....

Complete the drawings to show the position of the ports and the shape of the piston. Name the main parts and show the direction of crankshaft rotation.

(a) Show fuel entering crankcase.

(b) Show fuel transferring to cylinder and exhausting.

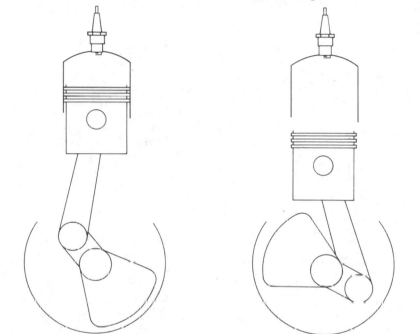

Summary of two-stroke cycle		
Stroke	**Upward**	**Downward**
Events above piston	Closing of transfer port Completion of exhaust Compression	Expansion of gases Commencement of exhaust Transfer of mixture from below piston
Events below piston	Induction of new mixture into crankcase	Partial compression of new mixture in crankcase

Name the parts indicated on the engine shown opposite.

1. ....
2. ....
3. ....
4. ....
5. ....
6. ....
7. ....
8. ....
9. ....
10. ....
11. ....
12. ....
13. ....
14. ....
15. ....
16. ....
17. ....
18. ....
19. ....
20. ....
21. ....
22. ....
23. ....
24. ....
25. ....
26. ....

20

COMPRESSION-IGNITION (DIESEL) ENGINE — FOUR-STROKE CYCLE

The actual strokes, induction, compression, power and exhaust, are exactly the same as in the spark-ignition engine.
The operating principle is, however, slightly different.

....
....
....
....
....
....
....
....
....
....
....

List the main differences of the compression-ignition engine when compared with the spark-ignition engine.

....
....
....
....
....
....
....

Investigation

Examine and compare the basic components of a spark-ignition and compression-ignition engine of similar size.

Component	Ways in which compression-ignition engine components differ from typical spark-ignition engine components
Piston	
Connecting rod	
Crankshaft	
Cylinder block	

What are the main advantages and disadvantages of a compression-ignition engine relative to a spark-ignition engine?

Advantages

....
....
....

Disadvantages

....
....
....

COOLING SYSTEMS

All types of internal combustion engines require some form of cooling.

Why is a cooling system necessary?

....

....

....

....

Any cooling system must be designed to prevent both under and over cooling.

AIR COOLING

This type of cooling is popular for motor cycles and is used on some older small cars.

On what basic principle does air cooling rely?

....

....

....

....

....

Complete the table in respect of a variety of vehicles having air-cooled engines.

Vehicle make	Model	Number of cylinders	Approximate engine capacity

A motor-cycle engine is not usually enclosed; the passage of air over the cylinders when the cycle is in motion provides an adequate cooling flow.

Investigation

Examine an air-cooled cylinder barrel and head. Add to the outline cylinder below the cylinder head, showing the cooling fins and the fins on the barrel. Show how the fins vary in length.

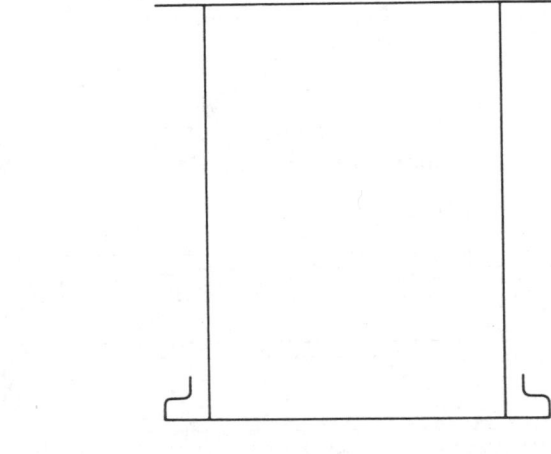

What is the reason for this variation in the size and shape of the cooling fins?

....

....

....

....

What periodic cooling-system maintenance should be carried out on air-cooled engines?

....

....

PUMP-ASSISTED WATER COOLING SYSTEM

On the diagram of the cooling system below, indicate the direction of water flow and identify the main components. Complete the sketch to show where the expansion tank would be fitted.

Show the recommended initial water level.

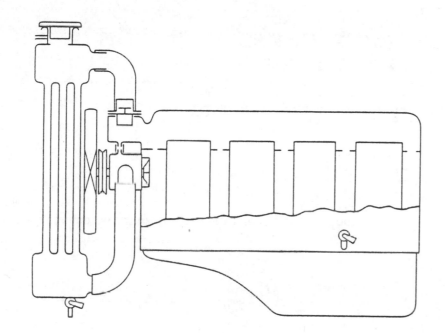

EXPANSION TANKS

Many modern cooling systems use an expansion tank. The layout will then be called, depending upon type, a sealed or semi-sealed system.

....

....

....

Describe the basic operation of the pump-assisted semi-sealed system.

....

....

....

....

....

....

....

....

....

....

....

....

What are four advantages of air cooling over water cooling?

1. ....

2. ....

3. ....

4. ....

What are four advantages of water cooling over air cooling?

1. ....

2. ....

3. ....

4. ....

23

LAYOUT AND PURPOSE OF MAIN PARTS IN FUEL SYSTEM — SPARK-IGNITION

Name the main parts of the fuel system layout shown.

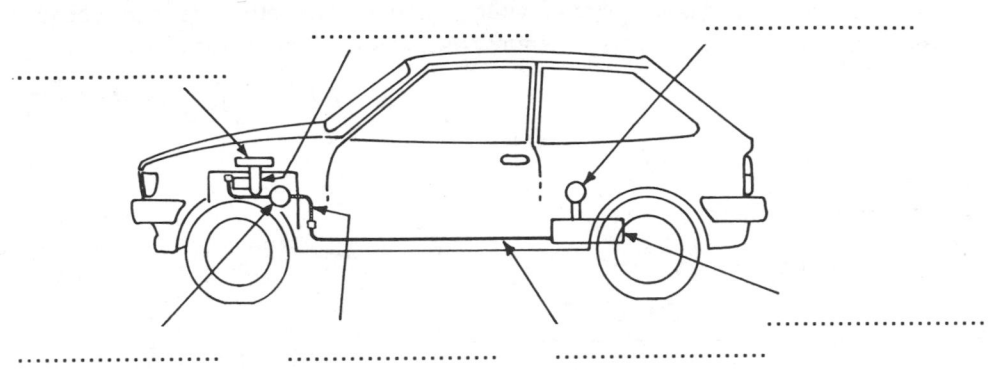

State the purpose of each part of the fuel system listed below and comment upon their construction or design.

Fuel tank ....
....

Tank unit ....
....

Pipe line ....
....

Filters ....
....

Lift pump ....
....

Carburettor ....
....

Air cleaner ....
....

Investigation

Examine a fuel system layout and complete the table.

Make of vehicle .... Model ....

Component	Type, position or material where applicable
Air cleaner or silencer	
Carburettor	
Filter	
Fuel pump	
Fuel pipes	
Fuel tank	

IDENTIFICATION OF CARBURETTORS

State which is the horizontal and which is the downdraught carburettor.

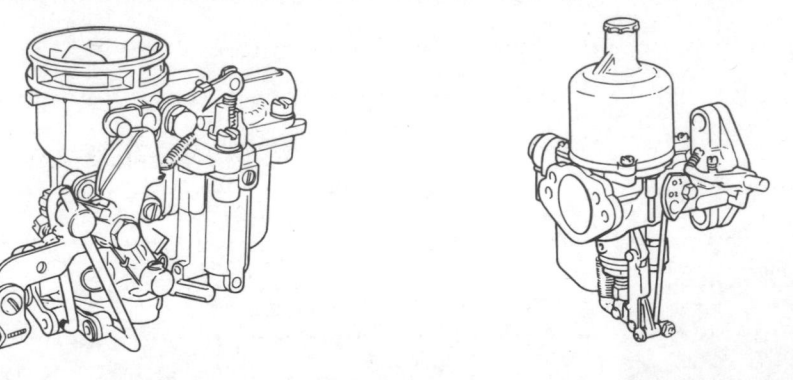

Type .... Type ....

THE SIMPLE CARBURETTOR

A simple single-jet, fixed-choke carburettor has all the main features of a modern sophisticated carburettor.

Using the outlines as a guide, sketch below a line diagram of a simple carburettor. Label the major parts.

Fuel
level

To engine

Explain the carburettor's basic operating principle.

....

....

....

....

....

....

What is the function of the venturi or choke tube?

....

....

What is the function of the float and needle valve?

....

....

A simple single-jet carburettor is not suitable for use on a modern variable speed engine. Why?

....

....

....

The graph below shows what would happen if a simple single-jet carburettor was fitted to a variable-speed engine.

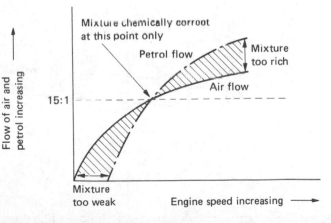

At low speeds the mixture strength would be ....

At high speeds the mixture strength would be ....

25

FUEL SYSTEM LAYOUT — COMPRESSION-IGNITION

The fuel system for the compression-ignition comprises: tank, pipelines, lift pump, filters, injection pump and injectors. Examine a vehicle fitted with a compression-ignition engine and add the fuel system components to the sketch below. Name the important parts.

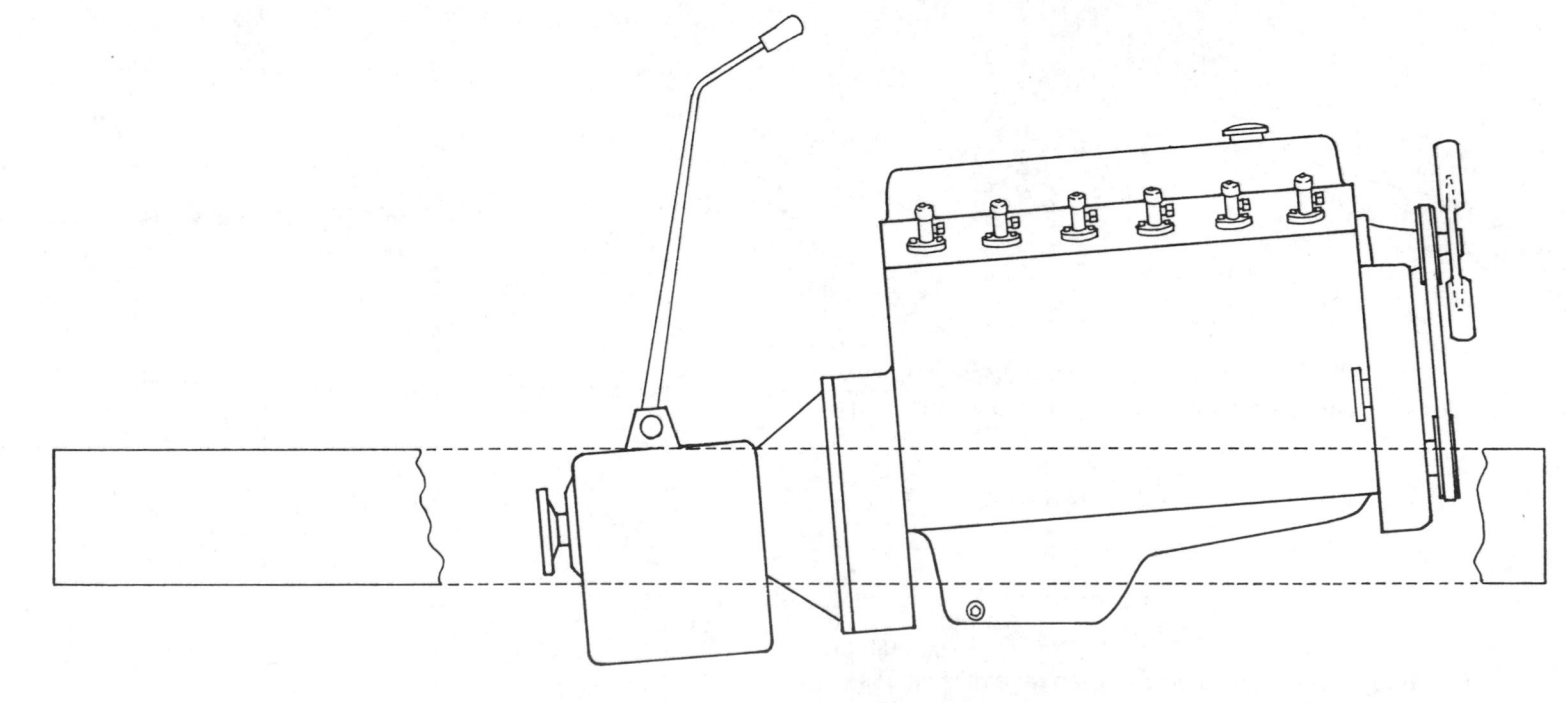

Inspect the pipelines and note whether there is a difference between the pipe from the tank to the lift pump and from the injection pump to the injectors. If so, state what the difference is, and why.

....

....

....

State how the fuel tank is mounted.

....

FUEL FILTRATION

From the examination of the layout it will be found that there are more fuel filters or that they are larger than those of a petrol fuel system.

Why is a better fuel filteration system necessary?

....

....

....

....

CLUTCH

The clutch is a form of coupling which is used to connect the engine crankshaft and flywheel assembly to the gearbox input or primary shaft.

One main function of the clutch is to allow the drive to be taken up gradually and smoothly as the vehicle moves off from rest.

State two more functions of the clutch.

1. ....

....

2. ....

....

SINGLE-PLATE CLUTCH

There are many different types of clutch in use on road vehicles but by far the most popular is the single-plate friction type. This type of clutch is operated by the driver depressing and releasing a pedal; it is used in conjunction with a *manual* type gearbox.

Name the type of clutch used with an automatic gearbox.

....

....

....

....

....

....

Main features of operation (single-plate clutch)

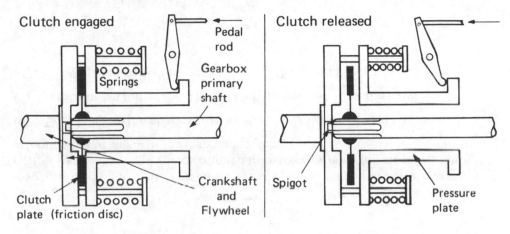

A very much simplified arrangement of a single-plate clutch is illustrated above.

Study the two drawings and state:

1. How the drive is transmitted from the engine to the gearbox.

....

....

....

....

....

2. How the drive to the gearbox is disconnected when the clutch pedal is depressed.

....

....

....

State the most important single factor with regard to the transmission of drive through this type of clutch.

....

THE DIAPHRAGM SPRING CLUTCH

As an alternative to using a number of coil springs to provide the clamping force, many clutches use a single *diaphragm* type spring. The diaphragm spring is rather like a saucer in shape with a hole in the centre.

A single plate clutch incorporating a diaphragm spring is shown below; complete the labelling on the drawing.

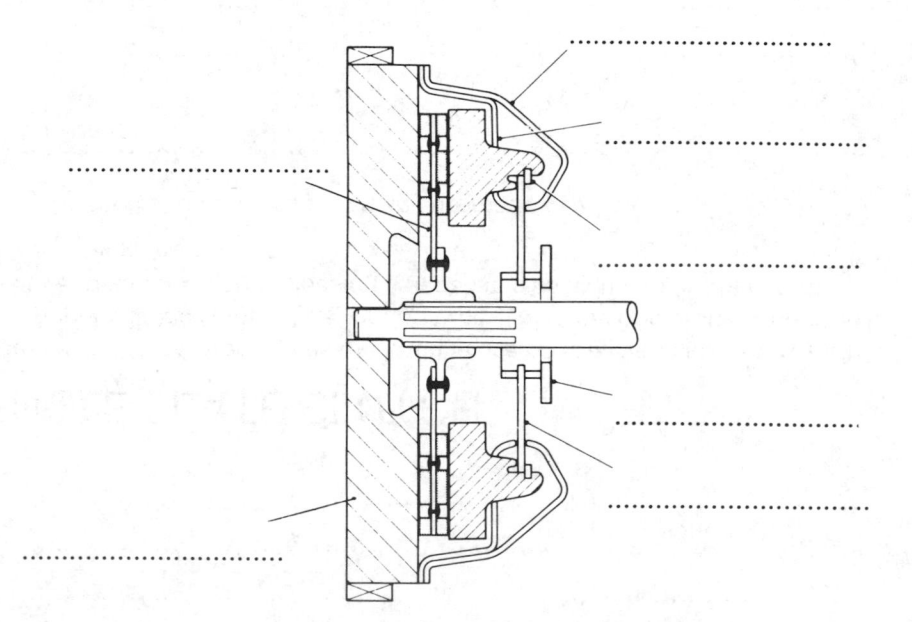

In this type of clutch the diaphragm spring serves two purposes:

(1)   It provides the clamping force.

(2)   ....
....
....
....
....

Investigation

Examine a diaphragm spring clutch assembly.

(a)   How does the clutch pressure plate compare in size and weight to a similar diameter coil spring type?

....

....

(b)   Which type of friction clutch has the least number of moving parts?

....

....

(c)   Make a sketch of the diaphragm spring by completing the circular outline below.

Inspect a diaphragm clutch assembly attached to an engine flywheel in the normal run position and when removed from the flywheel, paying particular attention to the shape of the diaphragm spring.

(d)   Sketch below the shape (SIDE VIEW) of the diaphragm spring;

(1)   in the normal run position and (2) when removed from the flywheel.

Normal run position   *Removed from engine*

1.4d GEARBOX — FUNCTION

In a motor vehicle the gearbox serves three purposes.

(1) To multiply (or increase) the torque (turning effort) being transmitted by the engine.

(2) ....

(3) ....

Under many operating conditions the torque requirement at the driving wheels is far in excess of the torque available from the engine.

(a) State four operating conditions under which the engine torque would need to be multiplied at the gearbox.

(1) When the vehicle is heavily laden.

(2) ....

(3) ....

(4) ....

Types of gearbox

The FOUR types of gearbox are:

(1) Sliding mesh   (2) Constant mesh

(3) ....   (4) ....

(b) Which of the four types of gearbox are used in most modern cars?

....

....

....

....

....

....

Types of gearing

The spur gear, the helical gear and the double helical gear are all types of gears used in gearboxes.

By observation in the workshop, complete the sketches below to show the tooth arrangement for each type.

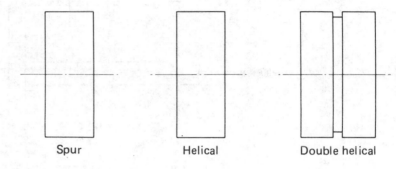

Spur   Helical   Double helical

Epicyclic gears

The sketches below show a simple epicyclic gear train. This extremely compact arrangement of gears is used in

.... and ....

(c) Name the main parts of this gear train by completing the labelling on the drawing. Name the type of gearbox shown on the right.

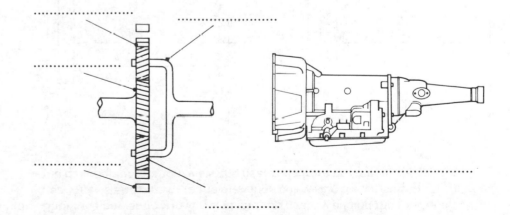

1.4d SIMPLE SLIDING-MESH GEARBOX

The drawing below shows a three-speed sliding-mesh type of gearbox. To obtain the various gear ratios the gearbox layshaft is made up of different sized gearwheels which are connected in turn to the gearwheels on the mainshaft. The drive to the layshaft is through a pair of gearwheels which are permanently in mesh.

Complete the labelling on the drawing:

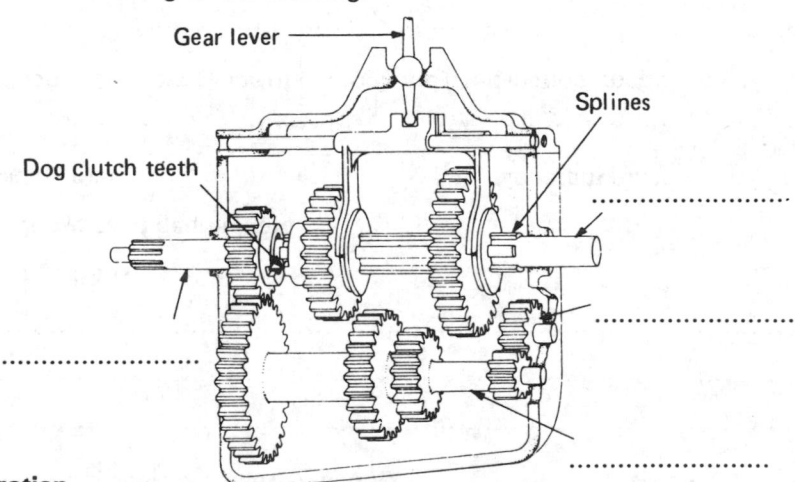

Gear lever

Splines

Dog clutch teeth

....

....

....

....

Investigation

Examine a sliding-mesh gearbox and answer the following questions:

(a) What type of gearing is used? ....

(b) How are the gears engaged to provide the various gear ratios?

....

....

....

....

(c) Why is the mainshaft splined?

....

....

(d) Show the power flow in 1st, 2nd and top gear by adding the mainshaft gearwheels and arrows to the drawings below. On the wheels in (4) show the direction of rotation; view the gear train from the rear of the gearbox.

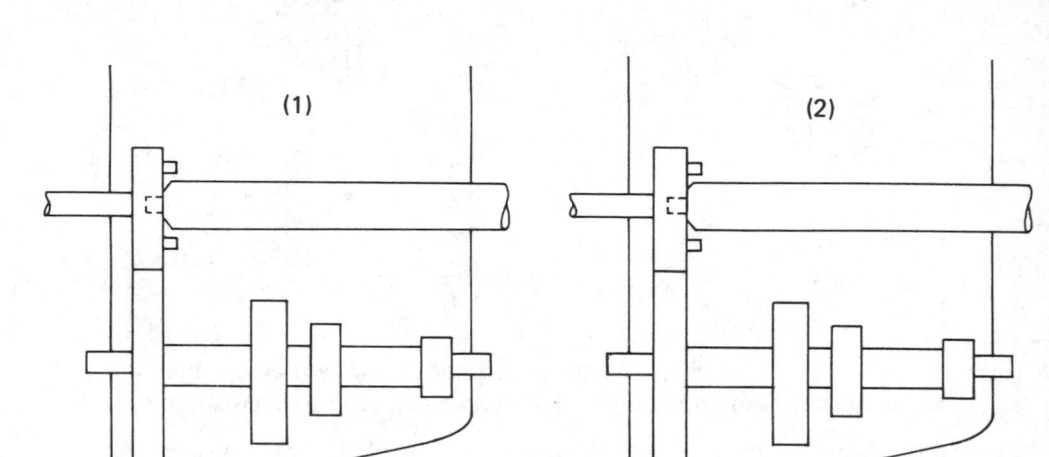

(1)

(2)

First gear

Second gear

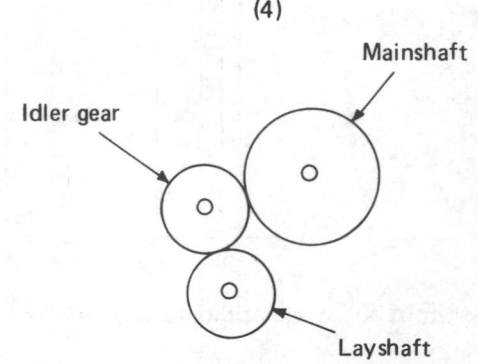

(3)

(4)

Top gear

Mainshaft

Idler gear

Layshaft

PROPELLOR SHAFTS AND DRIVE SHAFTS

On a vehicle of conventional layout the purpose of the propellor shaft is to

transmit the drive from the .... to the ....

.... Drive shafts (or half shafts) transmit the drive from

the .... to the ....

(a) Give three examples of vehicle layouts in which external drive shafts may be used as opposed to conventional type half shafts enclosed in the axle casing.

1. Front engine, rear wheel drive with 'independent' rear suspension.

2. ....

3. ....

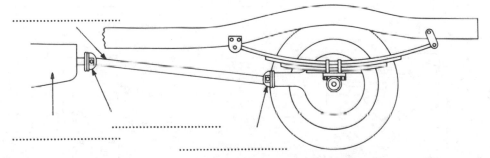

(b) Complete the labelling on the 'open' type propellor shaft arrangement shown above.

(c) Why is it necessary to have a universal joint at both ends of the propellor shaft?

....

....

....

Universal joints are also used on drive shafts to allow for the rise and fall of the road wheels relative to the final drive assembly on cars with independent rear suspension.

As the rear axle swings up and down with spring deflection the distance between the gearbox and axle varies. It is therefore necessary to enable the propellor shaft effectively to vary in length. The splined *'sliding joint'* in a propellor shaft assembly provides this facility.

Investigation

Examine a vehicle and make a sketch below to show the propellor shaft sliding joint arrangement.

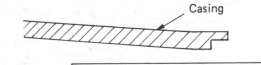

Casing

Splined mainshaft

(b) Is the propellor shaft solid or tubular?

....

(c) State three advantages to be gained by using a tubular shaft.

1. ....

....

....

2. ....

3. ....

TRANSVERSE ENGINE — FRONT WHEEL DRIVE TRANSMISSION LAYOUT

This is a typical front wheel drive layout for a small car. State three vehicles which use this (or very similar) layout and name the numbered transmission parts.

COMBINED GEARBOX AND FINAL DRIVE

The drawing shows a gearbox, differential and inner constant velocity joints; these joints are covered by their rubber shrouds.

Name the main parts and show with arrows the power flow from the first motion shaft to the drive shafts, assuming top (4th) gear to be selected.

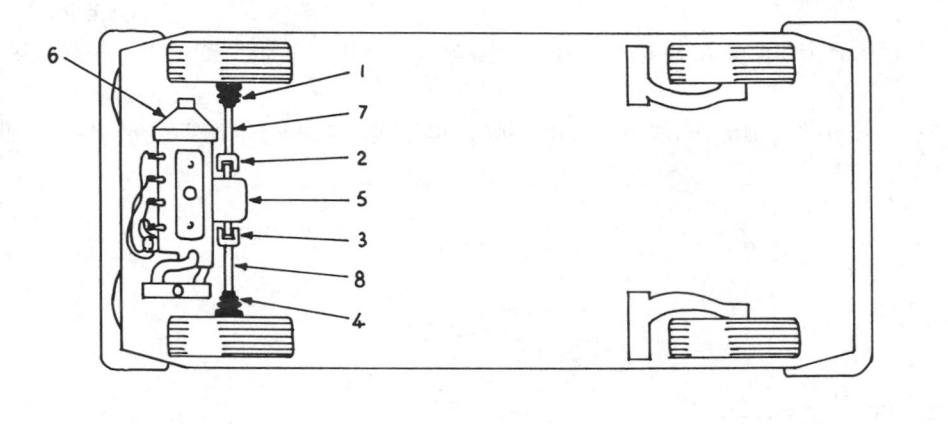

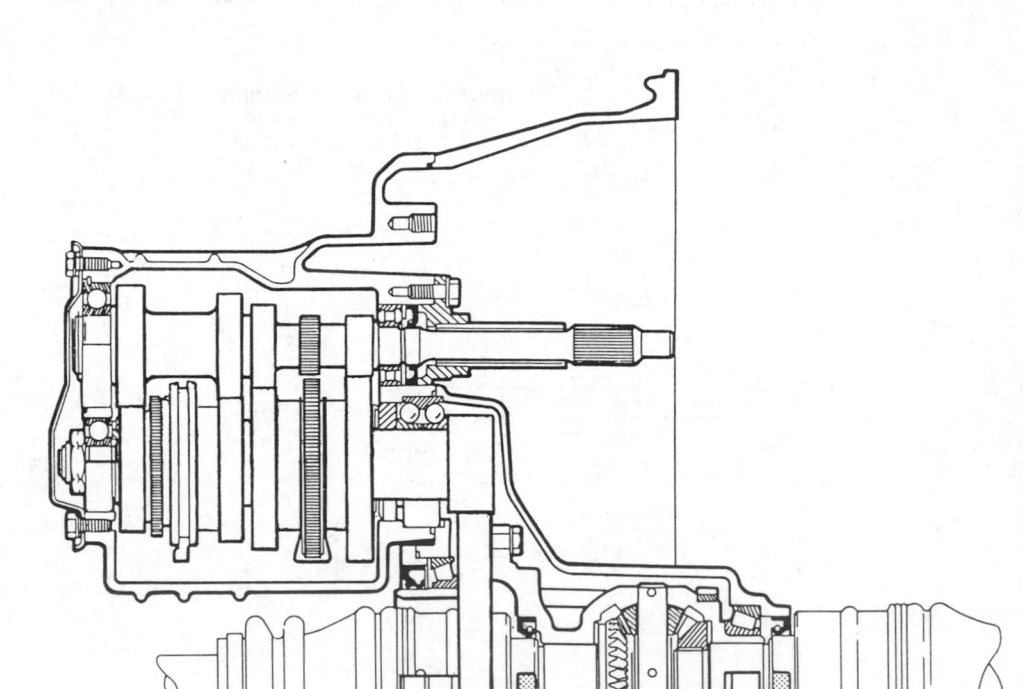

Make	Model	Engine Size

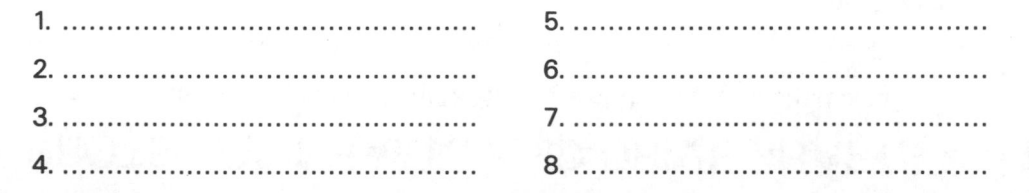

1. ....
2. ....
3. ....
4. ....
5. ....
6. ....
7. ....
8. ....

THE FINAL DRIVE

The final drive consists basically of a pair of gears which provide a permanent gear reduction, thereby multiplying the torque being transmitted from the gearbox.

In most conventional transmission arrangements (for example, front engine with rear live axle) the final drive fulfils another purpose; this is

....

....

The two gears forming the final drive are named

1. .... 2. ....

Investigation

Examine a rear axle and complete the drawings below to show how the final drive gears are positioned relative to each other to give the desired motion.

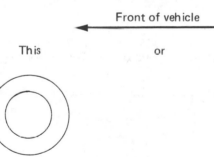

Complete the table below for the axle you examine.

Number of teeth on crown wheel	Number of teeth on pinion	Final drive gear ratio

Investigation

(a) Three types of final drive gear are: STRAIGHT BEVEL, SPIRAL BEVEL and HYPOID. Examine each of these and indicate below the type illustrated.

(b) List alongside each drawing the advantages of the particular gear design.

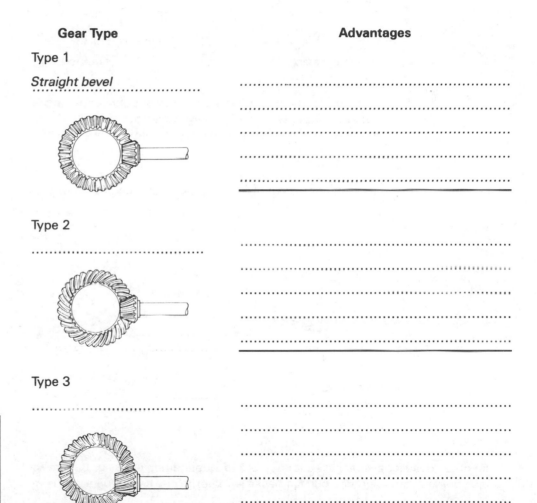

Gear Type   **Advantages**

Type 1

Straight bevel ....
                                                      ....
                                                      ....
                                                      ....
                                                      ....

Type 2

....
                                                      ....
                                                      ....
                                                      ....
                                                      ....
                                                      ....

Type 3

....
                                                      ....
                                                      ....
                                                      ....

33

THE DIFFERENTIAL

When a vehicle is cornering the inner driven wheel is rotating slower than the outer driven wheel. It is the *differential* which allows this difference in speed to take place while at the same time transmitting an equal driving torque to the road wheels.

Why does this difference in speed between inner and outer road wheels need to occur?

....

....

....

The differential is normally an assembly of bevel gears housed in a casing (or cage) which is attached to the crown wheel. The essential parts of a differential are

1. Planet wheels

3. ....

2. ....

4. ....

The differential could be described as a *torque equaliser.* Why is this?

....

....

....

....

During cornering the inner driven wheel is rotating at 100 rev/min and the outer driven wheel is rotating at 200 rev/min. The torque in the half shafts would be

(a)　double in the outer

(b)　the same in each

(c)　double in the inner

Answer (　　)

Investigation

Examine a final drive and differential assembly and complete the drawing below by adding the main components of the differential; clearly label each component.

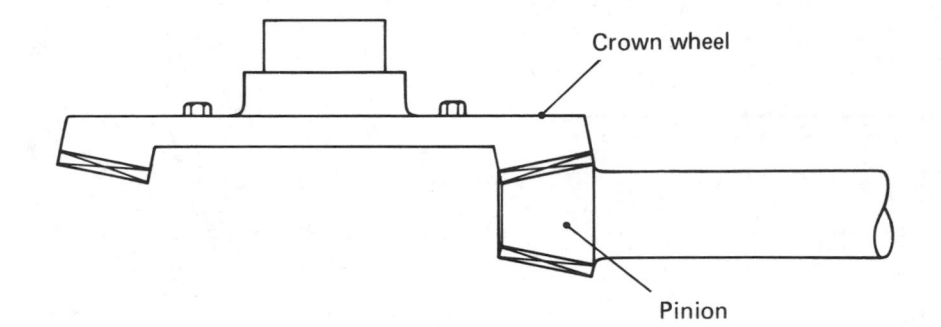

Crown wheel

Pinion

Which gearwheels transmit the drive to the axle shafts?

....

Power is transmitted from the final drive pinion to the axle shafts via the components listed below. Rearrange the list in the correct sequence in accordance with the power flow through the differential.

Components	Power flow
Cross pin	1. ....
Sunwheels	2. ....
Crown wheel	3. ....
Planet wheels	4. ....
Axle shafts	5. ....
Pinion	6. ....
Differential cage	7. ....

WHEELS AND TYRES

The road wheel assembly (tyre and metal wheel) transmits the drive from the drive shafts to the road surface, and back the opposite way during braking. It also provides a degree of springing to accommodate minor road irregularities.

TYPES OF ROAD WHEEL

Various designs of road wheels are in use on both cars and goods vehicles. On cars the pressed steel type of wheel has been used more than any other. Name two other types of road wheel in use on cars.

1. .... 2. ....

Investigation

Remove a wheel from a hub and complete the drawing below (with labels) to show how the wheel is secured and located.

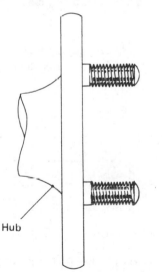

Hub

What is the purpose of the taper on the wheel nuts?

....

Three types of car road wheels are shown opposite. Name the types and list the advantages and disadvantages of each.

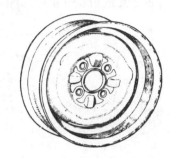

.... Advantages

....

....

.... Disadvantages

....

....

....

.... Advantages

....

....

.... Disadvantages

....

....

.... Advantages

....

....

.... Disadvantages

....

....

TYRES

The pneumatic tyre was originally developed for use on vehicles by J.B. Dunlop in the year 1888. Its main advantages over the solid tyres, in use at that time, were that it provided a cushion for the vehicle against road shocks and it rolled with greater ease.

However, pneumatic tyres also fulfil a number of other functions:

1. ....
2. ....
3. ....
4. ....
5. ....

Tyre construction

The tyre is a flexible rubber casing which is reinforced or supported by other materials, for example, rayon, cotton, nylon, steel.

Label the main parts on the tyre section shown below.

....
....
....
....

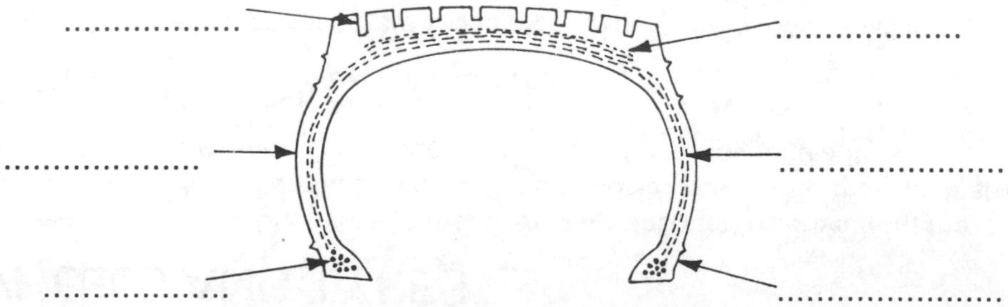

TUBED AND TUBELESS TYRES

Tubeless tyres have now largely superseded tubed tyres on cars. Outline the essential differences between the two designs.

Tubed tyres

....
....
....

Tubeless tyres

....
....
....
....
....
....

The drawings below show tubed and tubeless tyre valves. Label the parts of the sectioned valve.

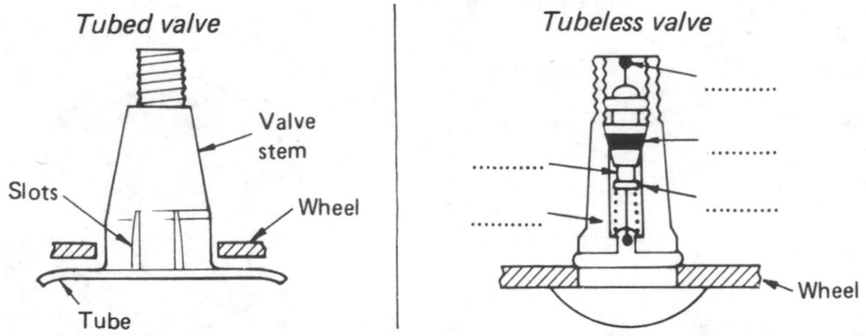

Tubed valve

Valve stem

Slots

Wheel

Tube

Tubeless valve

Wheel

What is the purpose of the slots in the outer stem of the tubed valve?

....
....

State three advantages of tubeless tyres over tubed tyres.

....
....
....
....
....
....
....
....

Types of tyre construction

The two principal types of tyre construction used on road vehicles are

1. ....

2. ....

A tyre casing consists of *plies* which are layers of material looped around the beads to form a case. The basic difference in structure between radial and diagonal ply tyres is in the arrangement of the casing plies.

With diagonal ply construction the ply 'cords' form an angle of approximately

.... to the tyre bead

Radial ply cords form an angle of

.... to the tyre bead.

Radial ply tyres are in use on most cars and on many goods vehicles.

Add lines to the two outlines at the top opposite to show the position of the cords in relation to the tyre bead.

Radial ply   *Diagonal ply*

Label the tyre sections illustrated below.

....

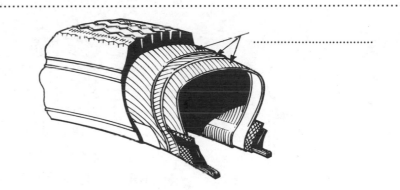

....

....

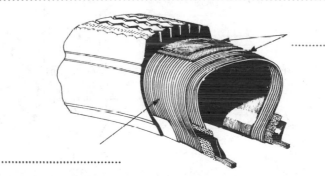

....

One feature of the radial ply tyre is that the walls are more flexible than the diagonal ply tyre. Why is this?

....
....
....

TYRE FAULTS

Certain tyre defects make it illegal to use a vehicle on a public road. Outline the main legal requirements with regard to the tyre faults listed below.

Tread wear

....

....

....

....

Cuts

....

....

....

....

Lumps and bulges

....

....

....

....

Investigation

Examine the tyres on a vehicle and complete the table below.

Position	Tread depth		Pressure	Other defects	Serviceability
	Maximum	Minimum			
Front O/S					
Rear O/S					
Front N/S					
Rear N/S					
Spare					

TYRE SIZE MARKINGS

The size of a tyre is indicated by two dimensions on the sidewall, for example

5.20 — 13   or   145 — 13

Identify the part to which each tyre size refers by adding these dimensions to the diagrams below.

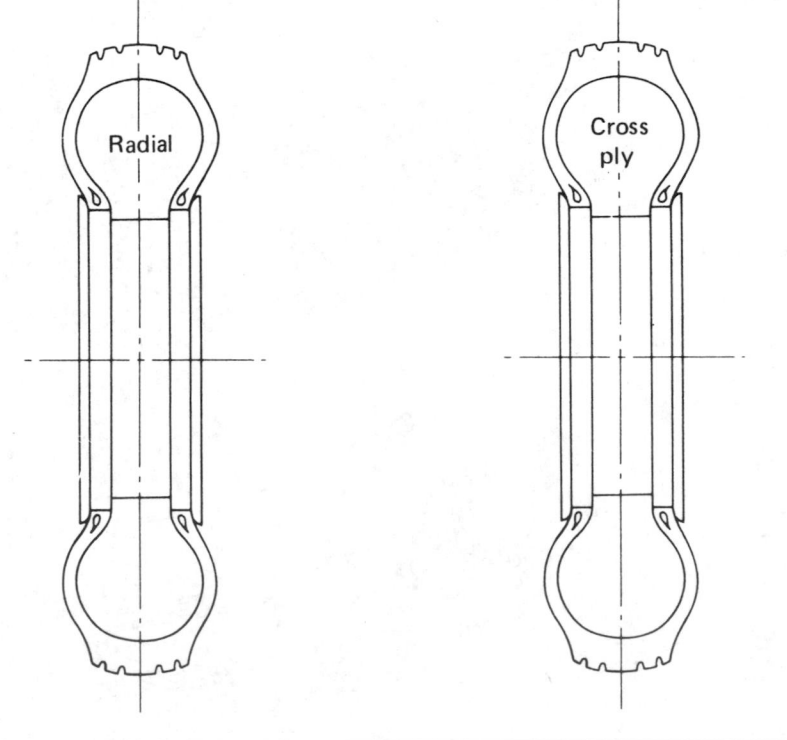

SUSPENSION SYSTEMS

The suspension on a vehicle performs two functions:

1. It insulates the vehicle body, hence the passengers or load, from shocks as the vehicle travels over irregularities in the road surface.

2. It assists in keeping the tyres in close contact with the road surface to ensure adequate adhesion for accelerating, braking and cornering.

One of the simplest and most widely used forms of suspension was the *beam axle semi-elliptic leaf spring* arrangement. This system is still used at the rear of some cars and at both the front and rear of most heavy commercial vehicles.

BEAM AXLE SEMI-ELLIPTIC LEAF SPRING SUSPENSION

(a) Complete the labelling on the drawing:

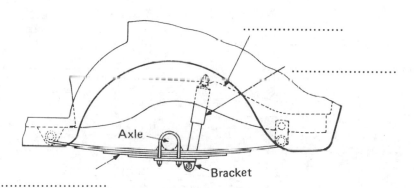

Axle

Bracket

....

....

....

....

....

....

(b) Name and briefly describe the four suspension conditions illustrated below.

....

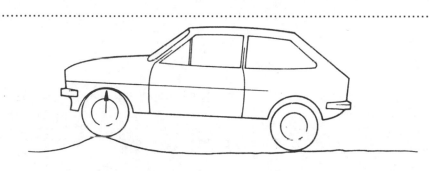

....

....

....

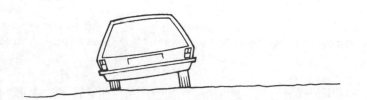

39

THE LAMINATED LEAF SPRING

The drawing below shows a leaf spring. Label the drawing and state the purpose of each part.

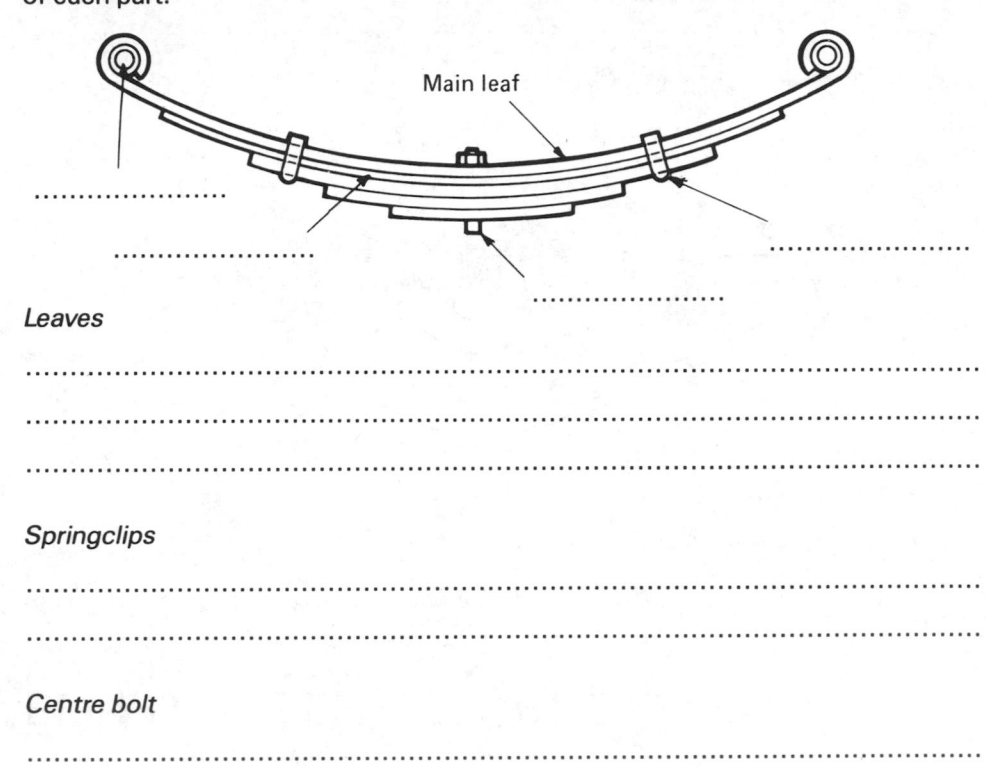

Main leaf

Leaves

....

....

....

Springclips

....

....

Centre bolt

....

....

Spring eye bushes

....

Why is this type of spring said to be semi-elliptical?

....

....

....

The simplified sketch (a) below shows how the leaf spring is attached to the chassis.

State the purpose of the swinging shackle and complete sketch (b) to show the action of the shackle as the spring is deflected.

....

....

Swinging shackle

(a)   (b)

Investigation

(a) Examine a leaf spring and axle assembly (car type) and make a sketch to show how the spring is secured and located on the axle.

(b) Sketch and label the spring eye bush.

HELICAL SPRINGS

(a) State the advantages of a helical or coil spring over a laminated leaf spring.

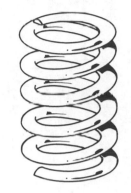

Advantages

1. ....

2. ....

3. ....

4. ....

5. ....

As the term implies, 'independent suspension' describes a suspension system in which the suspension at one wheel operates completely independently of the opposite wheel on the other side of the vehicle. This is not the case with a beam axle suspension when, if one wheel rises over a bump, the other wheel on the same axle is also affected.

Complete the sketch below to show how the other wheel is affected as one wheel rises over a bump with beam axle suspension.

View of axle from front

INDEPENDENT SUSPENSION

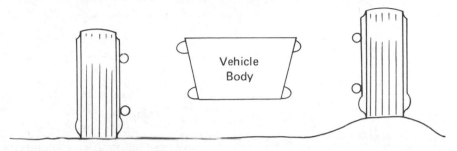

The drawing above is a simplified representation of a double-link independent suspension system. Complete the drawing to show the springs and the suspension as one wheel rises over a bump.

Investigation

Examine a vehicle fitted with Macpherson strut independent front suspension which uses a helical spring, and complete the drawing below to show one side. Label all major components.

Vehicle make/model .... Year ....

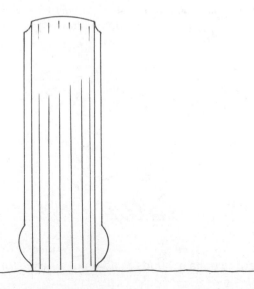

41

(a) State the meaning of the terms i.f.s. and i.r.s.

i.f.s. ....

i.r.s. ....

(b) State the advantages of independent suspension over beam-axle suspension.

1. ....

2. ....

3. ....

4. ....

5. ....

The main disadvantages of independent suspension are that it is usually more complicated and costly and the tyres tend to wear unevenly.

(c) In the suspension arrangement shown below 's' is the spring. Complete the labelling on the drawing and name this type of spring.

.... spring.

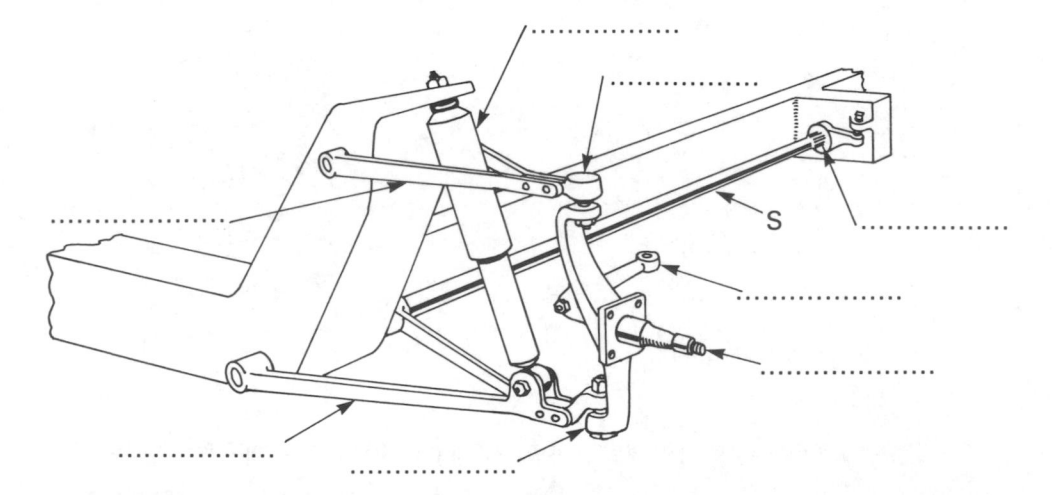

(d) Name the type of spring in each of the suspension arrangements shown below.

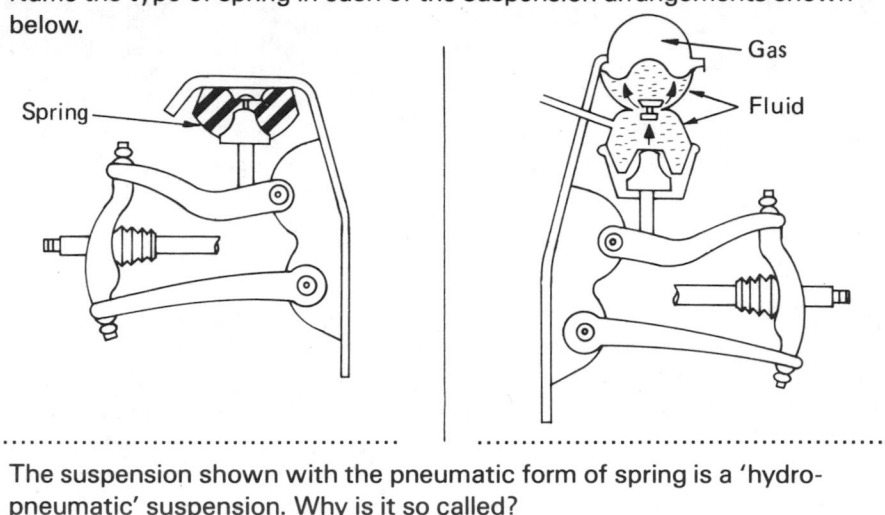

.... | ....

(e) The suspension shown with the pneumatic form of spring is a 'hydro-pneumatic' suspension. Why is it so called?

....

....

....

(f) In the hydro-pneumatic suspension system the individual suspension units are interconnected. How are they interconnected?

....

(g) Give examples of modern vehicles which use the types of suspension springs illustrated on this page.

Vehicle	Type of spring

SUSPENSION DAMPERS

Why is it necessary to use dampers in a suspension system?

....

....

....

....

....

....

The dampers used on very many cars are the hydraulic telescopic type.
Telescopic dampers are fixed at one end to the axle or suspension link and
at the other to the

....

Principle of operation

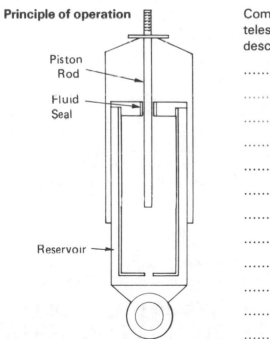

Piston
Rod

Fluid
Seal

Reservoir

Complete the simplified drawing of the
telescopic damper shown and briefly
describe its operation.

....

....

....

....

....

....

....

....

....

....

....

COMMERCIAL VEHICLE SUSPENSION

As already mentioned, some commercial vehicles use semi-elliptic suspension
springs. Some heavy commercial and passenger vehicles use quite different
systems, for example, pneumatic (air) suspension.

AIR SUSPENSION

Air springs usually consist of reinforced rubber bellows containing air under
pressure, situated between the axle, and an air capacity tank mounted on to the
chassis. They have an important advantage in that by fitting levelling valves to
each wheel unit, the height of the vehicle can be kept constant whatever the
load.

The main features of air suspension are shown below; label the drawing.

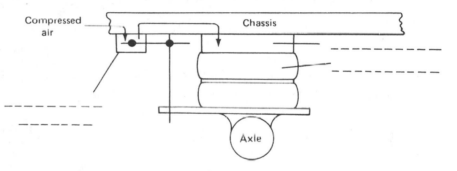

Compressed
air

Chassis

Axle

By observation, list three vehicles using air suspension.

Vehicle make	Model	Gross vehicle weight	Air suspension manufacturer

STEERING SYSTEMS —
TYPICAL BEAM AXLE LAYOUT

The front wheels on a normal vehicle rotate on stub axles which swivel or pivot about what is known as the 'swivel axis'. This provides a means of steering the vehicle. To make the stub axles pivot a control gear, operated by the driver via the steering wheel, and a linkage to the stub axles are necessary.

One of the simplest steering arrangements is that used with a beam axle system. Complete the beam axle steering layout below and label each part.

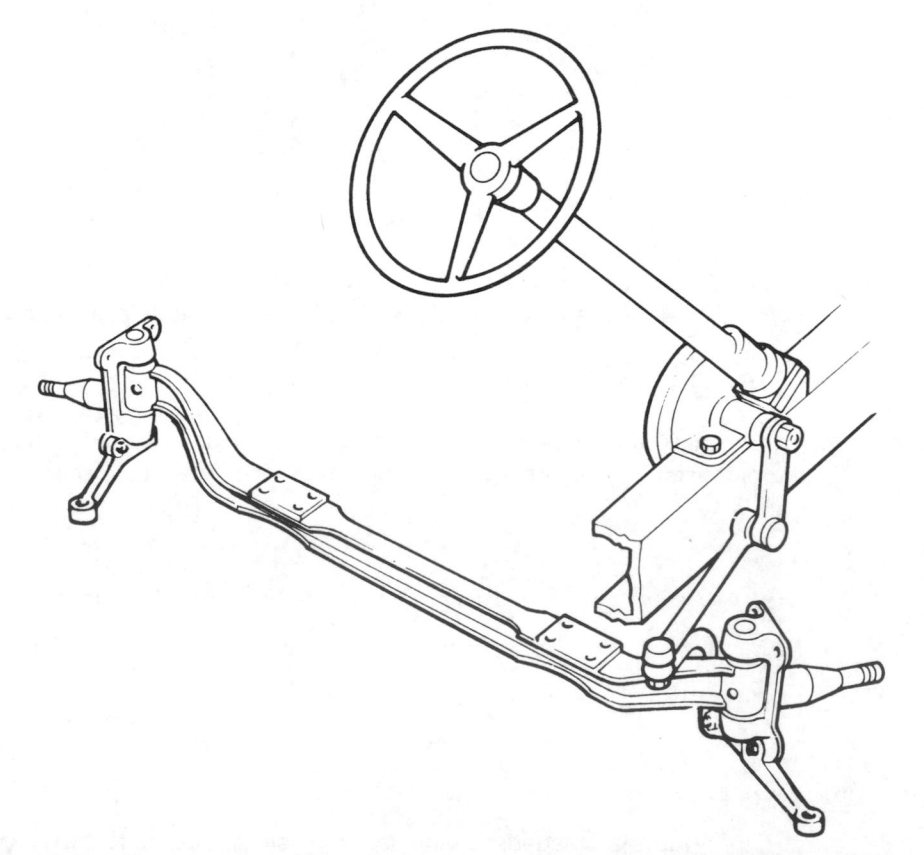

On what type of vehicle is the system shown above normally found?

....

State the purpose of each of the following steering components:

Steering gearbox

....

....

....

....

Drop arm

....

....

Draglink

....

....

Steering arms

....

....

Track rod

....

....

Ball joints

....

....

....

The *steering swivel axis* in the arrangement shown opposite is formed by 'king pins' and 'bushes'. That is, the stub axles pivot on hardened steel king pins which are held firmly in the beam axle; bushes in the stub axles provide the necessary bearing surfaces.

1.4g CAR STEERING SYSTEM

Most cars have independent front suspension (i.f.s.), and the steering linkage must therefore be designed to accommodate the up and down movement of a steered wheel without affecting the other steered wheel. In most systems two short track rods which pivot in a similar arc to the suspension links, are connected to the stub axles.

One system in use on cars can be described as a steering gearbox with 'idler' and three track rod layout.

Complete the drawing of such a system shown below by adding the linkage and labelling the parts.

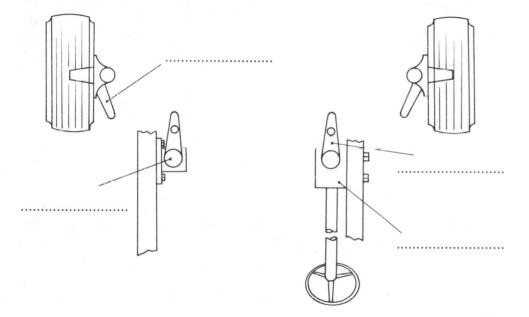

What are two main disadvantages of this layout?

....

....

Investigation

Examine a vehicle fitted with a 'rack-and-pinion' steering system and complete the drawing below to illustrate this; label all the parts.

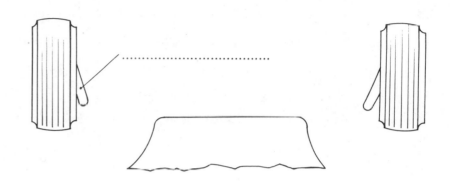

Draw a centre line through the steering swivel axis on the stub axle arrangement shown below.

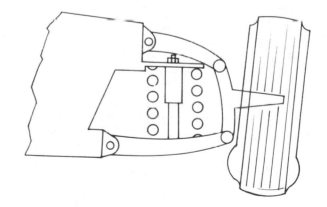

What provides the steering swivel action on this arrangement?

....

45

BRAKING SYSTEM

The braking system provides the driver of a vehicle with a means of safely slowing down (or retarding) the vehicle and bringing it to a halt, and preventing movement when stationary. When the

brakes are applied, ... is generated which converts the energy

of movement, ... energy, into .... energy.

Simple mechanically operated drum brake

The drawing on the left below shows a simple 'cam' operated drum brake in the 'off' position. Complete the drawing on the right to show the brake in the applied position.

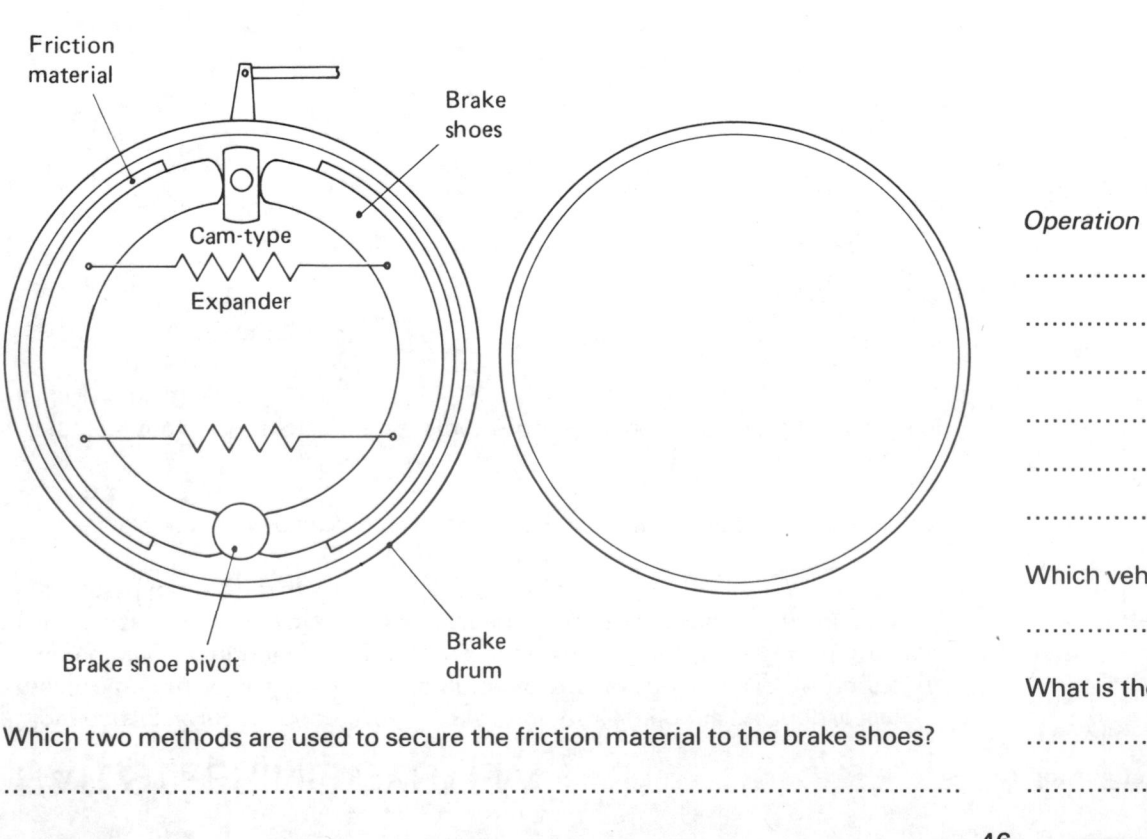

Friction material

Brake shoes

Cam-type

Expander

Brake shoe pivot

Brake drum

Which two methods are used to secure the friction material to the brake shoes?

....

HYDRAULICALLY OPERATED DRUM BRAKES

Most modern car braking systems and many light commercial vehicle braking systems are operated hydraulically. Label the parts on the single-line hydraulic drum brake layout below.

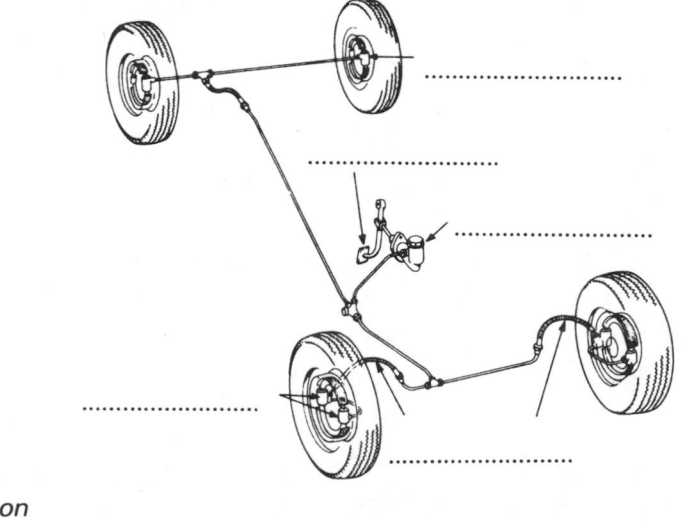

Operation

....
....
....
....
....
....

Which vehicles usually use drum brakes at each wheel?

....

What is the reason for using flexible pipes in parts of the hydraulic system?

....

SINGLE-LEADING SHOE BRAKE

The drawing shows a 'double-piston wheel cylinder' acting on a *leading brake shoe* and a *trailing brake shoe*. The leading shoe is pressed harder against the drum by drum rotation whereas the trailing shoe tends to be forced away by drum rotation. A much greater braking effect is therefore obtained from a leading shoe.

Name the parts in drum brake assembly.

Indicate drum rotation and show which is the leading and which is the trailing shoe.

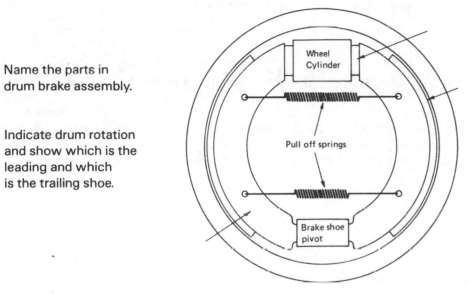

Why does the leading shoe wear at a greater rate than the trailing shoe?

....

....

What friction material may be used for brake linings?

....

What health hazards are associated with the dust from this friction material?

....

....

....

BRAKE COMPENSATION

A hydraulic braking system is said to be 'self-compensating'. What is meant by brake compensation and why are hydraulically operated brakes self-compensating?

....

....

....

....

....

....

....

....

....

PARKING BRAKE (HAND BRAKE)

With a mechanically operated parking brake a 'brake compensator' is usually incorporated in the linkage to ensure that both brake units receive the same applying force.

Investigation

One type of handbrake compensator is shown below. Examine a vehicle fitted with this type and label the drawing.

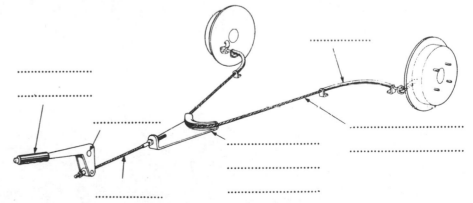

TWO-LEADING SHOE BRAKE

Front drum brakes are normally two-leading shoe arrangements. What is the reason for this?

....

....

....

....

....

....

....

....

....

....

Investigation

Examine the front drum brake assembly of a car and complete the drawing at the top opposite to show the 2LS arrangement. Add arrows to the drawing to indicate forward drum rotation and the direction of wheel cylinder piston movement.

A leading shoe is said to have a 'self servo' action. State the meaning of this.

....

....

....

....

On what do the brakes shoes in a 2LS assembly pivot?

....

Front drum brake assembly (2LS)

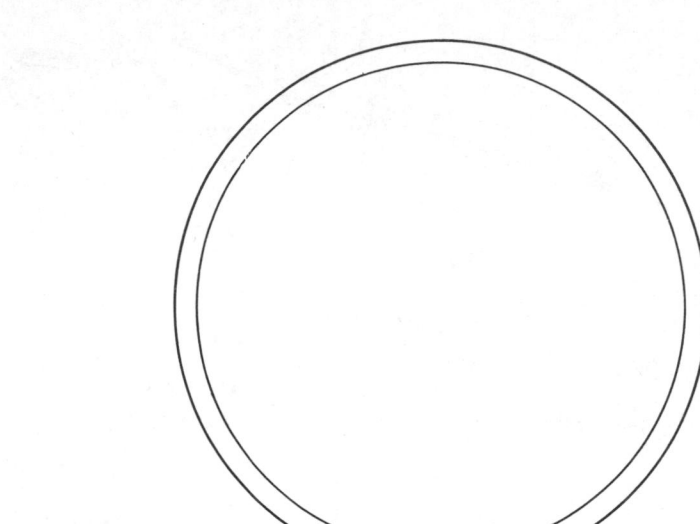

Name the type of braking system shown diagramatically below.

....

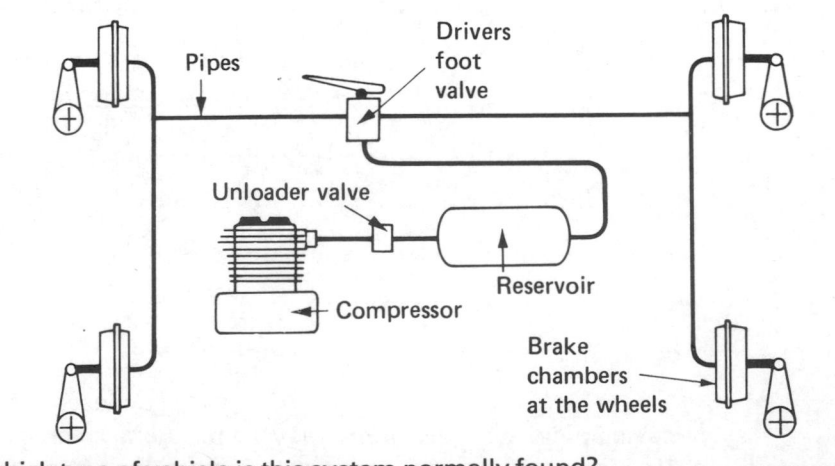

On which type of vehicle is this system normally found?

....

DISC BRAKES

1.4h

A disadvantage with drum brakes is that repeated brake applications at high speeds, for example, fast driving along winding roads or during long downhill descents, cause a gradual build-up in temperature of the brake assemblies particularly the linings and drums. Too great an increase in temperature reduces the efficiency of the brakes, making it more difficult to stop the vehicle. In effect the brakes may become temporarily useless.

This fall-off in brake performance is known as

....

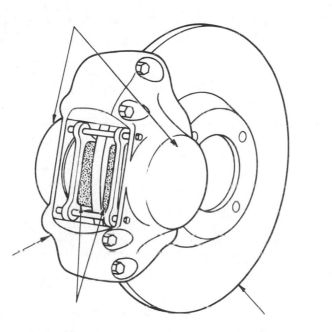

Investigation

Examine a front disc brake assembly and name the component to which the brake caliper is attached.

....

Disc brakes are now in use on most car front brakes and at both front and rear on many of the larger and faster cars. The disc brake, shown opposite, operates rather like a bicycle brake, that is friction pads are clamped on to a rotating disc by a caliper mechanism.

(a)   Label the parts on the simplified disc brake shown opposite.

(b)   List the advantages and disadvantages of the disc brake when compared with the drum brake.

Advantages

....

....

....

....

....

....

Disadvantages

....

....

....

....

....

A vacuum servo is part of the braking system on many modern cars, in particular vehicles with disc brakes. Why is the servo used?

....

....

....

....

....

ELECTRICAL SYSTEMS — ELECTRICAL CURRENT FLOW

To allow an electrical current to flow an electric circuit must consist of

(a)   A source of supply.

(b)   A device that will use the supply to do useful work.

(c)   Electrical conducting materials that will transfer the electric current from the supply source to the consuming device, and then return it to the supply source.

On a motor vehicle TWO sources of electrical supply are

1.   ....

2.   ....

Name FIVE different types of devices that consume the current to do useful work

1.   ....

2.   ....

3.   ....

4.   ....

5.   ....

What is meant by the term 'electrical conductor'?

....

....

What is meant by the term 'electrical insulator'?

....

....

Name SIX electrical conductors and SIX insulators.

Conductors	Insulators
1.	1. ....
2.	2. ....
3.	3. ....
4.	4. ....
5.	5. ....
6.	6. ....

VEHICLE ELECTRICAL CIRCUITS

Motor-vehicle electrical circuits can be classified under five basic headings:

1. Starter-motor circuit
2. Battery-charging circuit
3. Ignition circuit
4. Lighting circuits
5. Ancillary/accessory circuits

Under this last heading there are very many varied types of circuits but each is basically similar. They consist of a component which requires an electrical supply via a switch-operated circuit.

....

....

....

....

....

....

Name as many ancillary/accessory circuits as possible. (Two examples are given.)

1.	*Heater blower*	11.	....
2.	*Horn*	12.	....
3.	....	13.	....
4.	....	14.	....
5.	....	15.	....
6.	....	16.	....
7.	....	17.	....
8.	....	18.	....
9.	....	19.	....
10.	....	20.	....

ELECTRICAL SIGNS AND SYMBOLS

Each component on the list below can be represented by one of the symbols shown on this page. Write the appropriate name beneath each symbol.

Voltmeter	Gauge
Switches	Fuse
Battery	Diode
Ammeter	Horn
Light bulbs	Alternator
Fuel pump	Capacitor
Winding	Transistor

Ignition coil

Radio

Speaker

Starter motor with solenoid switch

Crossed wires not connected

Earth ground

Resistor fixed

Plug and socket connector

Multi plug and socket

Windscreen wiper motor

Contact-breaker points

Variable resistor

Heated rear window

Distributor cap and sparking plug

Crossed wires connected

Twin filament lamp

51

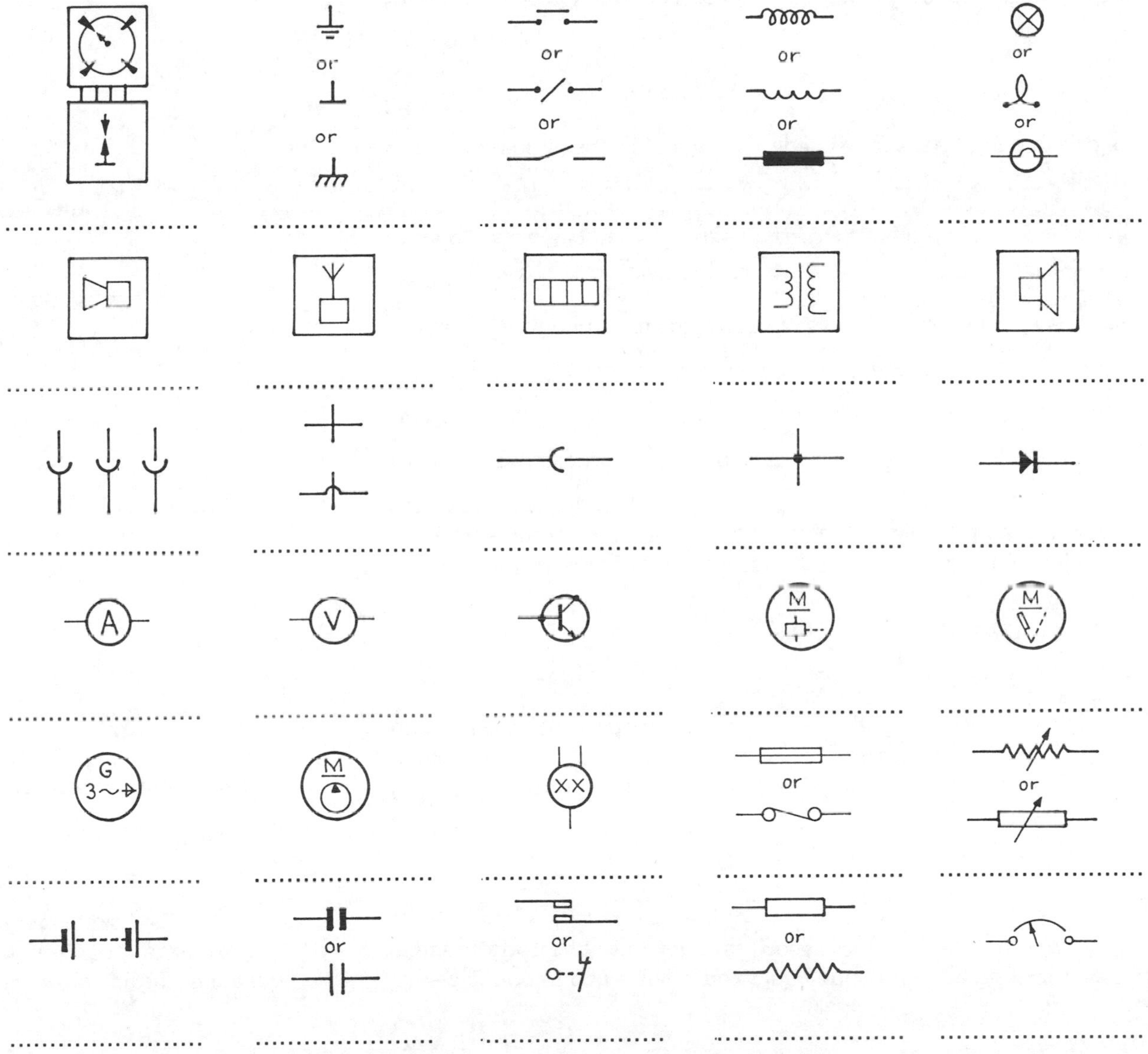

EARTH RETURN

On conventional vehicles it is common practice to allow the current, once it has passed through the electrical resistance that it has operated, to return to the battery through the body frame, instead of by a separate cable.

....

....

Sketch a wiring diagram showing four light bulbs connected in parallel, via a switch, to a 12 V battery. Incorporate the earth return symbol.

The advantages of this system are

1. ....

2. ....

3. ....

4. ....

Two types of vehicle that do not use this type of system are

1. ....

2. ....

They use a system called an insulated return.

....

....

The system is used because ....

....

CABLES

The selection of cable and type of insulation required for motor-vehicle use depends upon two main factors. These are

1. ....

2. ....

Cables are often bunched together in a harness or loom. This simplifies fitting and ensures less chance of breakage or short circuits. Each cable within the harness is colour coded.

....

....

The main feed cable to a specific switch may have a single colour and past the switch the lead has the same main colour but with a different coloured trace line passing through it.

Typical main colours for circuits are

Ignition .... Headlamp ....

Sidelamp .... Flasher ....

The amount of current a cable can pass is determined by its size. How are these

classified? ....

What does a cable having a size of 28/0.30 indicate?

....

What is a recognised safe current capacity for each strand of cable 0.30 mm

thick? ....

Investigation

Examine cables of various thickness obtained from or still held in a wiring harness.

From what material are the wires made? ....

Count the number of strands and measure their diameter.

LEAD-ACID BATTERY

1.4i

The lead-acid battery is of the secondary cell type and is used on most automobiles in either 12 or 24 V form. The 12 V is the most popular. The battery acts as a reservoir of electrical power. All other components take current from the battery; that is, except the alternator (or dynamo) which charges the battery while the engine is running.

Construction

A 12 V battery container consists of six separate compartments. Each compartment contains a set of positive and negative plates; each set is fixed to a bar which rises to form the positive or negative terminal. The plates have a lattice-type framework into which is pressed the chemically active material.

Between each plate is an insulating separator.

Name the parts on the sketch below.

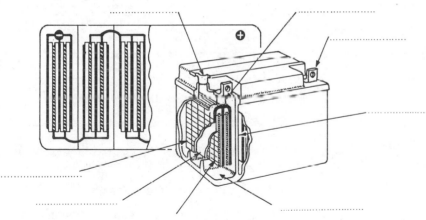

Investigation

Examine batteries suitable for dismantling. Dismantle a cell and state:

The colour of the active material.   The number of plates in each cell.

(a) Positive plate ....   (a) Positive ....

(b) Negative plate ....   (b) Negative ....

GENERATORS (DYNAMOS AND ALTERNATORS)

The basic operation of a generator is to

....

There are two basic types of generator.

....

Name the generators shown below.

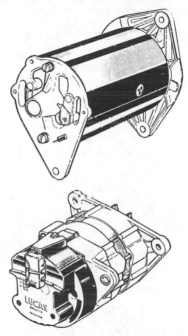

....

....

What advantages does the alternator have when compared with the dynamo?

....
....
....
....

53

IGNITION SYSTEM

The coil-ignition system must provide, at a precise time, a high voltage spark that will jump the plug gap inside the combustion chamber and ignite the compressed mixture.

The system may be considered to be made up of two parts:

1. Low-tension (primary) circuit—LT

2. High-tension (secondary) circuit—HT

....

....

....

....

....

....

....

....

....

....

....

....

....

....

....

What is the firing order of the system shown opposite, if the rotor turns

anticlockwise? ....

Name the main parts of the simple coil-ignition system shown and identify the primary and secondary circuits leads.

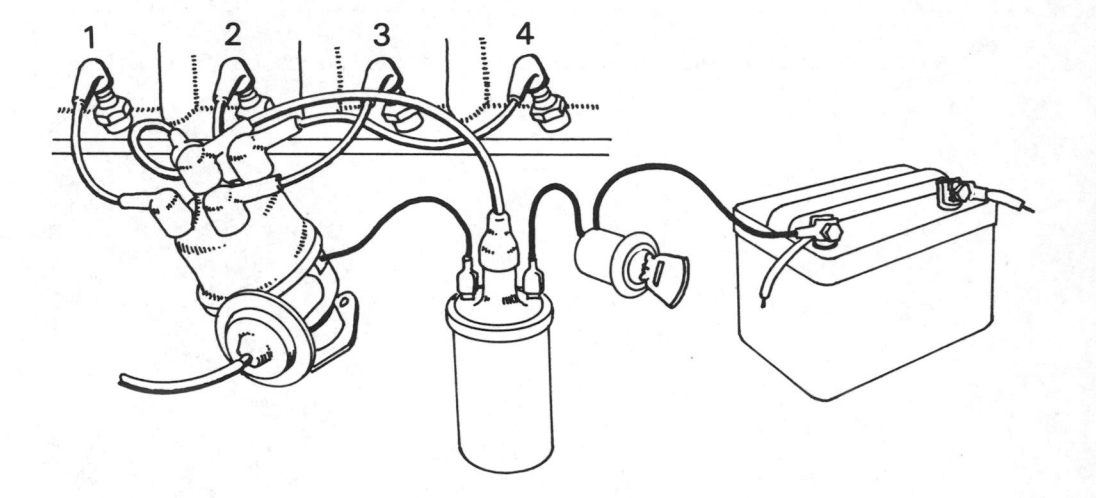

State briefly the function of the following main components of a coil-ignition system:

Battery ....

....

Ignition switch ....

....

Coil ....

....

Distributor ....

....

Sparking plugs ....

....

Investigation

Examine a coil-ignition system.

From observations, complete the wiring diagrams opposite and list, in order, the main component parts through which the current in both primary and secondary circuits passes.

Primary circuit	Secondary circuit
Battery	Coil

IGNITION COIL OUTPUT

The primary winding of the ignition coil is supplied at battery voltage (12 V) with a current of about 3 A. This supply builds up a magnetic field around both the primary and secondary coil windings.

Explain what happens to the output when the distributor contact breaker points are opened.

....

....

....

....

....

....

....

Pictorial diagram

Sketch a rotor in the centre of the distributor cap, show its direction of rotation and state the firing order. Sketch in cables as appropriate.

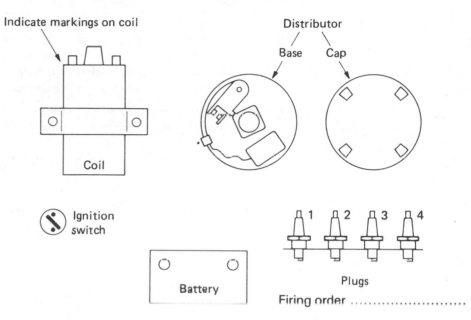

Firing order ....

Theoretical diagram

Complete the diagram and identify the basic symbols shown.

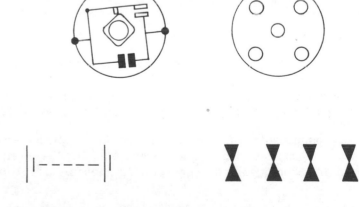

1.4i SPARK PLUG AND IGNITION LEADS

Name the parts of the spark plug shown below.

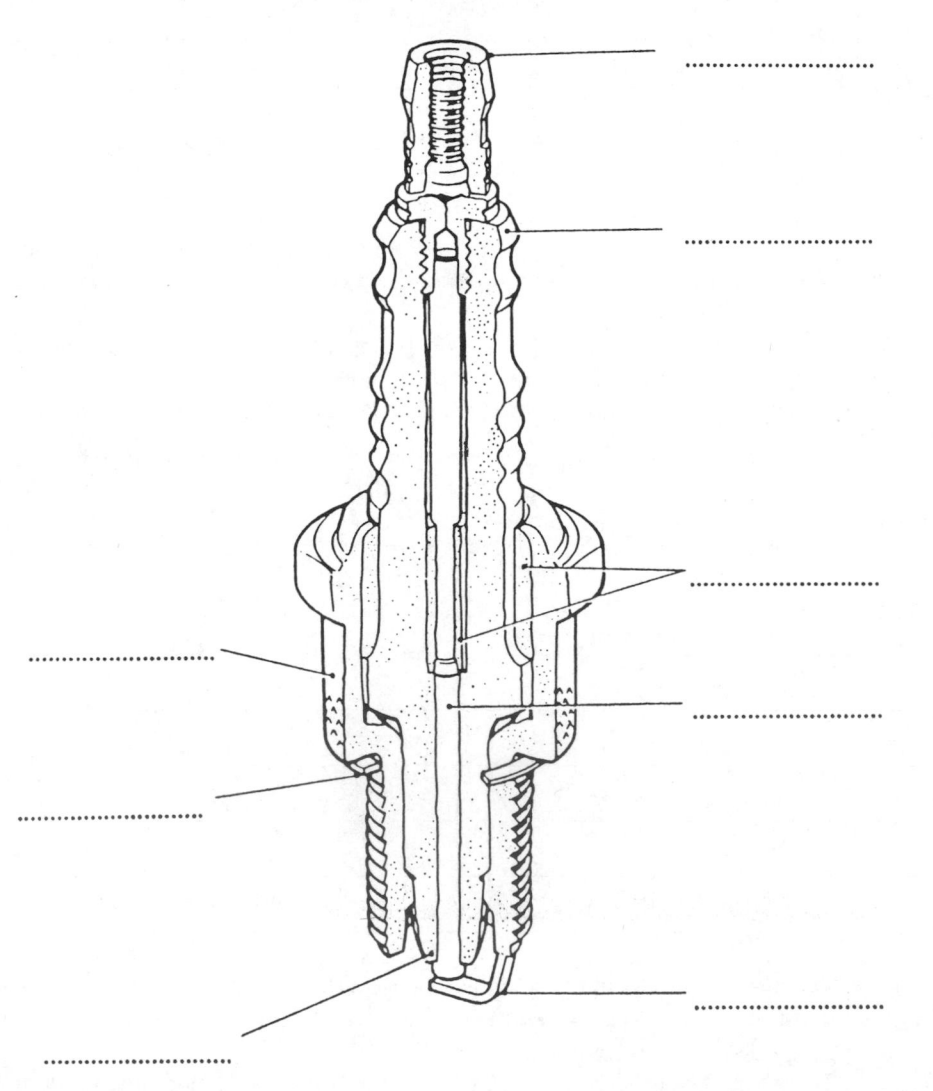

Indicate the plug diameter and gap.

The spark plug consists of a centre metal electrode which passes through a form of ceramic insulator. The lower part of the insulator is fixed to a metal case which screws into the cylinder head. This case forms the earth to the engine.

At normal atmospheric pressure the plug will readily spark with little voltage, but when in the running engine the voltage requirement may progressively increase, for example, over a period it can rise from 7000 V to 15 000 V. State four factors affecting the voltage requirement of the plug.

1. ....

2. ....

3. ....

4. ....

What may cause a spark plug to foul and not spark?

1. ....

2. ....

3. ....

4. ....

List the routine maintenance that should be given to a spark plug.

1. ....

2. ....

3. ....

4. ....

Examine spark plug leads.
Two types of lead are commonly used. In one type the centre core is made of stranded wire.
What is used as the core of the second type of lead?

....

....

Both types are highly insulated. Why is this? ....

....

VEHICLE LIGHTING SYSTEMS

The lighting system of a car may be split into two basic circuits. These are

....

List the basic essentials that make up a lighting circuit.

....

....

....

When more than one lamp is used the circuit is usually wired in ....

The side light circuit consists of two lamps at the front and at least two at the rear plus a lamp to illuminate the vehicle's rear registration plate.

....

....

....

The headlight circuit is basically two circuits, the main beam and dip beam.

....

....

....

Examine three vehicles of widely varying types, for example, commercial vehicle, Land Rover, and a modern saloon. Observe the correct working of head, dip and sidelights. If lights operate correctly, place tick in column. If inoperative, state which light is faulty.

Vehicle make			
Model			
Sidelights			
Tail lights			
Number plate light			
Headlight main beam			
Headlight dip beam			

Complete the following diagrams using the earth return system.

Sidelight circuit.

Lighting switch

Front

Rear

Headlight circuit

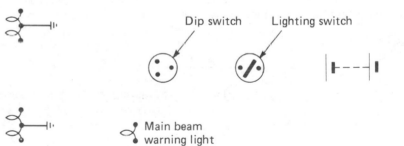

Dip switch   Lighting switch

Main beam warning light

Other circuits, which are sometimes considered as part of the basic lighting system, but which use lights for signalling purposes or for better visibility are the

1. ....

2. ....

3. ....

1.4i TYPES OF BULB

Examine light bulbs of different types.
Identify those shown and state where these may be fitted on a vehicle, in each case give a typical wattage rating.

Note: These sketches are not to scale.

1. ....

2. ....

3. ....

4. ....

5. ....

6. ....

7. ....

The inert gas used inside the bulb is usually ....

The resistance wire used for the filament is ....

the temperature reached by this wire is approximately ....

In what important way does bulb 3 differ from the other small bulbs?

....

....

....

Why does bulb 4 have a staggered pin fitment? ....

....

....

Bulbs 5 and 6 are known as pre-focus bulbs. What identifying feature gives them this name?

....

....

....

....

What does the unit 7 include? ....

....

For the same wattage rating the headlamp bulb 5 will give off a much brighter light than bulb 6. How is this improvement achieved?

....

....

....

....

METHODS OF DIPPING THE BEAM

Two-headlamp system

When on main beam the light rays illuminate the road as far ahead as possible.

What occurs when the lights are dipped?

....

....

....

Show the position of the dipped beams.

Four-headlamp system

With some systems, when on main beam the outer lamps are on permanent dip while the inner lamps throw out a brighter longer range beam along the road.

What occurs when the lights are dipped?

....

....

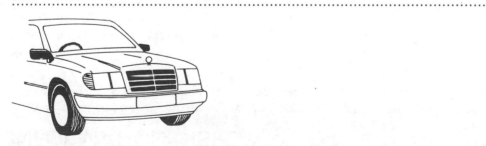

Show the position of the light beams when on main beam.

The direction indicator, stop light, reversing light and rear fog light are all obligatory lighting/warning systems on a modern car. Complete the simple wiring diagrams of the circuits shown.

DIRECTOR INDICATOR

Include flasher unit panel indicator lamps and, if required, side indicators.

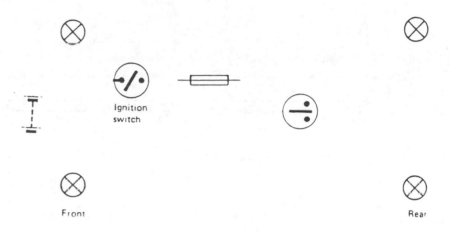

Front   Rear

STOP LAMPS

Indicate how they are operated.

59

DRIVER CONTROLS AND INFORMATION DISPLAY

Examine a car and a HGV and make sketches opposite to show the layout of the following driver controls and information displays.

Steering wheel
Clutch, brake and accelerator pedals
Hand brake lever
Gear lever (indicating gear positions)
Main lighting controls, e.g. main beam and dip
Side/tail, indicators, hazard, fog, screen wash/wipe
Bonnet release
Heater and ventilation controls
Speedometer, tachometer, tachograph
Fuel gauge
Warning indicators for brakes, lamps, engine oil
Coolant temperature, charging systems

Examine a car fitted with automatic transmission and sketch the auto-selector.

Name the selector positions.

Make .... Model ....

See also pages 262–264.

Car layout

Make .... Model ....

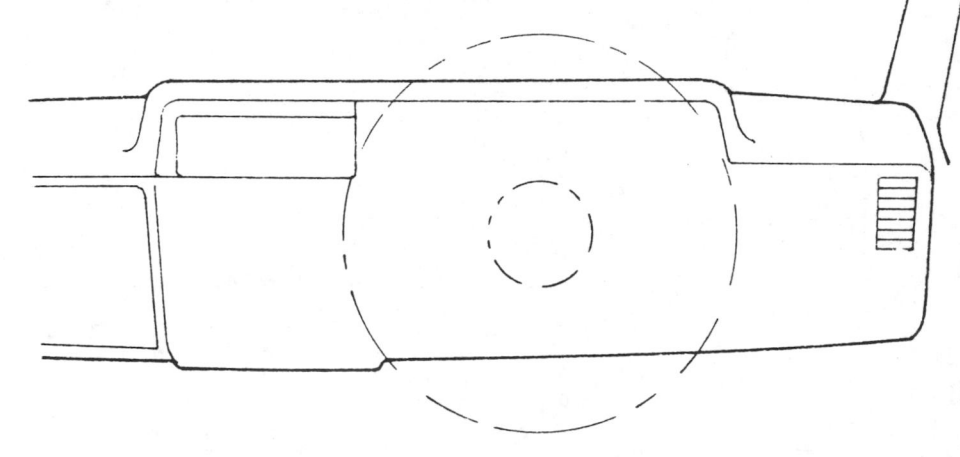

HGV Layout

Make .... Model ....

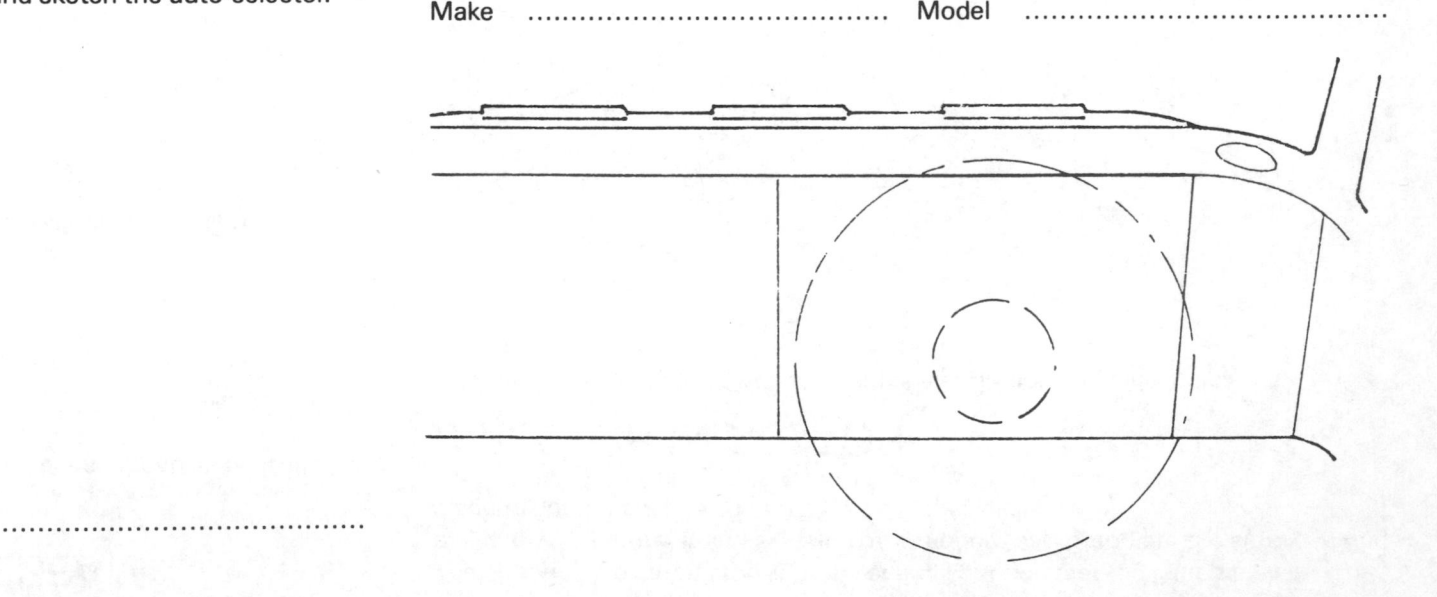

Chapter 2
Scheduled Servicing

ELEMENT 2   **PART OF UNIT 1**

TYPES OF SCHEDULED SERVICE

New vehicles must be in first class running order when delivered to the customer. They then must be regularly serviced to maintain this condition.

Name FOUR typical services scheduled by a manufacturer.

1. ....

2. ....

3. ....

4. ....

Suggest typical mileage service intervals.

....

....

What would be typical time-based service intervals?

....

....

Garage servicing does not mean that the owner has no need to carry out weekly or two weekly checks.

List typical owner weekly checks that should be carried out by the driver.

....

....

....

State the FUNCTION of the FOUR manufacturer-recommended servicing schedules.

1. Pre-delivery inspection (p.d.i.)

....

....

....

....

2. First service

This is usually scheduled at 500 or 600 miles, or even 1000 miles. (Some manufacturers incorporate this service with the pre-delivery inspection.)

....

....

....

3. Mileage-based service

....

....

....

....

....

....

4. Time-based service

....

....

....

The modern trend is to extend substantially the mileage service intervals.

List FOUR items that contribute towards this trend.

....

....

....

....

SERVICING DATA

Examine vehicle manufacturers' service schedules or oil company charts and basic service tasks under the following headings. State mileage/time intervals.

VEHICLE MAKE .... MODEL ....

Pre-delivery service

Mileage .... Time ....

....
....
....
....
....
....
....
....
....
....
....
....
....

First service

Mileage .... Time ....

....
....
....
....
....
....
....
....
....
....

Interim or Minor service

Mileage .... Time ....

....
....
....
....
....
....

Main service

Mileage .... Time ....

....
....
....
....
....
....
....
....
....
....
....
....
....

Seasonal service

Mileage .... Time ....

....
....
....
....
....
....
....
....
....

Safety check

Mileage .... Time ....

....
....
....
....
....
....
....
....

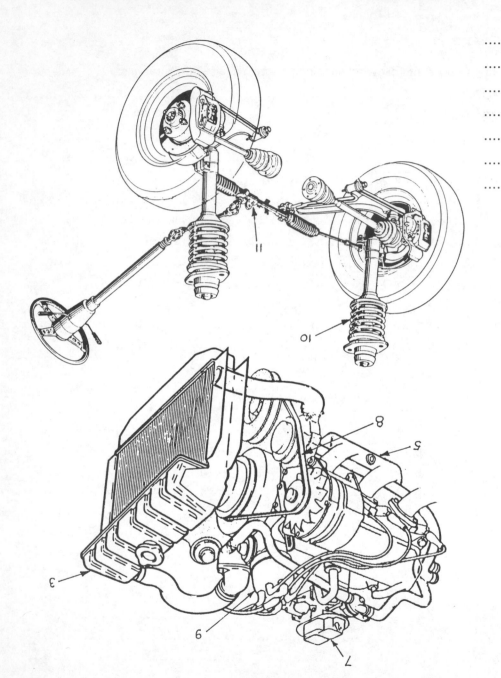

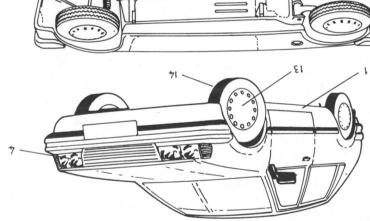

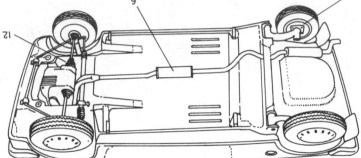

2.4 ITEMS AND SYSTEMS REQUIRING SERVICE CHECKS

Identify the vehicle systems shown below that would require basic service checks.

The illustrations are not of any one specific type of car.

1.	8. ....
2.	9. ....
3.	10. ....
4.	11. ....
5.	12. ....
6.	13. ....
7.	14. ....

BODY SERVICING

When carrying out an inspection service on the vehicle body, faults could be categorised under the headings below.

List common faults and where they might be expected to occur.

1. Paintwork

....
....
....
....
....

2. Corrosion to body panels

....
....
....
....
....

3. Underbody/chassis members for damage or corrosion

....
....
....
....

4. Door cover lock latch and hinge operation

....
....
....
....
....
....

5. Body and cab securing and locking devices

....
....
....
....
....

6. Seat belts, condition and security

....
....
....
....
....

What lubrication or adjustments might reasonably be expected to be done during a vehicle body check and service?

....
....
....
....

2.5a **Investigation**

Examine a vehicle in reasonable body condition and complete the table below.
Note: this exercise is related to routine maintenance, not body repairing.

Vehicle make .... Model ....

Examine	Faults	Possible causes	Treatment necessary
Body exterior	....	....	....
Inside the car	....	....	....
Engine compartment and boot	....	....	....
Body underside	....	....	....
Door locks, hinges, striker plates etc.	....	....	....

BRAKE SERVICING

Checking a braking system for faults may be divided into TWO sections:

1. Wheels on the ground.   2. Wheels removed.

What initial checks should be carried out with the wheels on the ground?

....
....
....
....
....

What basic checks should be carried out with the wheels removed?

....
....
....
....

Indicate and name the basic parts that require service checks.

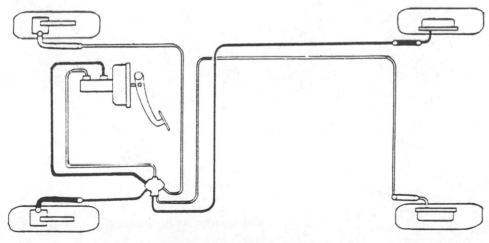

Car-dual line (hydraulic) braking system

Checks may also be made to see if the brake indicator warning circuits operate.

To what brake parts are warning indicators generally fitted and what do they monitor?

....
....
....
....

Heavy commercial vehicle brakes require extra attention. State THREE important items to check.

....
....
....
....

Indicate where checks should be made.

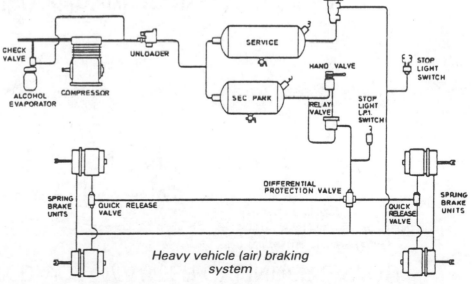

Heavy vehicle (air) braking system

FRONT DISC BRAKE ASSEMBLY

Name the parts that require service checks.

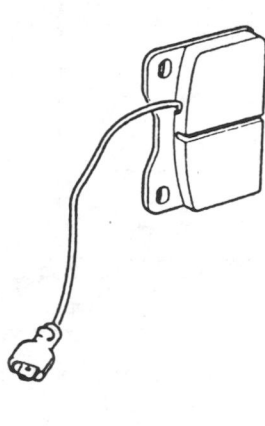
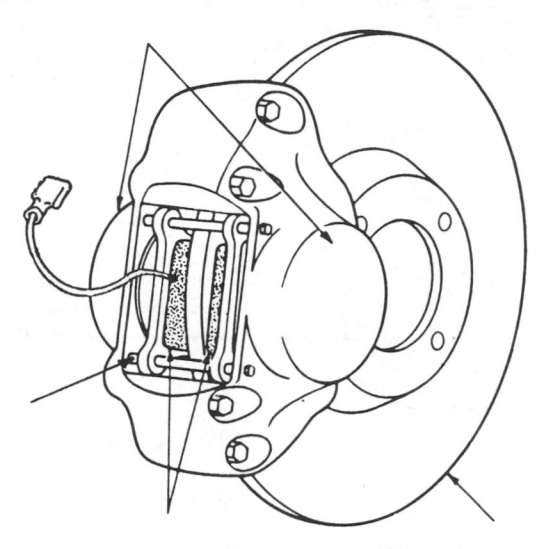

State faults that may be expected when checking a disc brake assembly.

....
....
....
....
....

What is the function of the cable hanging from the brake pad shown above.

....
....
....
....

PEDAL — MASTER CYLINDER LAYOUT

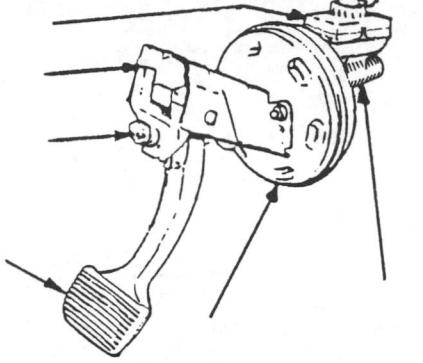

Name the arrowed parts.
Why is a split reservoir used on the master cylinder?

....
....
....
....
....
....
....

REAR DRUM BRAKE ASSEMBLY

Name the parts that require service checks.

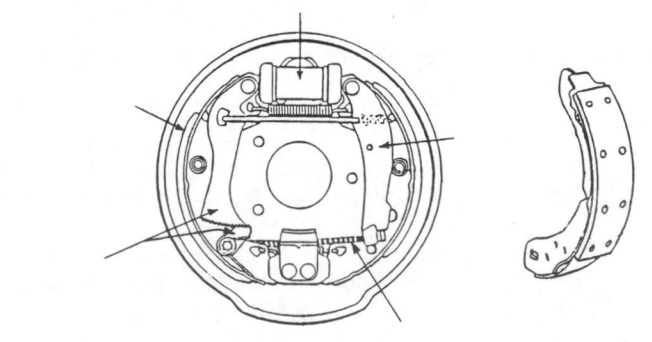

State faults that may be expected when checking a drum brake assembly.

....
....
....
....

COOLING SYSTEM SERVICE

Servicing the cooling system may largely consist of a visual check, with possibly a change of coolant or component.

The coolant level is usually checked by observing the fluid level in the translucent expansion bottle. What is the usual correct level of fluid in this bottle?

....

....

List TEN items that should be checked for leakage.

1. ....
2. ....
3. ....
4. ....
5. ....

6. ....
7. ....
8. ....
9. ....
10. ....

Identify using the above numbers possible leakage points.

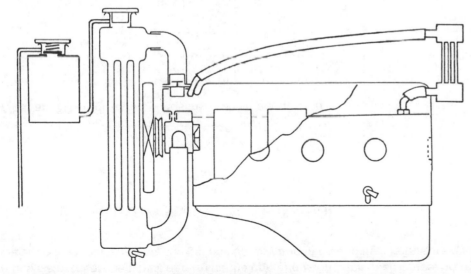

Indicate the direction of water flow and the recommended initial water level in (a) the radiator top tank, and (b) the expansion tank.

What effect does ageing have on the hoses?

....

....

When should a cooling system be drained and flushed?

....

....

How is the proportion of anti-freeze to water content usually checked?

....

....

How should anti-freeze/inhibitor be prepared before being put into the system?

....

....

....

....

Air locks occur in many coolant systems when refilled. How generally are these de-aerated? Consider the case of a car having air bleed valves.

....

....

....

....

The radiator matrix may eventually become clogged with dirt and flies. How should these be removed?

....

....

69

2.5d ELECTRICAL

A basic electrical check will determine the operation/condition of all lamps, horn, wiper and washer systems, the general battery condition and the alternator drive belt tension.

Name the main lighting systems that should be checked.

....

....

....

What are FOUR different windscreen wiper operations?

....

....

....

....

In what way may wiper blades be faulty?

....

....

The diagram shows, without using specialised equipment, the position of the main beams. What will occur when the lamps are dipped?

....

Distance between headlamp centres

Concentrated area of light

Height of lamp centres from ground

Distance for setting is at least 25 feet

Show the approximate dipped position of the concentrated light areas.

The battery needs little maintenance, usually only a visual check, but this should be made regularly.

Complete the table to give common faults that may cause premature battery failure.

Item	Possible fault
Casing	
Top	
Electrolyte	
Connections	
Securing frames	

What faults would make the drive belt unserviceable?

....

....

....

How would the drive belt shown in the diagram be adjusted for correct operation?

....

....

....

....

....

....

....

....

....

ENGINE SERVICING — OIL LEVEL CHECKS

The engine oil level must be frequently checked. It is therefore essential that the dip stick level readings are understood and the engine oil capacity known.

Indicate on the bottom of the dip stick the usual oil level markings and what they represent.

State typical engine oil capacity.

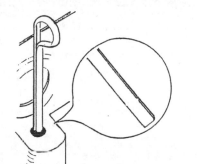

Vehicle make	Model	Engine size (cc)	Oil capacity (litres)

BREATHERS AND CAP FILTERS

On routine maintenance check, a check commonly overlooked is the cleaning of breathers, pipes and their filters.

How should the filler cap shown be serviced?

....
....
....

Why should the cap be cleaned?

....
....
....
....

Name and indicate the parts that require cleaning. Note that broad arrows show air flow.

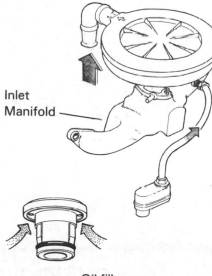

Inlet Manifold

Oil filler cap

OIL AND FILTER CHANGE

Oil filter fitments may be basically of two different types. Name those shown below.

1. ....   2. ....

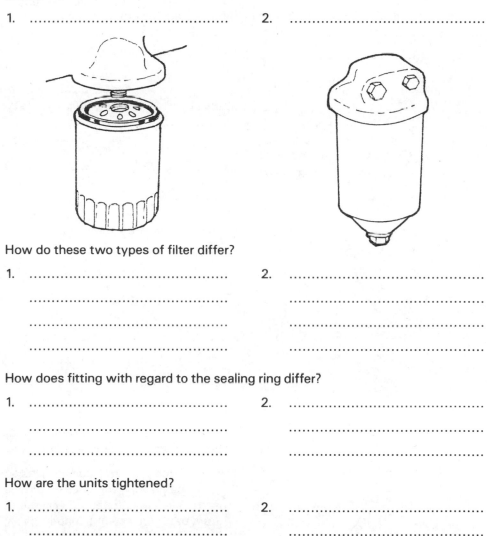

How do these two types of filter differ?

1. ....   2. ....

How does fitting with regard to the sealing ring differ?

1. ....   2. ....

How are the units tightened?

1. ....   2. ....

ENGINE SERVICING — OIL LEAKS

Indicated on the lubrication diagram of the engine below are typical points where oil leaks may occur.

Examine the sketch and name the possible leakage points that have been numbered.

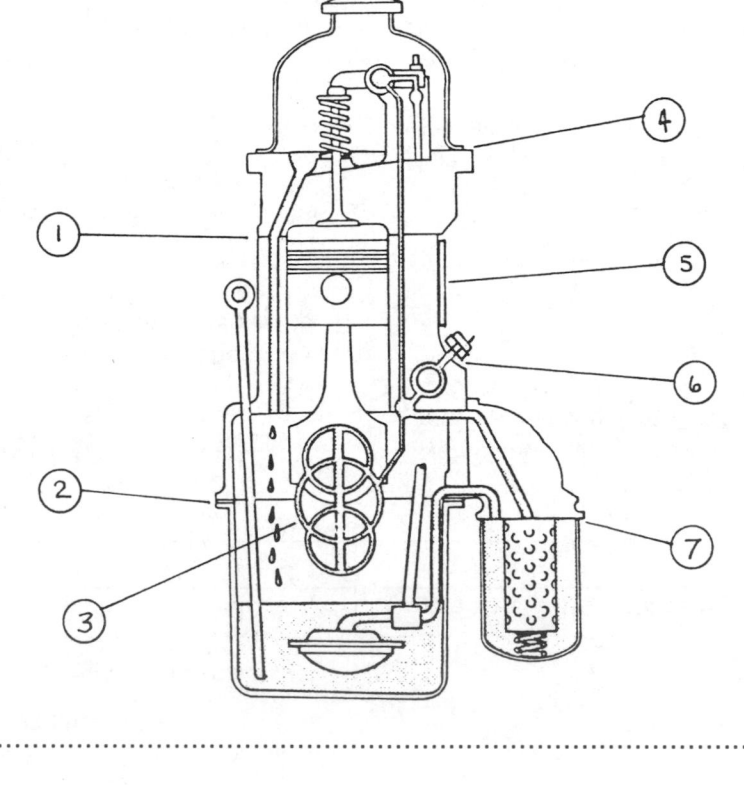

1. ....
2. ....
3. ....
4. ....
5. ....
6. ....
7. ....

TIMING BELT TENSION

Most modern engines are fitted with internally notched timing belts. These should be periodically checked for correct tension and condition.

How should a timing belt be checked for correct tension?

....
....
....
....
....
....
....
....

What faults would require the belt to be changed?

....
....
....
....

At what mileage should a timing belt typically be changed?

....

What may occur to the engine if the timing belt is not changed at the recommended mileage?

....
....
....

Name the parts indicated on the drive belt assembly.

1. ....
2. ....
3. ....
4. ....
5. ....

ENGINE SERVICING — VALVE CLEARANCE

The valves in an engine require clearance, there are two reasons for this:

(a) ....

(b) ....

Obtain data for a conventional four-cylinder engine for which the valve clearances will need to be adjusted during servicing.

Make of engine .... Type ....

State the engine's valve clearances in mm and inches.

Inlet valve   mm .... in. ....

Exhaust valve   mm .... in. ....

When the following valves are fully open	8	7	6	5	4	3	2	1
Check the clearance of valve nos.	1	2	3	4	5	6	7	8

The above method uses a 'law of 9' and is suitable for most four-cylinder engines.

....

....

....

....

Why do some engines not require the valve clearances to be adjusted?

....

....

....

....

Methods of valve adjustment

Below are shown some typical engine valve operating mechanisms. In each case show the position of the feeler gauge and explain how adjustment is made.

(a)

....

....

....

....

(b)

....

....

....

....

....

....

....

(c)

....

....

....

(d)

....

....

....

(e)

....

....

....

....

....

EXHAUST CHECK

An exhaust system should be replaced as soon as a box or pipe leaks. During routine service the condition of the exhaust should be checked. Indicate on the complete exhaust system where leaks are most likely to occur.

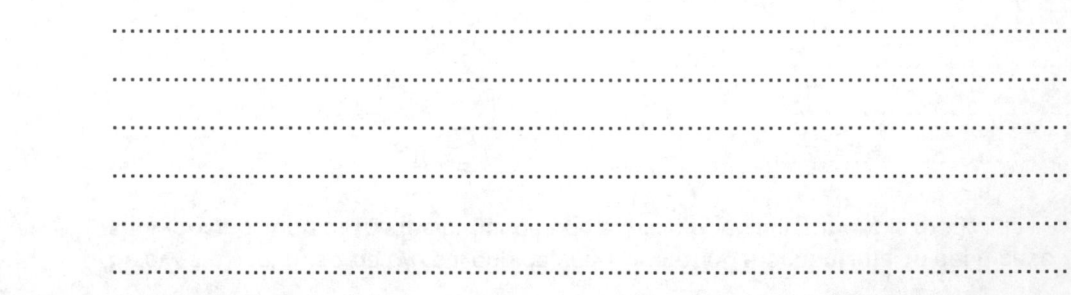

What faults may occur with the flange mountings below?

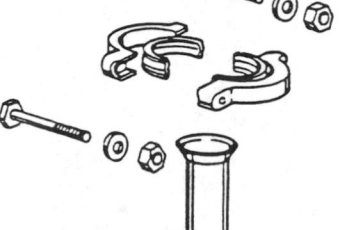

....

....

....

Identify the exhaust supports shown below.

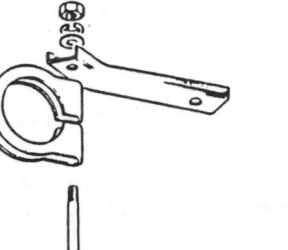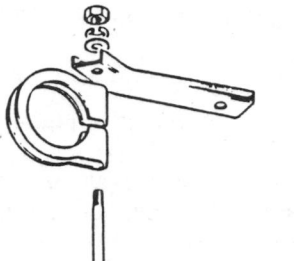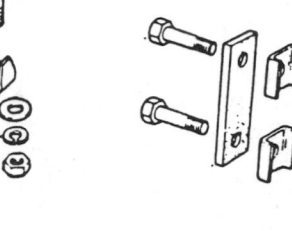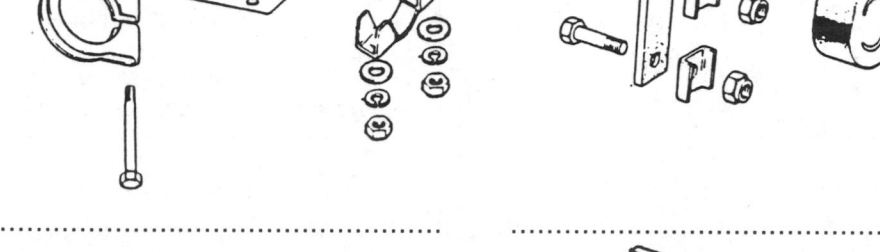

....

What routine checks should be given to the exhaust system?

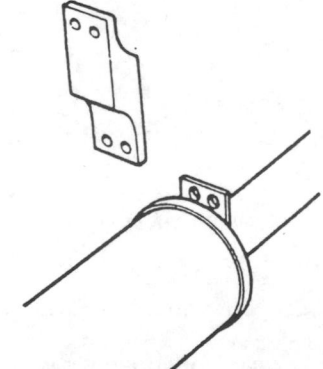

....

....

....

....

....

....

....

....

....

....

SERVICING AIR SUPPLY

The engine air cleaner has two functions:

1. To remove foreign matter (dust, grit) from the air before it enters the carburettor and engine.

2. ....

....

Below are shown two common types of air cleaner.
Name the types and describe how each should be serviced.

1. ....

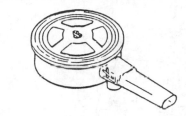

Oil level —
do not overfill

Wire
mesh

2. ....

The usual mileage between services is ....

1. ....

....

....

....

....

2. ....

....

....

....

....

....

....

....

AIR TEMPERATURE CONTROL

In European countries modern air cleaners have some means of allowing warm air to enter the engine during the winter period. This control may be a flap valve (operated manually) or by a thermostat.

Manually controlled air cleaner

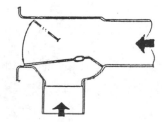

What service checks should be made?

....

....

....

Temperature controlled air cleaner

The thermostat moves the valve deflector plate to a position which will allow a mixture of hot/cold air to be supplied at a temperature between 23° and 28°C.

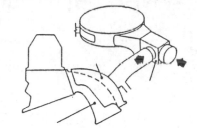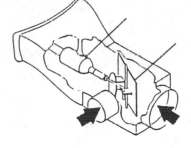

What service checks should be made?

....

....

....

....

FUEL SYSTEM PETROL

Show, on the drawing below, a typical petrol fuel system. Name the parts and indicate where service attention is likely to be required.

The diagrams show a typical constant depression carburettor. State the checks associated with the numbered parts.

1. ....
   ....
2. ....
   ....
3. ....
   ....
4. ....
   ....
5. ....
   ....

What checks should be carried out to the fuel system during a routine service?

....
....
....
....
....
....
....
....

FUEL INJECTION

A fuel injection layout is shown below. At this stage it is only necessary to check if all parts are secure and fitting correctly.

Name the parts indicated.

NOTE: if the fuel injection system is to be worked on, the fuel supply system must first be depressurised.

FUEL SYSTEM —
COMPRESSION IGNITION (DIESEL)

An in-line pump diesel fuel system is shown. Note the direction of fuel flow around the system. Name the parts indicated.

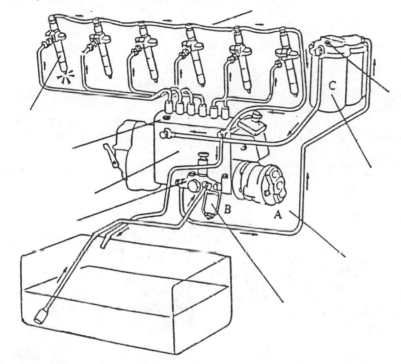

To what is part A connected? ....

What checks should be made to a diesel fuel system during routine maintenance?

....
....
....
....

Describe how filter B should be serviced.

....
....
....

Describe how filter C should be serviced.

....
....
....

When filters B and C have been serviced the system must be bled of air. Describe how this bleeding process is carried out.

....
....
....
....
....
....
....
....
....

What effects would occur if air was in the fuel system?

....
....
....

77

IGNITION SERVICE

Name the main parts of the simple coil-ignition system shown and draw the primary and secondary circuits leads.

What is the firing order if the rotor turns anticlockwise? ....

What items should be visually checked on the ignition system before dismantling and after removal of the distributor cap?

....

....

....

....

What is the speed relationship between the distributor and the crankshaft?

....

SPARK PLUG

terminal

insulator

thread

gap

At what typical mileage should the spark plugs be removed and checked? ....
What basic service should be given to a plug which is removed for cleaning?

....

....

....

....

....

....

DISTRIBUTOR

Name the parts indicated.

Describe how the distributor contacts should be replaced and adjusted.

....

....

....

....

....

....

....

....

SUSPENSION CHECKS — REAR

Shown below is a conventional rear wheel drive leaf spring suspension.
What service checks should be made to the numbered items?

....
....
....
....
....
....
....
....

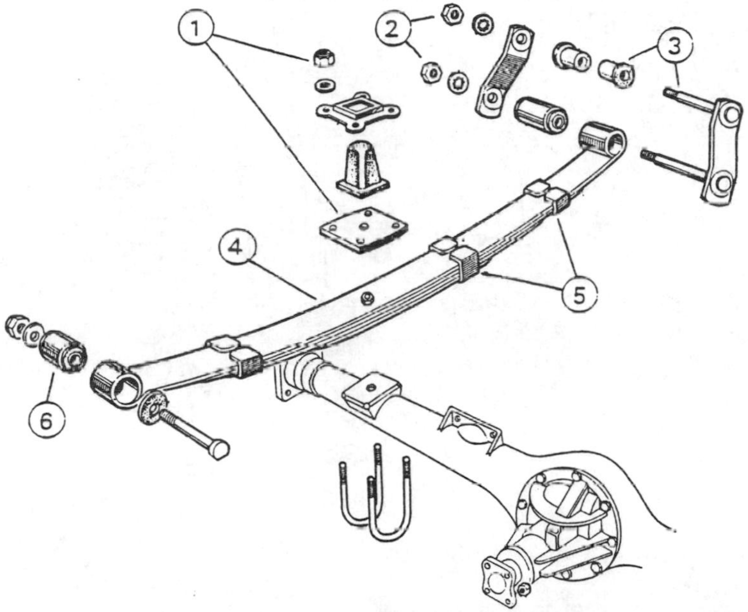

Shown below is a typical rear wheel drive independent suspension system.
Name the numbered items and state what service checks should be made to
them.

....
....
....
....
....
....
....

What is the component (5)? ....

What is a typical recommended mileage for its replacement? ....

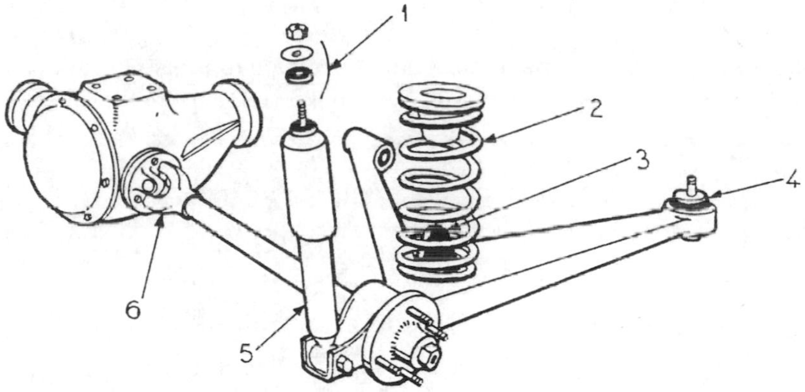

....
....

2.5j SUSPENSION CHECKS — FRONT

The type of suspension system shown is called?

....

Number the parts and state what service checks should be made to them.

....
....
....
....
....
....
....
....
....

If the ride (trim) height of a vehicle is incorrect (usually it is low), what checks should be made?

....
....
....
....

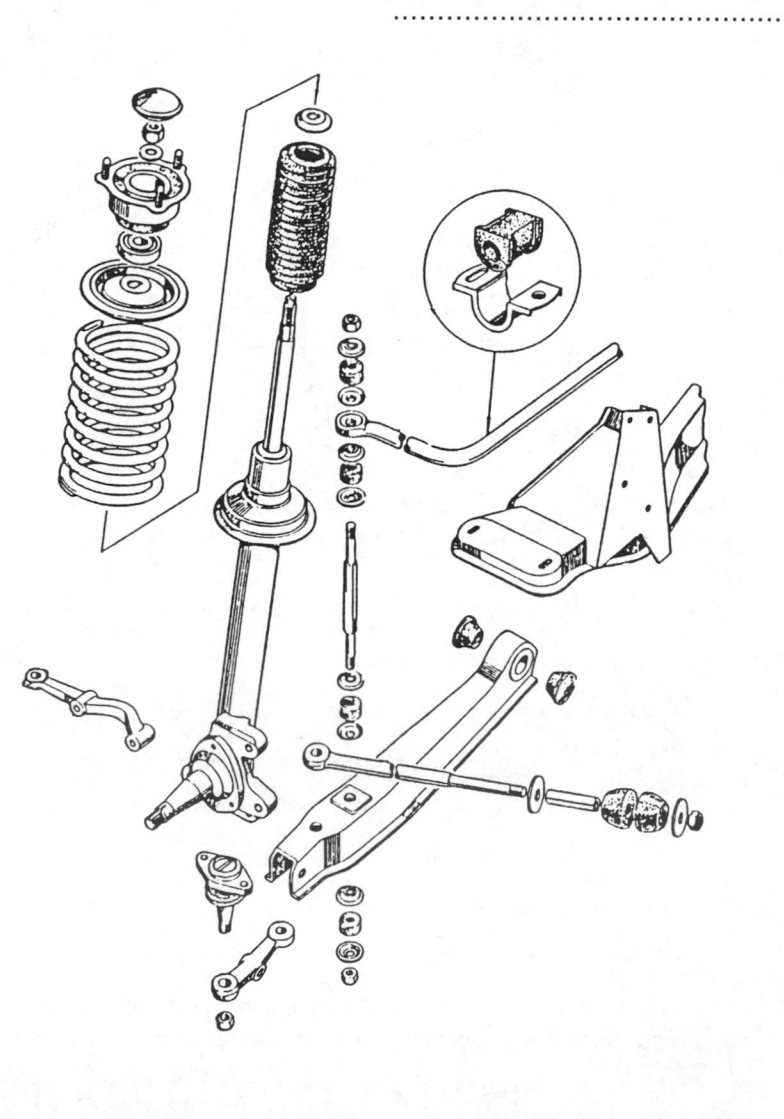

LUBRICATION

On all the three suspension drawings shown, the moving parts require no lubrication or are self-lubricating.

What parts on older models require lubrication by grease?

....

Some heavy commercial vehicles use an automatic chassis lubrication system by oil or grease.
What periodic maintenance should be given to such a system?

....
....
....

STEERING SYSTEM CHECKS

The type of steering system shown is the most popular arrangement used on modern cars.

It is called a ....

Indicate and name the items that should be checked for wear, if the steering wheel was rotated to and fro and excessive play was evident.

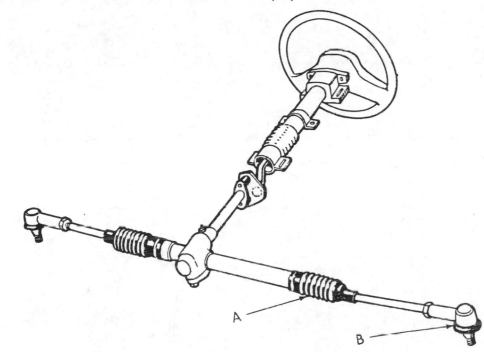

What are items A and B and what checks should be made to them?

....

....

What lubrication is necessary to the steering system?

....

....

Many modern vehicles use a power steering system. Name the main parts of the system layout shown below.

List three important checks that should be made to the power steering system?

1. ....

2. ....

3. ....

Both sides of a filler cap dip stick are shown. What is noticeable about the readings?

After repair, when the system is topped up with oil, a bleeding procedure must be carried out to expel all air.
Describe how this should be done.

....

....

....

....

....

TRANSMISSION CHECKS — CLUTCH OPERATION

The drawings show the clutch operating layouts that should be checked during service.

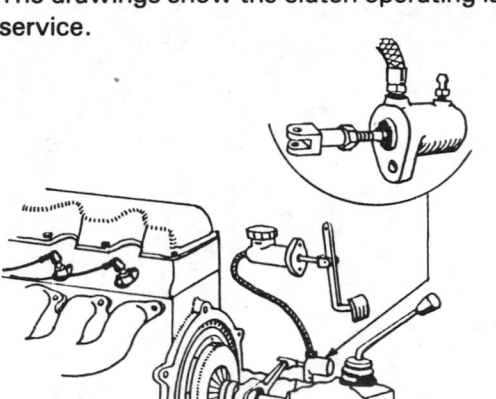

In both cases name the basic parts and state the items that should be periodically checked.

Hydraulically operated

....
....
....
....
....
....
....
....

Mechanically operated

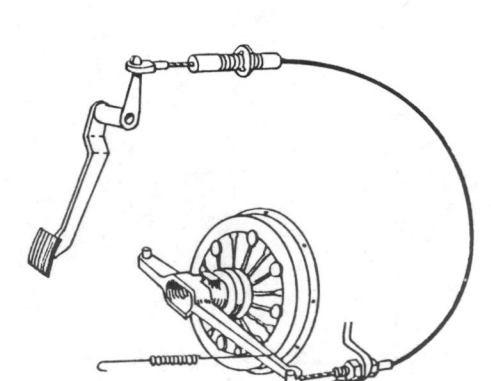

....
....
....
....
....
....
....
....

Some clutch and gear change layouts on PSVs and commercial vehicles are pneumatically assisted. What checks should be made to these systems.

....

BASIC OIL LUBRICATION

Indicate on the first three drawings from where the oil should be drained and/or checked for the correct level; also indicate from where oil leakage is most likely to occur.

MANUAL TRANSMISSION

Gearbox   *Rear axle*

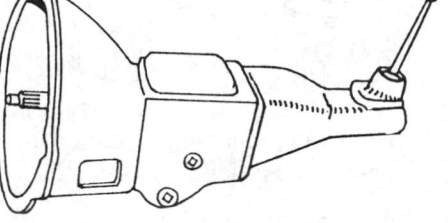

AUTOMATIC TRANSMISSION

Fluid flywheel   *Automatic gearbox dipstick*

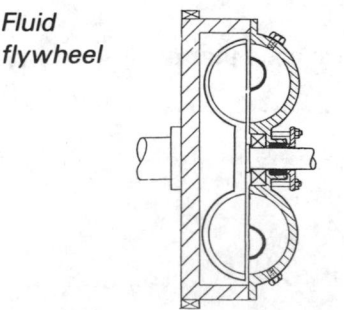

....
....

DRIVE SHAFTS

What service checks should be made to the drive shaft assembly shown?

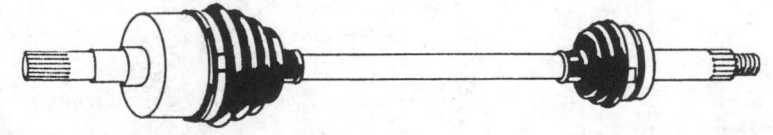

....
....

TYRE CHECKS

Certain tyre defects make it illegal to use a vehicle on a public road. Visual checks for tyre defects must be made at each service.

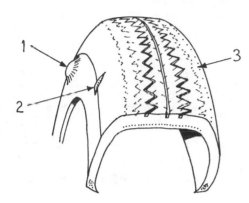

State the three tyre defects shown opposite.

....

....

....

....

....

....

....

....

Types of tyre

Two of the most important characteristics of a tyre are:
(a) type of construction, radial or cross-ply (see Chapter 1), and
(b) its speed rating.

How is it possible to determine these two factors by external examination?

....

....

....

Fitting all cross-ply tyres or all radial-ply tyres to a vehicle is legal; some tyre combinations, however, are dangerous and therefore illegal.

Below are shown three possible tyre fitment combinations. State which is legal and which is illegal.   cross-ply X   radial-ply III

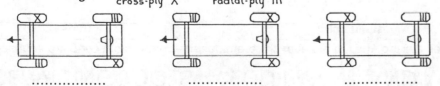

....

Ensuring that tyre pressures are correct is probably the single most important tyre check that can be made. Running with tyres incorrectly inflated is both illegal and dangerous.

Compare the recommended pressures for vehicles of the following types.

Type of vehicle	Make	Model	Pressure Front	Rear
Front engine rear drive				
Front engine front drive				
Rear engine rear drive				
Heavy commercial vehicle				

ROAD WHEEL CHECKS

The most important check on a wheel is to ensure that the wheel nuts are tight. Sketch a wheel nut in its correct tightened position and give reasons for its shape.

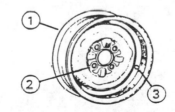

Hub

....

....

....

State three checks that should be made to road wheels during service.

....

....

....

....

....

....

What other wheel checks should be made?

1. ....

2. ....

2.6 SERVICING TOOLS — EQUIPMENT AND MATERIALS

Describe the main tools/equipment and materials required to carry out the servicing of the motor-vehicle systems listed.

System	Equipment	Materials
Braking		
Cooling		
Electrical		
Engine and transmission		
Fuel and exhaust		
Ignition		
Suspension and steering		
Wheels and tyres		

INSPECTION AND CARE OF TOOLS

Before commencing work, the condition of hand tools should be checked and any that are damaged should not be used. Similarly, any special service tool drawn from the store should be inspected to ensure that it is safe to use and capable of doing the work required. State examples of when hand tools should be discarded.

....
....
....
....
....
....
....

Certain test equipment should be checked against known standard readings. Name service items that require testing in such a manner.

....
....
....
....
....

How should the tools, equipment and materials described on the previous page be kept in good working condition to ensure that they

1. Are secured against loss?

....
....
....

2. Are undamaged?

....
....
....

3. Do not deteriorate?

....
....

SERVICING SEQUENCE

Every basic service, particularly the larger ones, should follow a predetermined sequence of operations to allow the service to be carried out in the most efficient manner possible.

Produce a list of such a service sequence from collecting the work order to completing the service sheet and report.

1. ....
....

2. ....
....

3. ....
....

4. ....
....

5. ....
....

6. ....
....

7. ....
....

8. ....
....

9. ....

SAFE WORKING

State the precautions to be observed to avoid injury or vehicle damage when carrying out scheduled servicing.
Itemise under the following headings:

Jacking vehicle, working in pits

....

....

....

....

Working under bonnet, removing battery

....

....

....

....

Running engine

....

....

....

....

Brake servicing

....

....

....

....

Basic servicing

....

....

....

....

Car body and interior protection

....

....

....

....

State the safety faults depicted by the drawings:

Tools

Electrical

Wearing jewellery

Making vehicle wheel free

Using pits

Parts storage

....

....

....

....

....

....

....

....

....

....

....

....

Chapter 3

Assembly and Dismantling

ELEMENT 8   **PART OF UNIT 4**

PURPOSE, FORMS and METHODS of ASSEMBLY and DISMANTLING

8.1, 2, 3

All the components that make up a modern vehicle are in their assembled position when the vehicle is in service. If a repair is required it is likely that some form of dismantling will be necessary. Give examples of vehicle components which require some form of dismantling to carry out:

1. Periodic inspection or maintenace

....
....

2. Repair of components

....
....

3. Replacement of components

....
....

After repair all components must be assembled, observing correct procedures. State important points that should be observed to ensure the correct assembly of a cylinder head.

....
....
....
....
....

When obtaining replacement parts from stores it is common practice to find that they are protected from minor damage or corrosion. Give examples of vehicle components and the method of protection given.

....
....
....
....

Give examples of items which typically may:

(i) be dismantled *in situ* on the vehicle, and repaired by fitting new parts

....
....

(ii) removed from the vehicle then dismantled, repaired and re-assembled on the workbench

....
....

(iii) removed from the vehicle and replaced with an exchange unit

....
....

On some vehicles it is necessary to remove the component for repair while on others the same component can be repaired *in situ*. State some consideration which may affect this decision.

....
....
....
....

What major differences could be expected in removing the engine sump on a

(i) small car	(ii) heavy commercial vehicle
....	....
....	....
....	....
....	....

RELATIONSHIPS BETWEEN ASSEMBLED COMPONENTS

Identify the motor vehicle drawings shown on this page and state which of the relationships below could describe the assembled components shown. In each case give three other motor vehicle examples.

Relationship	Other examples

1. 'Neither component moves relative to the other' is shown at drawing ....

2. 'The joint between non-moving parts must be fluid tight' is shown at drawing ....

3. 'One side slides relative to the other' is shown at drawing ....

4. 'The joint between sliding and fixed components is fluid tight' is shown at drawing ....

5. 'One part rotates relative to the other' is shown at drawing ....

6. 'The joint between the rotating and fixed components is fluid tight' is shown at drawing ....

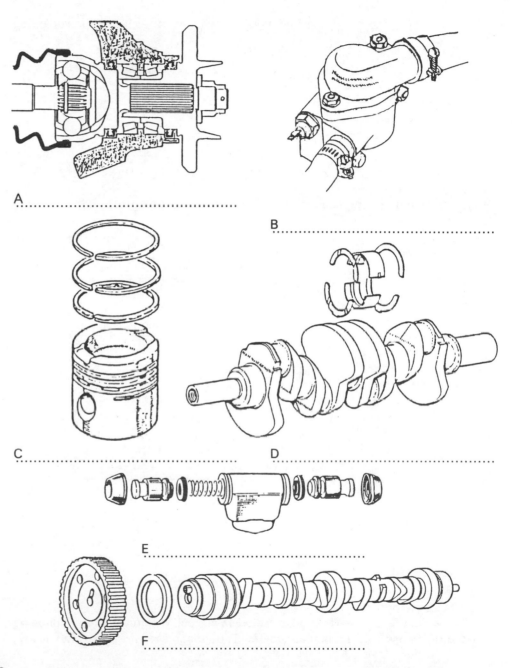

A ....

B ....

C ....   D ....

E ....

F ....

8.5 BEHAVIOUR OF MATERIALS UNDER APPLICATION OF FORCE

A force tends to produce or alter the motion of a body if it is free to move, or induce an internal reaction — called *stress* — in a body if it is not free to move.

When a bolt is tightened the applied force will always cause the material to deform — the material is thus said to be under *strain*. Excessive strain will cause permanent deformation.

Below are the main forces which act on a material.
State two motor-vehicle components subjected to each force.

Force	Motor-vehicle components
Tensile or stretching	
Compressive	
Torsional or twisting	
Shearing	

How would permanent deformation caused by overtightening affect nuts and bolts or studs.

....

....

....

....

Use arrows to indicate the directions in which the major forces would normally be acting after assembly when the vehicle is in normal use.

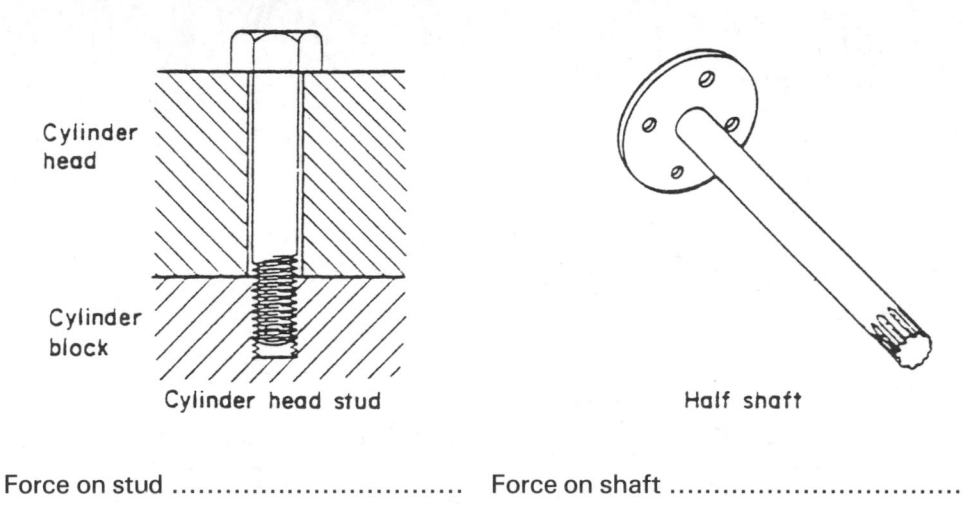

Cylinder head

Cylinder block

Cylinder head stud

Half shaft

Force on stud ....   Force on shaft ....

A leaf spring on a car bends or flexes.

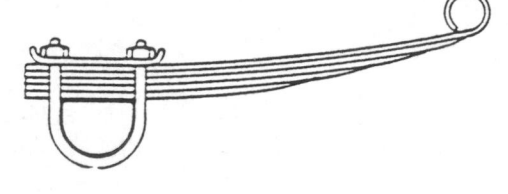

When the spring is loaded two forces are set up in each leaf. On the upper side a

.... force and on the lower side a .... force.

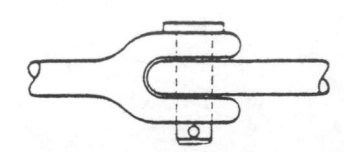

Coil spring

Force on spring ....

This type of pin is called ....

Force on pin ....

90

TOOLS USED for ASSEMBLY and DISMANTLING

Anyone employed in the active repair of motor vehicles should eventually build up a comprehensive set of tools suitable to his specialised type of work.
Name the tools shown and state the sizes or types it is desirable to have.

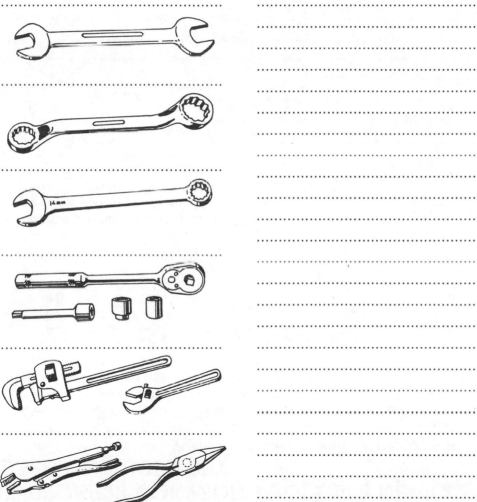

List any other basic hand tools you consider desirable.

Other specialised tools available will most probably be supplied by the garage. What are the most common tools in this area?

What is the basic function of a torque wrench?

What is the purpose of a lock 'C' spanner?

Why is a ring spanner made in the shape shown?

8.7 PURPOSE of COMMON TOOLS and DEVICES USED ON ASSEMBLY

I. *Fitting tools:* Those such as already described are used to secure together various parts or assemblies.

II. *Mechanical joining devices:* These provide the means of joining one component to another and are traditionally nuts, bolts, screws, keys and pins; plus adhesives on modern vehicles. All are adequately covered in other sections but as a reminder, can you identify the items shown?

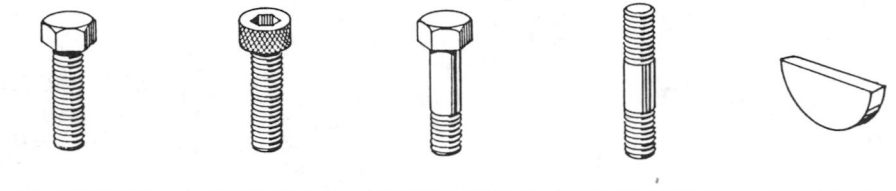

....

....

III. *Locking devices:* These prevent nuts and bolts from working loose as the vehicle is continually vibrated.
How does the nylon insert in the nut shown provide a self-locking action?

nylon insert

....

....

....

....

Name FIVE other locking devices.

....

....

....

....

....

IV. *Seals:* These ensure that joints are leakproof.
What may the seals be made from on a stationary joint?

....

What type of seal is most commonly used when the component is rotating?

....

V. *Presses:* The types of fit requiring a press for assembly would be ....

A press allows an even, steadily increasing load to be applied. Thus eliminating damage from shock loading that, for example, hammering could cause.
State FOUR vehicle components that require assembly by means of a press.

....

....

....

....

VI. *Measuring equipment used during assembly.* In order to ensure an accuracy of fit, before, during or after assembly it may be necessary to take measurements or align the components.
What measuring or testing equipment may be necessary for checking the circumstances listed below?

1. The size or position of a component before and during assembly

   ....

2. A horizontal or vertical datum

   ....

3. Angles

   ....

4. Clearances

   ....

5. Concentricity

   ....

6. Position

   ....

Presses may be operated mechanically or hydraulically. The hydraulic type is usually capable of exerting a higher pressure.

Sketch a press available to you for doing assembly work.

8.7 PURPOSE of COMMON TOOLS and DEVICES USED FOR DISMANTLING

I.   *Fitting tools,* such as already described, are used to dismantle components.

II.   *Cleaning agents:* What is their purpose before, during and after dismantling?

      ....

      ....

      ....

III. *Dyes and markers:* Why are these used?

      ....

      ....

      ....

      What type of markers are available?

      ....

      ....

      ....

IV.   *Stud removal:* The sketches show a stud remover and a stud extractor. Identify them and state how a stud remover should be used.

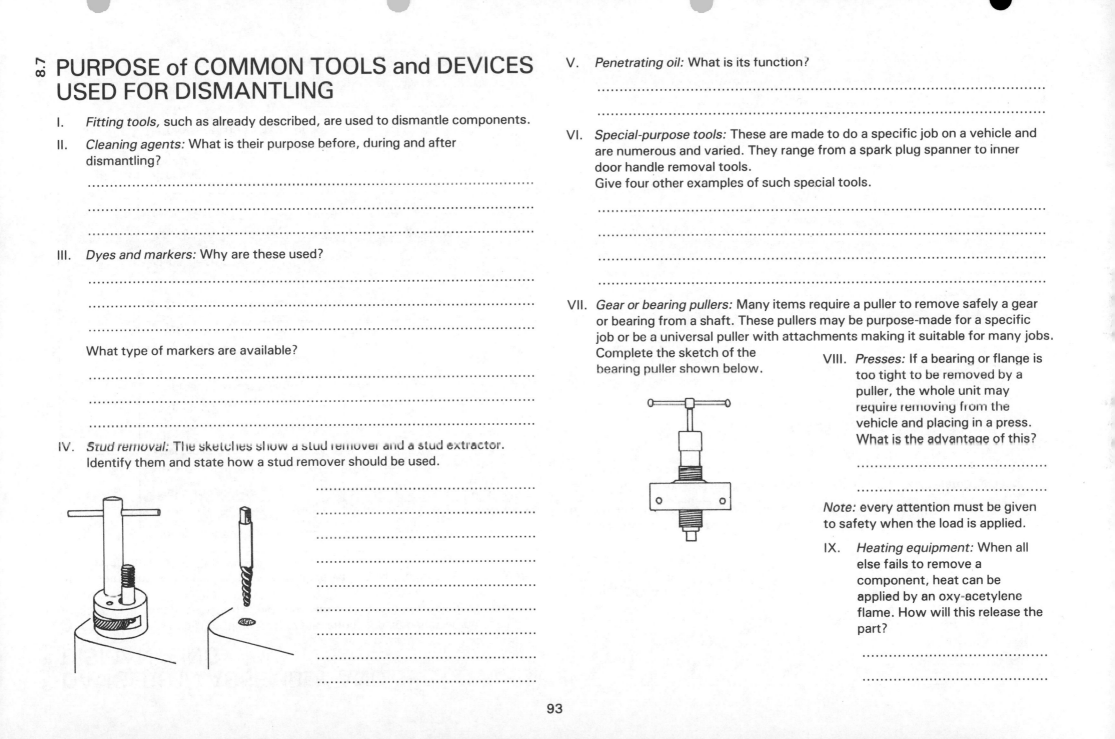

      ....

      ....

      ....

      ....

      ....

      ....

      ....

      ....

V.   *Penetrating oil:* What is its function?

      ....

      ....

VI.   *Special-purpose tools:* These are made to do a specific job on a vehicle and are numerous and varied. They range from a spark plug spanner to inner door handle removal tools.
      Give four other examples of such special tools.

      ....

      ....

      ....

      ....

VII. *Gear or bearing pullers:* Many items require a puller to remove safely a gear or bearing from a shaft. These pullers may be purpose-made for a specific job or be a universal puller with attachments making it suitable for many jobs. Complete the sketch of the bearing puller shown below.

VIII. *Presses:* If a bearing or flange is too tight to be removed by a puller, the whole unit may require removing from the vehicle and placing in a press. What is the advantage of this?

      ....

      ....

      Note: every attention must be given to safety when the load is applied.

IX.   *Heating equipment:* When all else fails to remove a component, heat can be applied by an oxy-acetylene flame. How will this release the part?

      ....

      ....

93

DANGERS IN ASSEMBLY AND DISMANTLING

When assembling or dismantling, safety precautions must be observed at all times. A lack of concentration could cause an accident to yourself or damage to the component.

State some important precautions to be observed under the following headings (note additional detail, Chapter 4).

Forces — weight of system and forces applied	Engine removal .... Jacks and stands .... Fuel tanks ....
Pressure and flammability	Air brakes .... Petrol tanks and pipe .... Garage pipework ....
Electricity	Battery .... Mains electricity ....
Temperature	Cooling systems .... Oil changing ....
Chemicals	Battery, cooling system, brake system ....

Component marking for re-assembly	....

GENERAL RULES FOR ASSEMBLY and DISMANTLING

The workshop manual provides a dismantling and assembly procedure which should be used at all times until the correct method is known.

State general rules that should be applied to ensure that successful dismantling and assembly occur.

1. ....
....

2. ....
....

3. ....
....

4. ....
....

5. ....
....

6. ....
....

7. ....
....

8.9 EFFECTS OF MATERIAL PROPERTIES ON ASSEMBLING AND DISMANTLING

All types of mechanical fastening should be tightened to their correct torque and this value should not be exceeded.

Bolts are graded according to their tensile strength. How can they be identified?

....

....

....

What is the advantage of using bolts of high tensile strength?

....

....

....

It is possible for bolts to be made stronger although produced from the same material? Indicate the principle on the sketches below relative to machined and forged-rolled bolts.

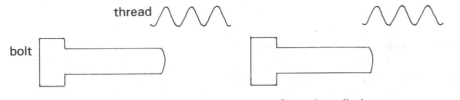

machined   forged – rolled

The material of a component must be known before it is tightened because different materials have different properties. For example, some may stretch easily, others may be very brittle.

State a type of material that is brittle ....

State two important considerations relative to assembling or dismantling cast components

....

....

....

When assembling vehicle components, different methods of sealing are used to ensure the best results in a given situation. This can vary from such as high pressures in the engine cylinder to high temperatures in the exhaust, or hot oil at high pressure in the engine.

Examine a complete engine gasket set and list the materials used for the different gaskets.

Gasket	Material
Cylinder head	

CORROSION

Corrosion, especially of bodywork, can seriously reduce vehicle life. What precautions should be taken to minimise corrosion due to service repairs?

....

....

....

Show the effect of corrosion after assembly when using component of dissimilar metals and indicate how corrosion can be avoided.

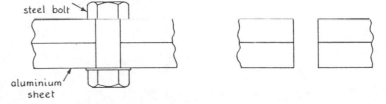

steel bolt

aluminium sheet

UNIT 02
PERSONAL SAFETY

INCLUDES

Chapter 4

Observing Safe Practices

4.1 HEALTH AND SAFETY AT WORK ACT

The Health and Safety at Work Act 1974 provides one comprehensive system of law, dealing with the health and safety of working people and the public as affected by working activities. The Act has imposed responsibilities on every person to be aware of health and safety hazards in their working environment.

General duties of employers to their employees

To safeguard health, safety and welfare. This relates to

(a) the condition of plant equipment and the systems of work adopted;

(b) the use, handling, storage and transport of articles and substances;

(c) the place of work (premises);

(d) facilities and arrangements for welfare.

State three other general duties of employers.

1. ....
....
....
....

2. ....
....
....
....

3. ....
....
....
....

The Factories Act 1961 was a major Act concerned with health and safety in factories, demolition and construction sites, docks, shipyards and power stations. Name SIX aspects of health and safety covered by this Act.

....
....
....
....
....
....

State THREE duties of employees with regard to health and safety at work.

1. ....
....
....

2. ....
....
....

3. ....
....

Give an example of a situation where an employee could be prosecuted under the terms of the Act.

....
....
....

Enforcement

A body called The Health and Safety Executive Inspectorate enforces the Act. Its inspectors have various powers and penalties at their disposal.

What procedures can be adopted by the inspectorate?

....
....
....
....
....
....

BASIC PRINCIPLES OF ACCIDENT PREVENTION

An accident is an unexpected, unplanned occurrence which can involve injury. The effects of an accident are not necessarily confined to the person or persons directly involved; other people may be affected in different ways. A minor accident may have trivial effects but a serious accident could affect one's whole life socially, domestically and economically. Accident prevention should therefore be a major concern at all times.

What are the basic requirements for successful accident prevention?

....
....
....
....
....
....

Causes of accidents

Generally speaking accidents are caused by:

1. Ignorance of the dangers involved.

2. Failure to take adequate precautions.

3. Tiredness causing lack of concentration.

4. Fooling about.

5. Lack of skill through inadequate training.

State four other causes of accidents in the workplace.

....
....
....
....
....

Indicate in the table below, how an accident, where, for example, a man loses a limb, could affect the persons listed.

People affected	Possible effects
Person injured	
Service manager	
Foreman	
Workmates	
Parents or family	

4.5 List below the major hazard or risk areas associated with a garage/workshop environment:

(a) Moving and running vehicles.

(b) Working with flammable liquids and gases.

....
....
....
....
....
....
....
....
....
....
....
....
....
....
....
....

Indicate below the possible injuries that could result from the situations listed.

Situation	Possible consequences
Poor spanner fit on nut	....
Undue effort needed owing to the use of short spanner	....
Using a file without a handle	....
Using a blunt screwdriver	....
Using a 'mushroomed' headed chisel	....
Banging two hammer faces together	....
Using a file as punch	....

4.5 FLAMMABLE LIQUIDS AND GASES

Many flammable substances are used in garages, for example

(a) ....*Petrol*.......... (c) .... (e) ....

(b) .... (d) .... (f) ....

Some liquids are *volatile*. What is meant by this and what particular hazards can this present during the normal course of repair work?

....

....

....

....

....

....

....

What procedure should be adopted in the event of a spillage of flammable liquid such as petrol?

....

....

....

....

....

....

....

....

Some accidents related to flammable liquids or gases are shown in the table below. Complete the table by stating possible causes of the accident.

Accident	Possible cause
Petrol tank explosion	
Battery explosion	
Fire in the pit	
Fire under a bonnet	
Fire at or near welding bench	

What special precautions should be taken with regard to the storage of

flammable substances? ....

....

....

....

....

....

....

....

What substance is the more dangerous with regard to storage, a substance with a high flash point or a substance with a low flash point?

....

HARMFUL SUBSTANCES

Certain areas in a motor-vehicle repair premises present particular health hazards. The hazards may, for example, be due to breathing in polluted air or coming into contact with harmful substances.

What is meant by the term *toxic* when used to describe a substance or gas?

....

....

....

....

....

List some of the toxic gases or substances likely to be present in a motor-vehicle repair workshop.

....

....

....

....

....

....

Asbestos dust is encountered when cleaning brake assemblies. What particular hazard is associated with asbestos dust and what precautions must be taken?

....

....

....

....

....

Complete the table below by describing the toxic hazards involved in the areas listed and briefly outline the precautions to be adopted.

Hazard area	Hazard	Suitable precautions
Engine tuning	*Exhaust fumes*	*Pipe gases outside, adequate ventilation, use of extractor fans, gas not aimed into confined space*
Welding bench	....	....
Degreasing plant	....	....
Body shop	....	....
Paint shop	....	....
Battery charging	....	....

State any hazards not already mentioned that may affect your own working environment.

....

....

SAFE USE OF MACHINERY AND EQUIPMENT

Many accidents in garages are caused either by the worker not taking adequate precautions or by faulty equipment.

State the precautions necessary when working on a vehicle raised by a jack.

....

....

....

....

....

What precautions should be taken when using the following items of equipment?

Compressed-air equipment

....

....

....

....

....

Chain lifting blocks

....

....

....

....

Slings and chains should be checked for wear at least once every ....

Vehicle hoist

....

....

....

....

Bench drills

....

....

....

....

Grinding wheels

....

....

....

....

Which is the correct way to lift an engine using a chain sling as shown below?

(   )

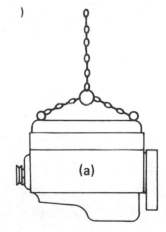

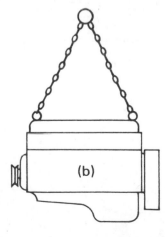

4.4 PERSONAL PROTECTION

A large proportion of accidents are due to the negligence of the person or persons involved. One very important factor with regard to accident prevention is the degree of 'personal protection' in relation to the particular hazards involved.

Personal protection can range from the use of adequate working clothes to the use of specialised protective equipment. The following headings all relate to personal protection. Describe the protective measures to be adopted, under each of the headings, for garage workers.

Ordinary working clothes (that is, protective clothing)

....

....

....

....

....

....

....

Eye protection

....

....

....

....

....

Skin protection

....

....

....

....

....

....

....

....

Tidiness

....

....

....

....

Which of the four sketches below shows the correct way to lift a heavy load?

| A | B | C | D |

.... is correct

4.6 ELECTRICAL SAFETY

Two dangers arising as a result of using electricity in a workshop are: *fire* caused by say overheating of an electrical circuit or a bursting bulb igniting fuel, and *electric shock* as a result of someone coming into contact with a live circuit.

An electric shock can cause death or serious injury to a person. Apart from electric shock, what other effects can result from a person coming into contact with a live electrical conductor?

....

Electric shock is caused by current passing through the human body; how does this occur?

....

....

....

....

....

For safety reasons hand-held electrically operated equipment, for example portable drills, should be .... volts and handlamps should be

.... volts.

What could cause a circuit to overheat?

....

....

....

....

....

The main hazards arising from the use of electrical equipment are

(a) Poor or damaged insulation on such as cables, plugs etc.

(b) Lack of adequate earthing for the equipment.

(c) ....

(d) ....

(e) ....

(f) ....

Describe briefly the action to be taken in the event of a person receiving an electric shock.

....

....

....

....

....

Note: see First-Aid section.

Accident reporting

Accidents of any kind should be reported to the employer. Describe normal procedure for reporting and recording accidents.

....

....

....

....

....

....

Investigation

Make a thorough inspection of your workshop or garage and make brief notes under the headings on this page to describe any potential safety hazards or lack of warning or guidance notices.

Fire risk/fire precautions

....

....

....

....

Machinery (drills, grindstones etc.)

....

....

....

....

Vehicle lifts and jacks

....

....

....

....

Electrical (hand drills, hand lamps etc.)

....

....

....

....

Lifting equipment

....

....

....

....

Welding area

....

....

....

Battery charging

....

....

....

....

Compressed-air equipment

....

....

....

General tidiness (floor condition etc.)

....

....

....

....

4.7 FIRE PREVENTION AND CONTROL

Protection against fire is normally organised in accordance with the requirements of the Factory Acts and in co-operation with the local Fire Prevention Officer. Fire fighting equipment must be readily available and kept properly maintained. Doors and passages must be kept clear and a positive routine established, to be followed in the event of a fire.

Briefly describe the procedure to be followed in the event of a fire in the workshop.

....
....
....
....
....
....
....

Investigation

What are the visible signs of fire prevention in your workshop?

....
....
....
....

Different types of fire extinguishers are intended for use on different classes of fire. What are the three main classes of fire?

....
....
....

Name three popular types of fire extinguisher and describe the circumstances in which they might be used.

Class 1 ....

Uses ....
....

Class 2 ....

Uses ....
....

Class 3 ....

Uses ....
....

Water from a hose, bucket or extinguisher is used on solid fuel fires. What effect has the use of water on burning flammable liquids?

....
....

List the types of extinguisher available in the college workshop.

....
....

State the colour code for the following portable fire extinguishers.

Foam ....

Water ....

Carbon dioxide ....

Vaporising liquid ....

Dry chemical powder ....

4.6.8 FIRST AID

Personnel should be familiar with the location and contents of First-Aid boxes. Cuts, abrasions and burns etc., however minor, should be cleaned and treated promptly owning to the dirty nature of motor-vehicle repair work.

Certain personnel trained in basic First-Aid should be available to provide treatment and advice during working hours; the staff should know how and where to contact these people promptly in the event of an accident.

Basic first aid
By reference to the British Red Cross Society First Aid Chart, briefly describe the procedure to be followed when dealing with the following accidents:

Bleeding
....
....
....
....
....

Fractures
....
....
....
....
....
....

Burns and scalds
....
....
....
....
....

Unconsciousness
....
....
....
....
....

Breathing stopped
....
....
....
....
....
....
....
....

General rules for observance of safe practices
List five major rules for the above:
(a) ....
(b) ....
(c) ....
(d) ....
(e) ....

Chapter 5

Moving Loads

MOVEMENT OF LOADS

Any heavy object which requires moving manually or by mechanical lifting equipment is considered to be a load.

State four typical items that may need to be physically carried from the garage workbench to the vehicle.

1. ....   3. ....

2. ....   4. ....

Before carrying such units, it is essential that the carrier is aware of the potential dangers that may be incurred if the item is not properly lifted and held.

Considering the simple sketch, what two important points are emphasised?

....

....

....

....

These TWO simple precautions are most important if personal injury is to be avoided when lifting heavy loads. List other precautions that should be observed when lifting or manually handling components.

....

....

....

....

....

....

....

....

....

....

LIFTING DEVICES

Lifting devices may be classified by their power sources. State the power source of the lifting devices shown.

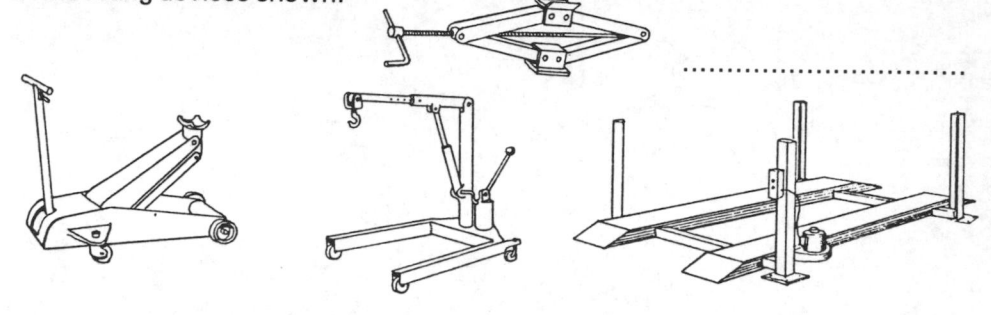

....

....

Above is shown basic garage lifting equipment. What other power lifting sources are available even though they are not commonly found in a garage workshop?

....

....

As a general rule any load over .... requires some form of powered lifting gear to support or move it. State safety rules that should be observed when moving a swinging load across the workshop.

....

....

....

....

....

....

....

....

LIFTING GEAR ACCESSORIES

When removing an engine from a vehicle the accessories required to support the engine to the lifting frame would be hooks, chain or sling, and eye bolts or shackles.

Examine your lifting equipment at work and note what is provided.

Lifting hook

Show a sketch of a typical safety hook.

For safety the expected colour of the hook should be

....

Position of chains and slings

The angle made by the slings is very important. What is the maximum recommended angle (A) between the slings? ....
If the angle (A) were to be substantially increased, what would be the effect of the 'pull' on the slings?

....
....

State FOUR rules to be observed when using slings.

....
....
....
....

Eye bolt and shackles

Sketch an eye bolt, shackle and spliced wire sling all correctly connected.

Name lifting and supporting equipment which is specialised to the motor vehicle workshop.

....
....

Transportation of loads

In a large garage or parts department, heavy loads may be transported in the manners shown. Name each method of transport.

1. .... 2. .... 3. ....

Which of the above units is loaded correctly? ....

Below is shown a wheeled stand. When would such a unit be used for moving loads in a workshop?

....
....
....
....
....

Show, with the aid of simple sketches, methods of chocking to avoid overbalance or shifting.

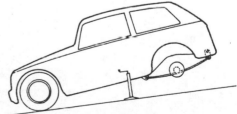

UNIT 03

PLANNING SKILLS

INCLUDES

Chapter 6

Measurement and Dimensional Control

MEASUREMENT AND DIMENSIONAL CONTROL

Many workshop processes, e.g. manufacturing, construction or repair operations, involve some form of measuring. Measuring is done by COMPARING the dimension or object to be measured with a similar object or some kind of measuring tool or instrument.

Give simple examples of how measurement information can be obtained by means of a simple COMPARISON process.

(a) Where, say, a series of bolts needs to be replaced, the new ones can be easily checked against the existing bolts.

(b) ....
....
....
....

Measuring equipment may be NON-INDICATING or INDICATING; describe briefly the difference between the two types of equipment.

....
....
....
....
....
....

Name the measuring instruments shown below and state whether they are indicating or non-indicating.

....
....

DIMENSIONAL PROPERTIES

Some important dimensional properties which can be measured are

(a) LENGTH (width, height, depth, diameter, radius)

(b) ....   (c) ....

(d) ....   (e) ....

(f) ....   (g) ....

How might you check the surface of a cylinder head for FLATNESS in garage conditions?

....
....
....

6.2 For the two road wheels shown at (a), measurements taken at x and y would give an indication of

....

Which measuring instrument could be used to determine the 'relative position' of the road wheel shown at (b) to the vertical plane?

....

(a)

(b)

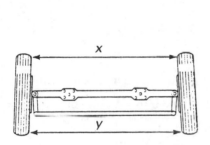

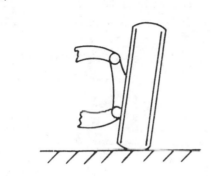

STANDARDS

Standards of measurement and dimensional control have been agreed on a national and international basis. These standards relate to:

(a) Quantities and units used in measurement.

....

....

....

The International Organization for Standardisation (ISO) sets the standards relating to measurement and dimensional control on an international basis.

Who is the recognised authority for the preparation and publication of standards in the UK?

....

The SI system (Système International) is an international system of units set up to standardise quantities and units used in measurement on an international basis. Some quantities used in the SI system are listed below; state the correct SI unit for each quantity (and its correct abbreviation).

Quantity	Unit	Abbreviation
Length		
Time		
Mass		
Velocity		
Force		
Pressure		

Quality specifications for tools and measuring equipment

If standards applied to measurement are to be achieved, the tools and equipment used for measurement must have a higher degree of accuracy than those required for dimensional properties being measured.

To maintain the standard of accuracy required, tools and equipment must be HANDLED, MAINTAINED and STORED with great care.

ENVIRONMENTAL STANDARDS

Because most materials expand when subjected to an increase in temperature, an agreed environmental temperature of .... is used when calibrating and setting up measuring tools and equipment.

What is the purpose of the STANDARDS ROOM?

....
....
....
....
....
....

State the advantages of having agreed standards.

1. Interchangeability of component parts.

....
....
....
....
....

MEASUREMENT OF LENGTH

The equipment used for measuring length depends on:

(a) The actual purpose for which it is to be used.

(b) ....

Frequently used instruments for measuring length are shown below:

(i) Name the instruments and (ii) state the degree of accuracy to which they can be used.

....
....

....

....

....

....

....
....

6.5 The scientific unit of measurement for length is the metre. A simple measuring instrument is the rule. This is used for most general purposes. If an accuracy to a limit of 0.01 mm is required, then a vernier or micrometer caliper may be used.

Using a rule measure the lengths of the lines below. State answer in units required.

Draw accurately lines to the requirements below.

_____	.... mm	5 mm
_____	.... mm	17 mm
_____	.... mm	32 mm
_____	.... mm	0.04 m

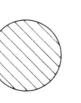

Sketch an external caliper being used to obtain the diameter of the shaft.

Sketch an internal caliper being used to obtain the diameter of the bore.

MICROMETER

The micrometer caliper is used to measure the diameter of shafts to an accuracy of 0.01 mm (1/100 mm).

State the principle on which it operates to achieve this accuracy.

....
....
....
....
....
....
....
....
....
....

Micrometers are made in size ranges of 0-25 mm, 25-50 mm, 50-75 mm etc. A big end bearing journal of 45.50 mm diameter would be measured by using a 25-50 mm micrometer.

Examine a micrometer and make a sketch of one positioned measuring the bar below. Name the important parts.

Bar

Reading the micrometer scale

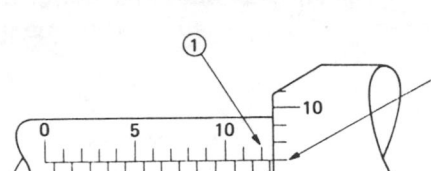

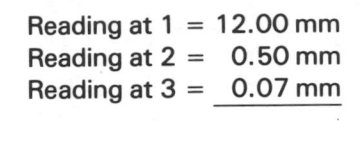

Reading at 1 = 12.00 mm
Reading at 2 = 0.50 mm
Reading at 3 = 0.07 mm

Micrometer
reading = 12.57 mm

State the readings of the scales of the metric micrometers below.

0-25 mm   0-25 mm   25-50 mm

0 — 35   5 — 15   20 — 0
  — 30   — 10   — 45

....

25-50 mm   50-75 mm   50-75 mm

15 — 25   0 — 5   10 — 45
   — 20   — 0   — 40

....

Sketch scales on the micrometers to give the readings indicated.

8.17 mm   14.76 mm   5.22mm

VERNIER CALIPER GAUGE

The degree of accuracy of a measuring instrument depends upon the fineness of the divisions marked on its scales. The metric rule gives an acceptable degree of accuracy up to 0.5 mm while the vernier caliper gauge can provide an accuracy of 0.02 mm. (*Note:* 0.02 mm is smaller than 0.001 in.)

Name the arrowed parts of the vernier caliper shown below.

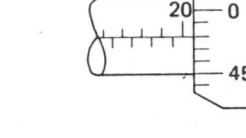

Some differences between vernier calipers and micrometer calipers are

(a) The degree of accuracy on a metric micrometer is 0.01 mm; on the metric vernier scale it is 0.02 mm.

(b) ....
   ....
   ....

(c) ....
   ....
   ....

PRINCIPLE OF READING SCALES

The vernier caliper consists of two slightly different scales, one fixed and one moving.

These gauges may be found calibrated in both English and metric scales.

There are two types of metric scales, in both cases the reading on the sliding scale is multiplied by 0.02.

(a) 25-division vernier (sliding) scale, the main scale is graduated in 0.5 mm divisions.

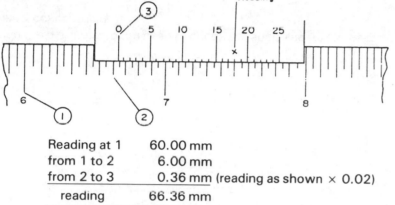

Reading at 1	60.00 mm
from 1 to 2	6.00 mm
from 2 to 3	0.36 mm (reading as shown × 0.02)
reading	66.36 mm

(b) 50-division vernier (sliding) scale. The main scale is graduated in 1 mm divisions.

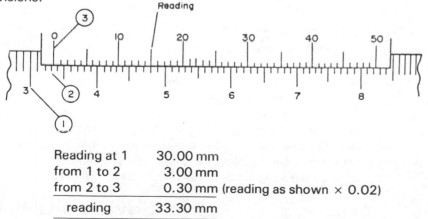

Reading at 1	30.00 mm
from 1 to 2	3.00 mm
from 2 to 3	0.30 mm (reading as shown × 0.02)
reading	33.30 mm

State the readings on the scales below.

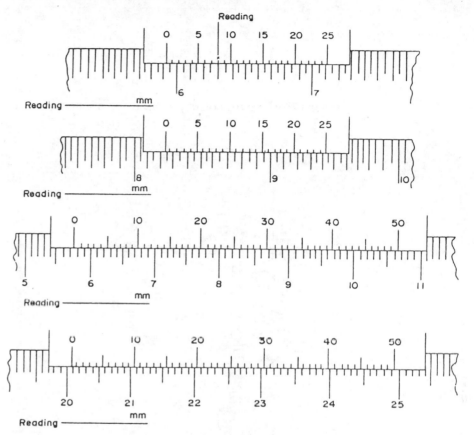

Reading ——————— mm

Reading ——————— mm

Reading ——————— mm

Reading ——————— mm

Sketch vernier readings of 17.86 mm and 53.24 mm.

119

6.5 DIAL INDICATORS

A dial test indicator (DTI) is an instrument which may be used to give comparative measurements from an item of specific or standard size. The main type of indicator used in motor-vehicle repair work is the plunger type. Slight upward pressure on the plunger moves it upwards and the movement is indicated by the dial finger.

A typical clock gauge with a measuring range of 10 mm would have an accuracy of 0.01 mm.

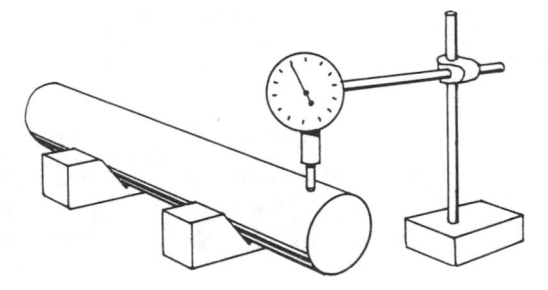

How would the dial indicator be used to check the shaft shown above for roundness or concentricity?

....

....

Give three examples of the uses of a DTI in motor-vehicle repair.

(a) ....

(b) ....

(c) ....

The cylinder bore gauge

An internal micrometer takes direct readings but requires a sensitive touch to obtain accurate readings. When a cylinder bore gauge is used, it must be calibrated by using either a ring gauge or an external micrometer.

The cylinder bore gauge converts the horizontal movement of the spring-loaded plunger into a vertical movement, which is transferred by a push rod (in the gauge shaft handle) to a dial test indicator clamped to the top of the handle.

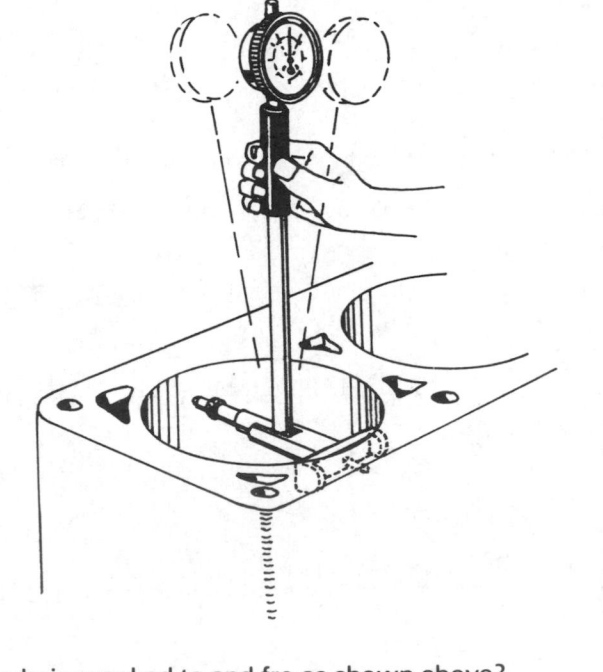

Why is the gauge being rocked to and fro as shown above?

....

....

....

6.6 ANGLES AND THE UNIT OF ANGLE

Angles are formed when a circle is divided radially into parts. The unit of angle is obtained by dividing the circle into .... equal parts and 1/360 of a circle is a .... which is the UNIT OF ANGLE. The circle shown is divided into four equal parts whose angles are .... Divide the circle further, without using measuring equipment, to show approximate angles of 45°.

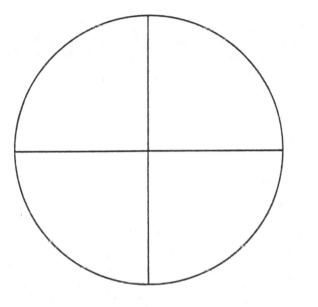

Each degree can be divided into 60 equal parts:

1/60 of a degree = 1 ....

or 1 degree   = 60 .... and

if 1′ is further divided by 60 the ....

is obtained.

1′ = 60 ....

ANGULAR MEASUREMENT

Angles and squareness can be checked using:

try squares

....

....

The try square is the most common tool used for checking squareness. Show by simple sketches how the try square would be used to check the angles (a) and (b) for squareness on the workpieces shown below.

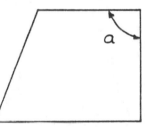
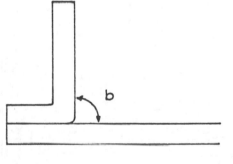

When measuring angles other than 90°, a protractor can be used; the type of protractor depends on the particular application and the degree of accuracy required for the measurement.

COMBINATION SQUARE

A useful instrument for measuring angles is the universal bevel protractor or combination square. A combination square consists of a blade which may be used with any one of three heads; these are illustrated opposite.

State the purpose of a 'centre square' and describe how it would be used. Show by sketching how the workpiece would be positioned when using the centre square opposite.

....

....

....

....

....

....

....

Indicate on the protractor opposite where the angle being checked is read.

Vernier protractor

The vernier protractor is a protractor with a vernier scale which can be adjusted to give a higher degree of accuracy when measuring angles; however, using it requires skill and experience.

How does the accuracy of a vernier protractor compare with that of the bevel protractor shown below.

Normal bevel protractor accuracy = 0.5°

vernier protractor accuracy = 0.5′

Square

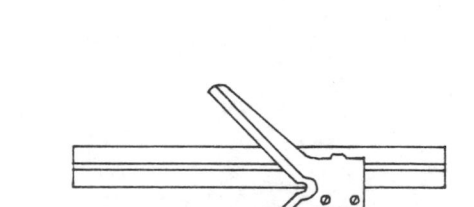

square

Centre square

centre square

Protractor

protractor

SURFACE TABLES AND SURFACE PLATES

Surface tables and plates both fulfil the same purpose in a workshop. The surface plate is the smaller of the two and more portable. Both are to be found in a mechanical engineering workshop, whereas in a motor-vehicle repair workshop a surface plate is quite adequate.

State the purpose of surface tables and plates and describe their main constructional features.

....

....

....

....

....

....

....

....

Spirit level

Its function is to ....

....

Sketch a typical spirit level in the space below.

Note: see section 8.4 for other associated tools.

DIMENSIONAL DEVIATION

It is not possible to measure or produce a workpiece or component *exactly* to size or to duplicate *absolute* accuracy between workpieces. When components are being manufactured, therefore, a DEVIATION from a specified dimension is allowed.

A standard system of SIZE LIMITS controls the dimensional accuracy.

Definitions

Nominal Size

This is the design size, and if it were possible to work to an exact size a component would be made to the nominal size.

Limits ....

....

....

Tolerance

....

....

Deviation

....

....

State the nominal size, high and low limits, tolerance and dimensional deviations for the following dimensions.

	$50\,{}^{+0.5}_{-0.5}$	$25\,{}^{+0.5}_{-0.2}$	$30\,{}^{+0.6}_{-0.0}$
Nominal Size			
High Limit			
Low Limit			
Tolerance			
Deviation			

123

ACCURACY IN MEASURING

The degree of accuracy is directly related to the tolerance. If high accuracy is not required for a particular component, the manufacturing tolerance can be greater. The choice of measuring equipment for a particular job depends on the tolerances being worked to. For the tolerances given at (a), (b) and (c), name the measuring equipment to be used.

	Tolerance	Equipment
(a)	1.0 mm	....
(b)	0.25 mm	....
(c)	0.04 mm	....

Factors Affecting Accuracy

Give some examples of things which can affect accuracy when taking measurements.

(a) Variations in temperature affecting measuring tools and workpieces.

....

....

....

....

....

Many errors in measurement are caused by incorrect use of the measuring equipment.

Some common causes of error are shown below; make simple sketches to illustrate correct measuring techniques.

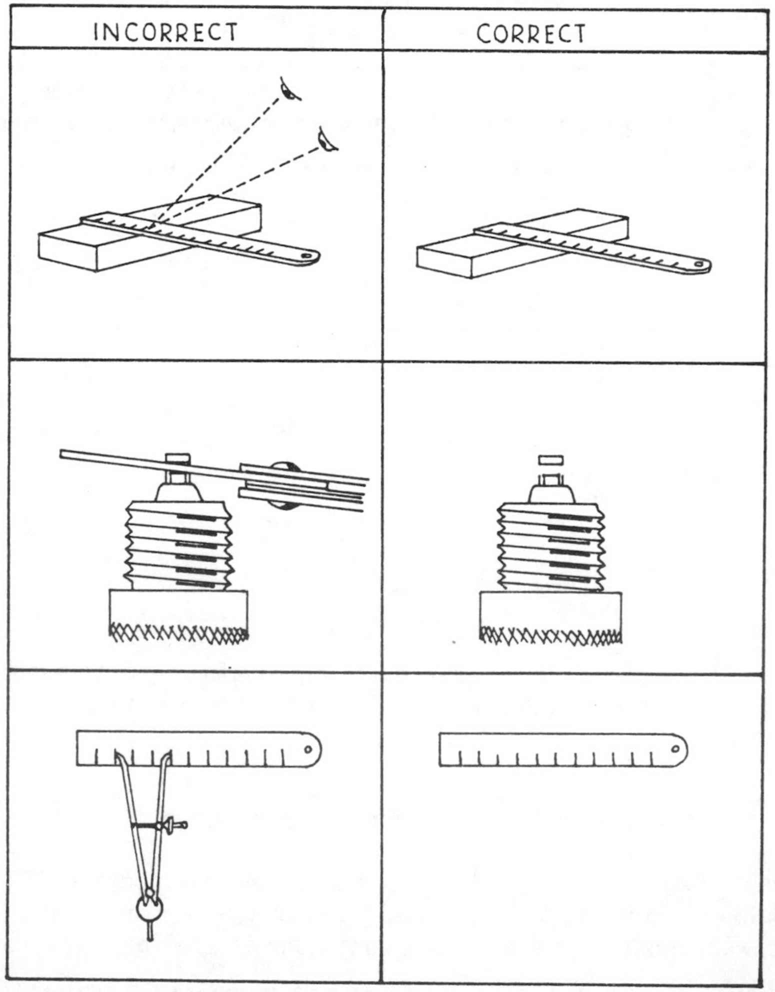

INCORRECT	CORRECT

TERMINOLOGY

Define the following terms:

(a) *Measuring range*

....

....

(b) *Reading value*

....

....

(c) *Indicated size*

....

....

....

....

....

(d) *Mean size*

....

....

The accuracy of the measuring equipment depends on its *condition* and *quality*. A measuring tool may indicate a size which can deviate from the dimension being measured.

Define *tool accuracy*.

....

....

....

CARE AND MAINTENANCE OF MEASURING EQUIPMENT

Keeping measuring tools and equipment in good condition depends on

(1) the way in which they are handled and used in the workshop;

(2) how the equipment is stored when not in use;

(3) the maintenance of the equipment.

List some important points with regard to the upkeep of:

Rules

....

....

Squares/Feeler gauges

....

Micrometers/Verniers/Dial indicators

....

....

....

....

Very often measuring tools and equipment are damaged as a result of misuse, e.g. using rules, feeler gauges, squares for purposes other than measuring.

Measuring equipment should always be:

....

....

Chapter 7

Interpreting Drawings, Specifications and Data

DRAWINGS SPECIFICATIONS AND DATA

Engineering drawing is a means of communication. It is a simpler, more accurate and less ambiguous form of communication than the spoken or written word. By 'reading' and understanding a drawing, the engineer can determine:

(a) the shape and dimensions of a component
(b) the constructional features, layout and location of components.

How could (a) and (b) above be of use to a motor-vehicle mechanic?

(a) ....
....
....

(b) ....
....
....
....
....

To understand drawings it is necessary to learn the 'language' and the simple rules of engineering drawing. Although motor engineers mostly need to read workshop manual drawings, it is useful to know something about engineering drawing.

To enable all engineers to understand and use the same rules when drawing, British Standard 308 is used.

Look through BS 308 (Student Edition) and list the main items of content.

....
....
....
....
....
....
....
....

DIN, SI and SAE are abbreviations for standards/conventions relevant to the transport industry; give a brief description of each.

DIN

....
....
....

SI

....
....
....

SAE

....
....
....

Many different forms of drawing are used by engineers. These vary from simple freehand sketches to a variety of other types of drawing. List below different types of engineering drawings.

....
....
....
....
....
....
....
....

COMMUNICATING TECHNICAL INFORMATION

Communication of technical information can be achieved in a number of ways. List some of the methods by which information, in some standardised form, is made available in engineering and in the operation of a modern garage.

....

....

....

....

....

....

....

....

Give examples of the use of microfiche and visual display units in a modern garage.

MICROFICHE

....

....

VDU

....

....

....

What are the advantages of using microfilm?

....

....

....

....

Rack and pinion steering gear

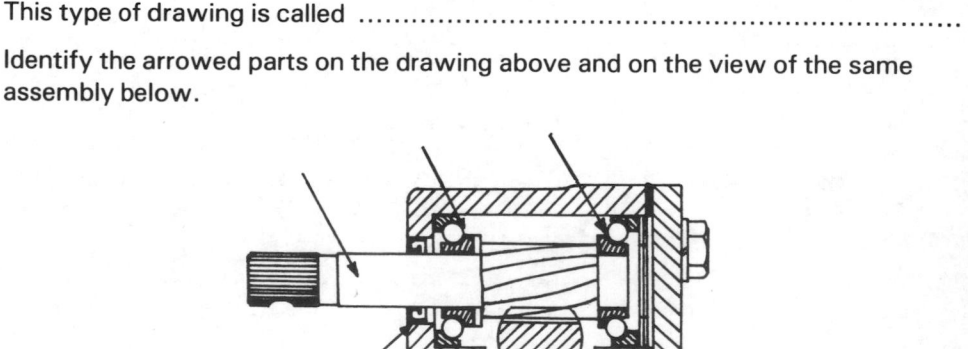

This type of drawing is called ....

Identify the arrowed parts on the drawing above and on the view of the same assembly below.

This type of drawing is called ....

128

7.4 TECHNICAL DRAWING — ORTHOGRAPHIC PROJECTION

Orthographic projection is a method used to present the various faces of an object when viewed squarely. For relatively simple objects, three views are sufficient to fully describe and give dimensions.

The three views are

....

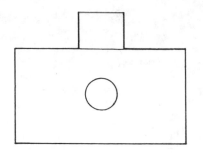

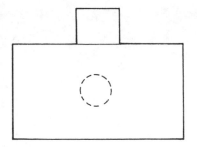

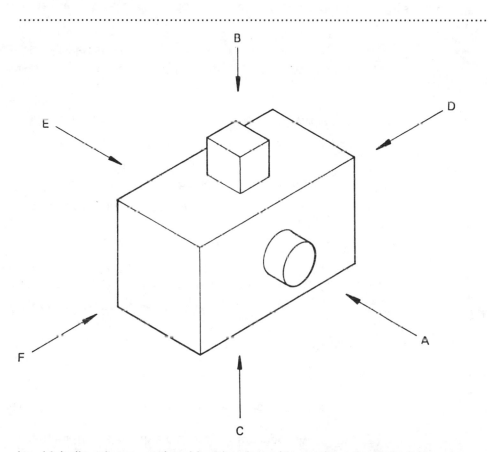

.... A ....

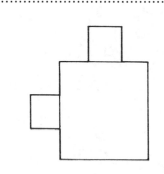

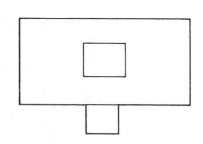

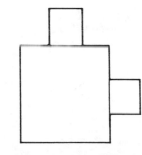

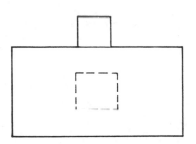

In which direction must the object be viewed to produce the views shown opposite, taking 'A' as the FRONT VIEW. Put the appropriate letter under the view.

....

PICTORIAL PROJECTION

A pictorial view of an object gives a three-dimensional impression where its height, width and depth are shown simultaneously.

Two methods of representing an object pictorially are by

1. .... projection

and

2. .... projection

Features of isometric projection

1. The lines receding from the horizontal are drawn at .... to the horizontal.

2. Circles are drawn as ....

Features of oblique projection

1. The lines receding from the horizontal are drawn at .... to the horizontal.

2. The front face is drawn as a .... face.

3 The lines receding from the horizontal are drawn at .... full size.

Sketch two 2 cm cubes to illustrate isometric and oblique projection at the top of the page opposite.

Name the method of projection under each of the pictorial drawings shown opposite.

Why are the receding lines reduced in length in oblique projection?

....

....

....

Isometric   *Oblique*

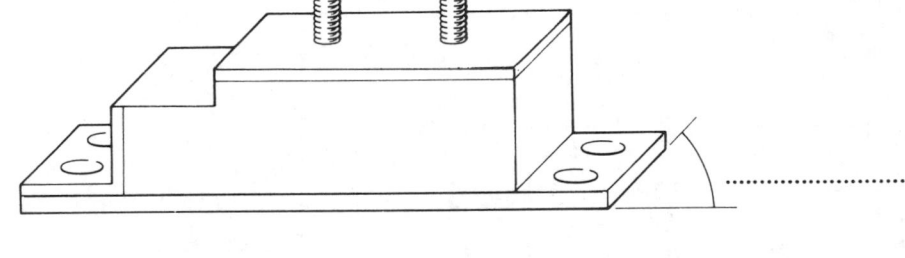

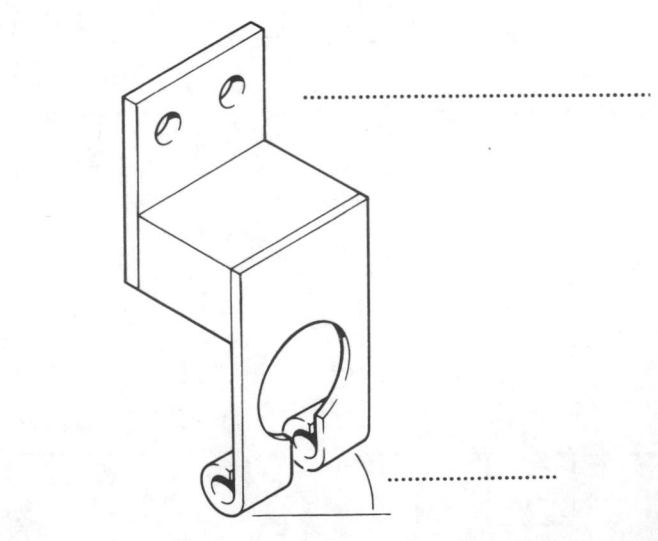

7.4 First angle and third angle projection

Two systems of orthographic projection are *first angle* and *third angle*. The difference between the two systems is the relative positioning of the three views on the drawing.

Consider the motor-vehicle battery shown below.

First angle

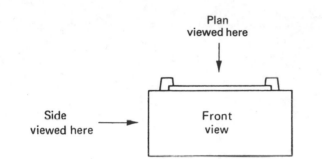

Plan
viewed here

Side
viewed here

Front
view

Side drawn
here

Plan
drawn here

Third angle

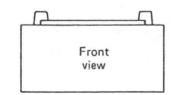

Front
view

Label the 'third angle' drawing above to describe 'third angle' projection and show where the two views would be shown. Will the actual drawings produced for first angle be different from the drawings for third angle projection? ....

....

....

Name the angle of projection used in each 'three view' drawing below.

....

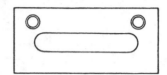

Plan view

Side view

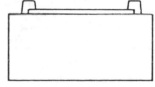

Front view

....

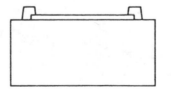

Front view

Side view

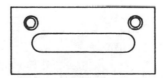

Plan view

7.4 The arrow on the pictorial drawings of the mounting brackets shown represents the front view. Study the views opposite and complete the table to indicate the correct front, side and plan views for the different brackets.

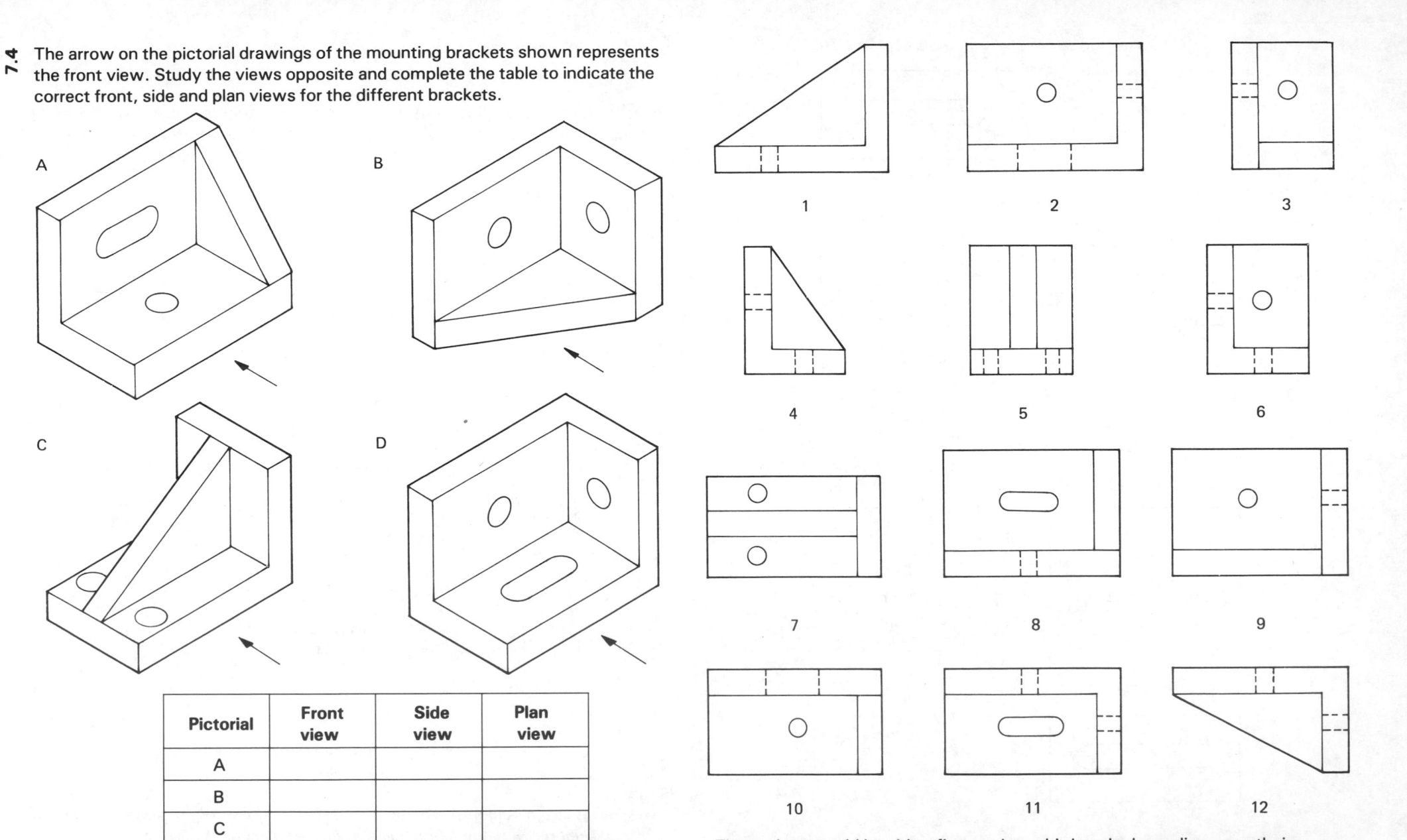

A

B

C

D

1

2

3

4

5

6

7

8

9

10

11

12

Pictorial	Front view	Side view	Plan view
A			
B			
C			
D			

These views could be either first angle or third angle depending upon their relative positions on the actual three view drawing.

CONVENTIONAL REPRESENTATION

To avoid wasting time on engineering drawings common features are often simplified, that is, they are shown by conventional symbols.

Complete the table to show the convention for the subjects shown.

TITLE	SUBJECT	CONVENTION
external screw threads	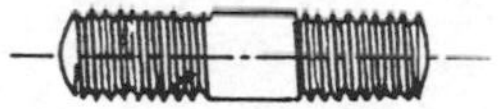	
splined shafts	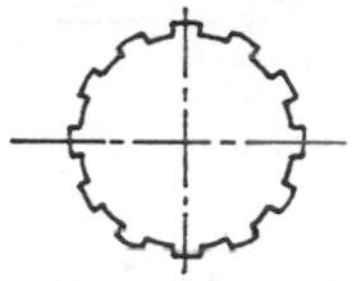	
semi-elliptic leaf spring with eyes	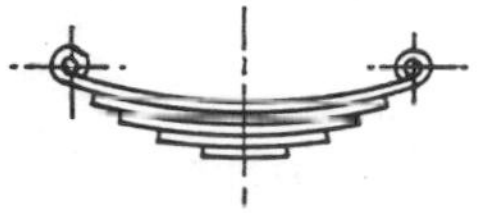	
square on shaft	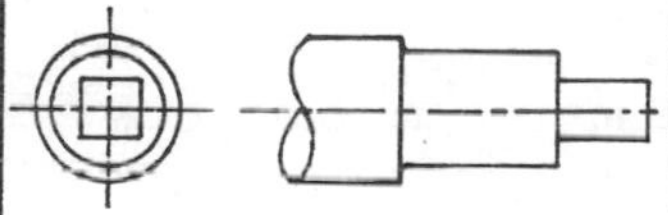	
bearings	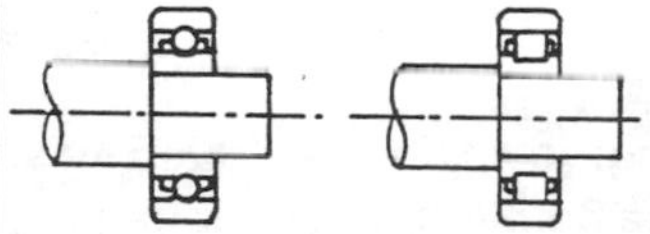	

INFORMATION ON DRAWINGS

List typical examples of BASIC and ADDITIONAL information to be found on drawings.

Basic information

....
....
....
....
....

Additional information

....
....
....
....

Indicate the PROJECTION SYMBOL for the two systems of projection.

Projection   **Symbol**

First angle

Third angle

....
....
....
....
....

GENERAL RULES

Types of lines

The types of lines used in engineering drawing are shown below. Complete the description of the lines by giving examples of their applications in drawing.

——————————————— Thick continuous

....

—————————————— Thin continuous

....

....

– – – – – – – – – – – Thin short dashes

....

—— · —— · —— · —— · Thin chain

....

—— · —— · —— · —— · Thick chain

....

∿∿∿∿∿∿∿∿∿ Thin wavy

....

....

To produce the correct type of line to suit the application, not only requires some expertise but well-sharpened pencils of the correct grade. Give examples of the grades of pencils used for:

1. Visible outlines ....

2. Projection or centre lines ....

ABBREVIATIONS

By reference to BS 308, complete the list at (A) below to give the recognised abbreviations for the terms stated and complete the list at (B) to give the terms for the abbreviations stated.

(A)		(B)	
Drawing	....	SCR	....
Machined	....	SK	....
Hydraulic	....	SPEC	....
Millimetre	....	STD	....
Minute	....	U'CUT	....
Hexagon	....	PCD	....
Figure	....	NO	....
Centre line	....	CRS	....
Assembly	....	LG	....
Across flats	....	CHAM	....
Cylinder	....	SPH	....
Diameter	....	MATL	....
Galvanised	....	C'BORE	....
British Standard	....	NTS	....
Countersunk	....	RH	....
Centres	....	Int	....
Left hand	....	Max	....
Minimum	....	Sq	....

....

....

....

....

7.4 DIMENSIONING (MAIN RULES)

The simple drawing below is dimensioned in accordance with recognised standards.

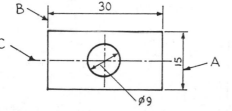

Line A is a ....

Line B is a ....

Line C is a ....

List the main rules for dimensioning a drawing.

....

....

....

....

....

....

....

....

....

....

....

The symbol ⌀ represents ....

State the units used for linear dimensions on drawings

....

DIMENSIONING FROM A DATUM

A datum is a line, point or a face from which each dimension is measured, it is used as a base for a number of dimensions. A machined surface is often used as the datum.

Measure and dimension the drawing below taking (a) as the datum.

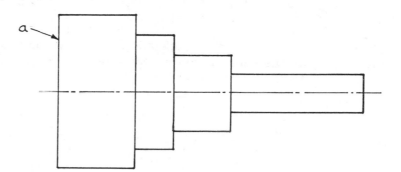

What is the reason for dimensioning from a datum?

....

....

....

....

....

7.3 BLOCK AND LINE DIAGRAMS

Block and line diagrams are used to illustrate, in a simplified form, component construction, layout of relative components or layout of certain systems (for example, hydraulic systems).

Name the type of diagram and the component or system illustrated below.

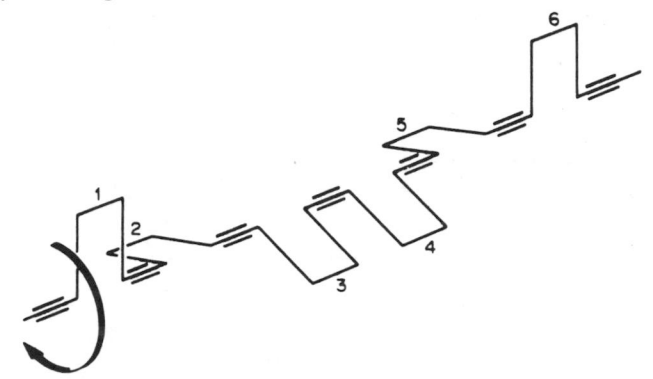

Diagram type .... Component ....

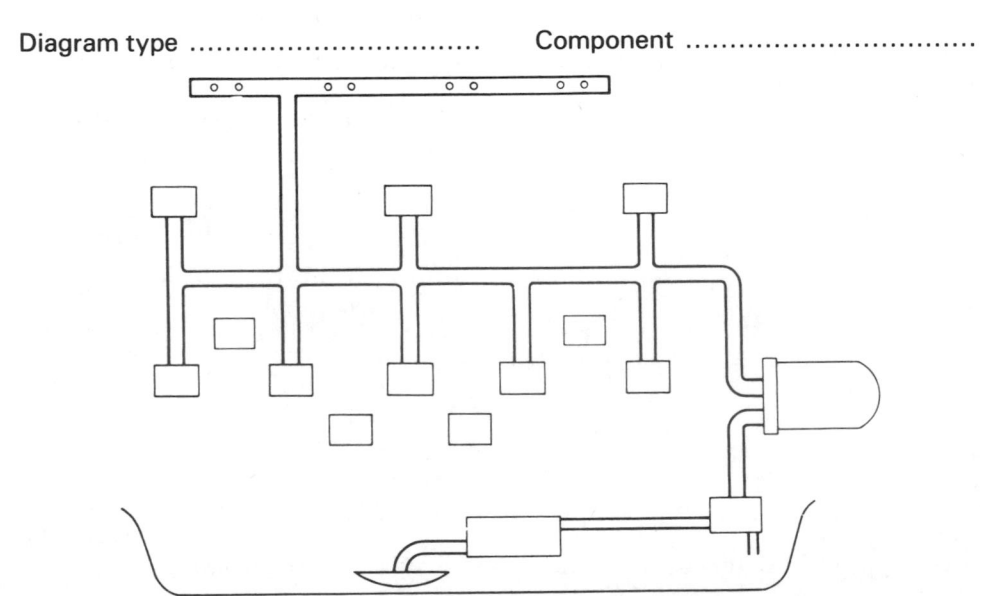

Diagram type .... Component ....

The simple line diagram above represents a ....

Label the diagram.

Illustrate below the layout of a petrol engine fuel system by using a block diagram.

The drawings on the left show a piston assembly and a valve. Make simple line diagrams on the right to illustrate the same.

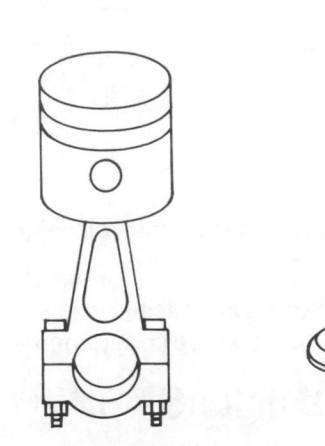

Assembly drawings

This type of drawing shows two or more components assembled together.
Usually dimensions are not shown but a list of parts is included.

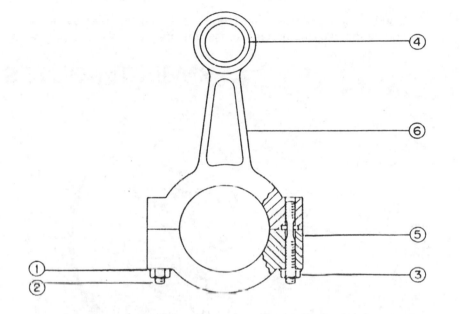

State the purpose of the assembly drawing shown on the left

....

....

....

Shown below is a typical bush used in motor-vehicle construction.

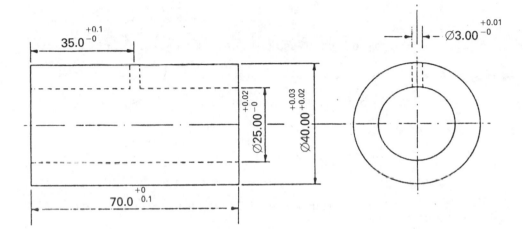

All dimensions in mm
Material — Phosphor bronze
Standard of finish — as turned

Item	Description	Drg. No.	Material	No. off
6	Rod	31127/6	Drop forged steel	1
5	Cap	31127/5	Drop forged steel	1
4	Bush	31127/4	Phosphor bronze	1
3	Nut	31127/3	Low carbon steel	2
2	Stud	31127/2	Low carbon steel	2
1	Washer	31127/1	Low carbon steel	2

Name and state the purpose of the type of drawing shown above.

....

....

....

....

....

The type of drawing shown below is often referred to as a LOCATION DRAWING and is used frequently in repair manuals. State the role of the location drawing.

....

....

....

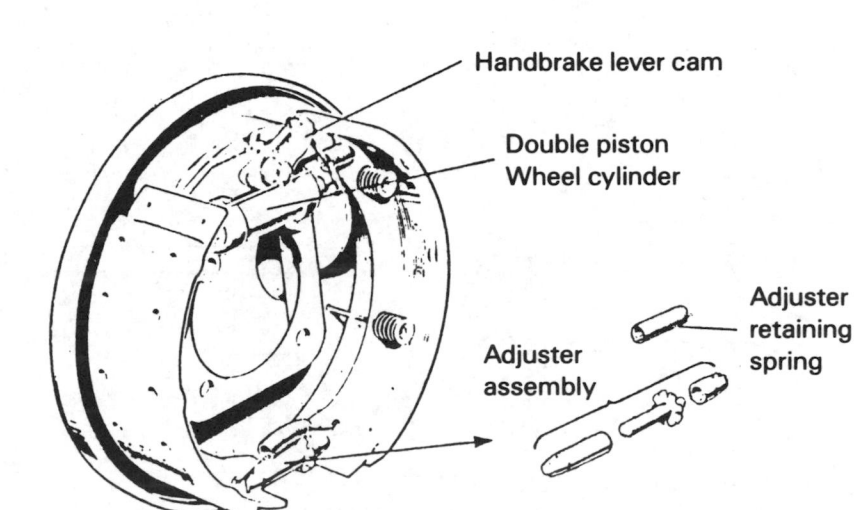

Handbrake lever cam

Double piston
Wheel cylinder

Adjuster
retaining
spring

Adjuster
assembly

SECTIONAL VIEWS

To get a true indication of the actual cross-sectional shape of an object, it is often necessary to produce a 'sectional view' — as shown at right.

State two uses of a sectional view to a motor engineer.

1. ....

2. ....

....

The view below shows a piston assembly in section.

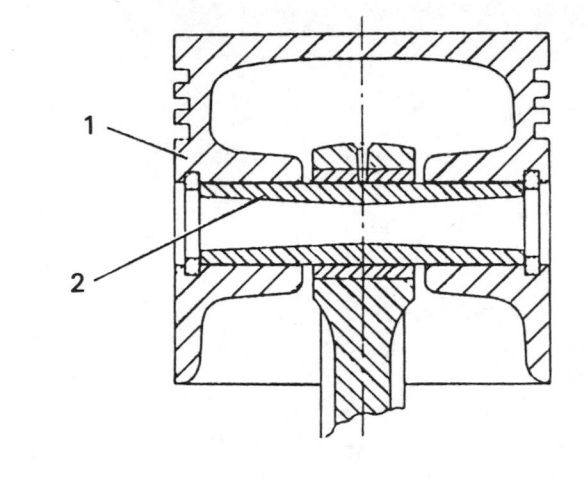

1

2

What parts of the sectional view are cross-hatched?

....

....

....

Why are the cross-hatch angles different on parts 1 and 2?

....

At what angle to the horizontal do the cross-hatch lines lie?

....

To improve the clarity of a sectional view, certain parts when lying on a longitudinal cutting plane are not cross-hatched. These include such items as

1. *Solid shafts and rods*

2. ....

3. ....

4. ....

5. ....

OPERATIONS SCHEDULES

An operations schedule outlines, in a logical sequence, the procedure to be followed when manufacturing a component or when assembling and dismantling a component. Very often the instructions within the schedule refer to a drawing or photograph to aid communication.

Draw up operations schedules for

(1) the manufacture of the chassis plate shown in detail at (a), and

(2) the removal and replacement of the thermostat shown at (b)

(b)

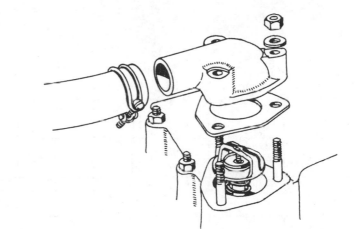

(a)

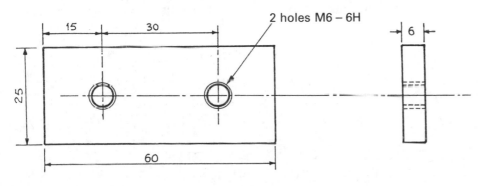

2 holes M6 – 6H

7.7 Name and state the purpose of the gauges shown below.

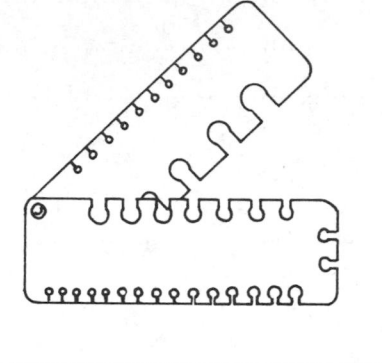

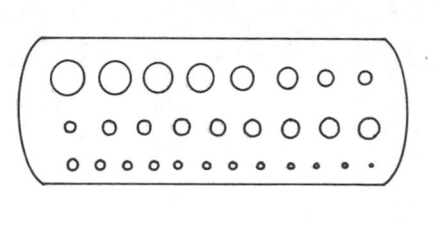

The graph below shows the POWER and TORQUE curves for a modern car engine. Use the graph to interpret:

(a) Maximum engine power and speed at which this occurs

....

(b) Maximum engine torque and speed at which this occurs

....

(c) Torque at maximum power ....

(d) Power at maximum torque ....

....

....

....

....

....

Use the tables in the workshop or stores to complete the table below giving twist drill sizes for the bolts indicated.

Clearance Hole Size (mm)								
Thread Diameter (mm)	2	3	4	5	6	12	16	20

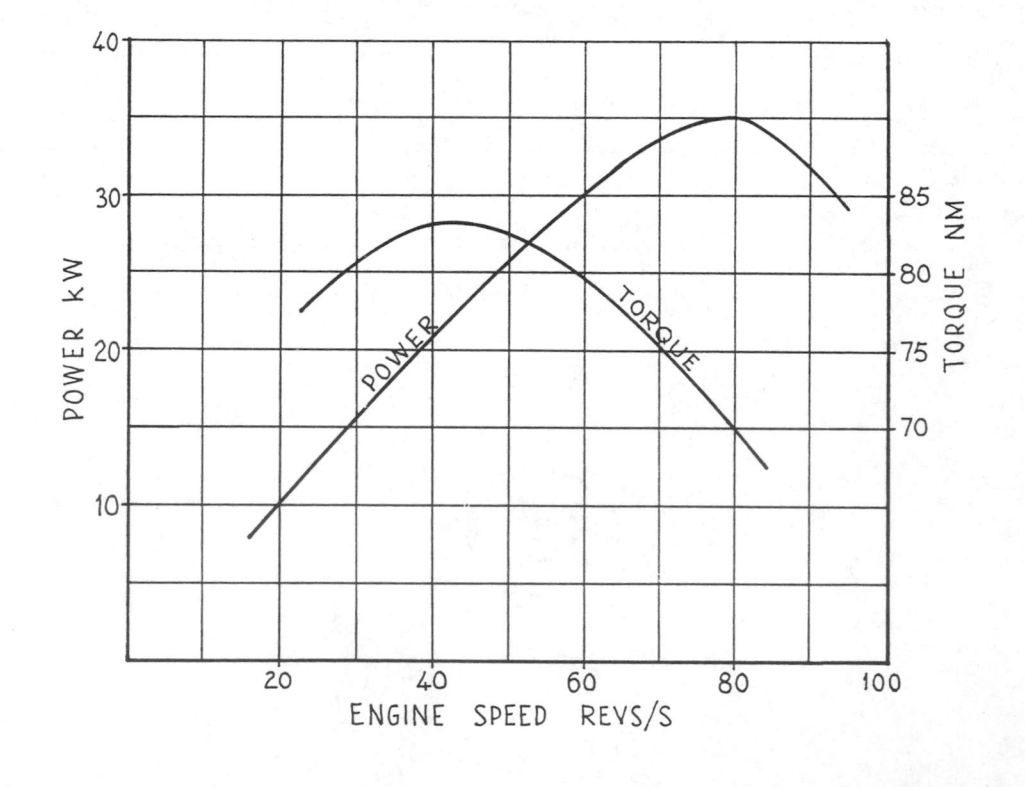

GRAPHS

A graph is a means of communicating information; it gives a pictorial illustration of the relationship between two variables, e.g. Engine speed and Power, or Time and Distance.

The graphical means by which information is conveyed depends very often on the subject and the type of relationship involved.

BAR AND PIE CHARTS

An alternative method of communicating information in a pictorial way is by means of BAR or PIE charts. Construct a BAR chart opposite to show car sales figures over a six month period using the following data.

Month	1	2	3	4	5	6
Sales	£120 000	£150 000	£100 000	£140 000	£170 000	£200 000

The PIE chart opposite shows the floor area occupied by the various departments of a garage business. Given the following data on floor area for the business, label the sections on the PIE chart to illustrate the proportion of floor area occupied by each department.

WORKSHOP   —   2000 m²

CAR SALES   —   1500 m²

FORECOURT   —   1000 m²

PARTS DEPT   —   500 m²

BAR CHART

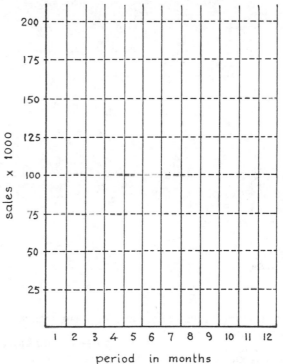

PIE CHART

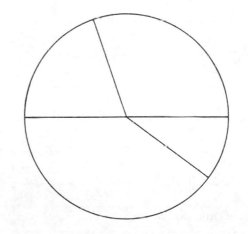

141

7.8 COLOUR CODING

Colour coding of components, equipment, piping, wiring etc. serves two purposes:

(1) It assists in identification when selecting and using, or when assembling or dismantling components or systems.

(2) ....
....
....
....
....

....
....

Indicate, by labelling the
plug shown, the colours of
the wires for a correct connection.

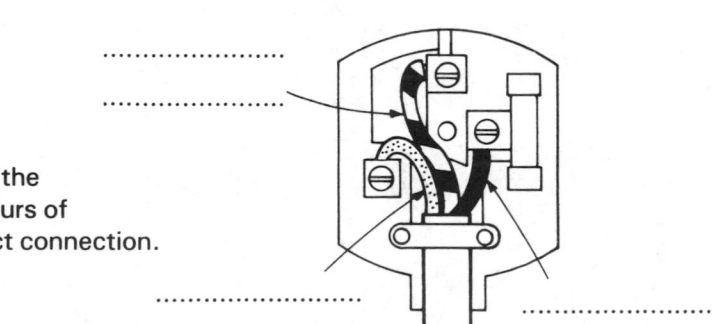

....

Resistors in electrical circuits are colour coded to indicate their value. Examine a number of resistors. Show the colour coding on the resistors shown below for resistors of value: 68 kΩ   220 kΩ

	Colour convention	
	Pipes	**Cylinders**
Oxygen		
Acetylene		
Comp. Air		
Natural gas		
Butane		
Propane		

In accordance with current colour-coding conventions, complete the table above to indicate the colours for the items given.

Examine a modern vehicle and state the colour coding for lighting cables and fuses.

Vehicle make ....   Model ....

Lighting cables

....
....
....
....

Fuses

....
....
....
....

UNIT 04

MANUAL SKILLS

Chapter 8

Bench Fitting

BENCH FITTING

9.1, 2, 3, 4

All mechanics at some time in their work will be required to make (fabricate), modify or repair motor-vehicle components. To do this kind of work the skilled mechanic must have a basic knowledge of bench-fitting skills. These skills can be divided into specific categories and they form the basis of this chapter.

Examine the titles on the following pages up to the 'Care and Maintenance of Bench-fitting Tools', and list below the various bench-fitting operations.

1. ....
2. ....
3. ....
4. ....
5. ....

6. ....
7. ....
8. ....
9. ....
10. ....

MARKING OUT AND MEASUREMENT

When a simple component is to be made, lines are reproduced on the material's surface from an engineering drawing. This is known as marking out.

The tool used for marking straight lines on a component is called ....

State the purpose of the following with regard to marking out.

Dividers ....

Oddleg calipers ....

....

Bevel protractor ....

....

Combination set ....

....

Trammels ....

....

Identify the tools associated with marking out.

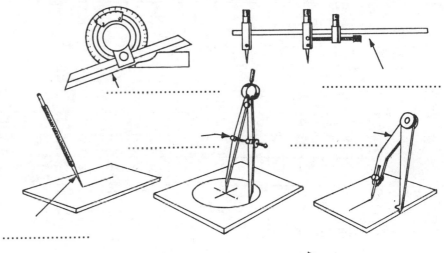

....

....

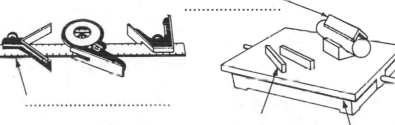

....

....

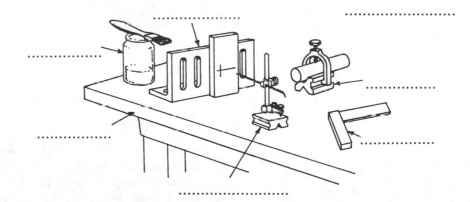

....

....

145

State a typical purpose of the following with regard to marking out.

Set square ....

....

Vee blocks and clamps ....

....

Surface table or *surface plate* ....

....

Angle plate and *surface gauge* ....

....

Parallels and *parallel blocks* ....

....

What is a template?

....

....

Why would it be useful to use a template to produce the following?

(a) 10 brackets as shown below.

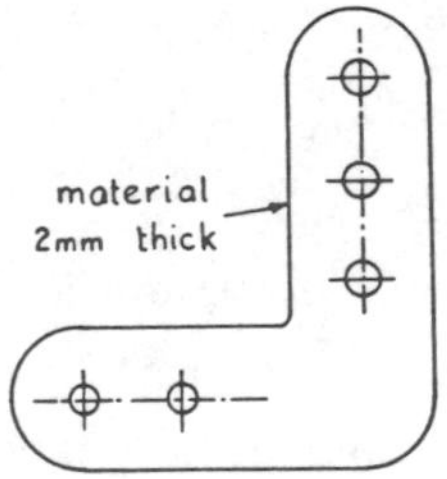

material
2mm thick

(b) A replacement piece for a lower wing.

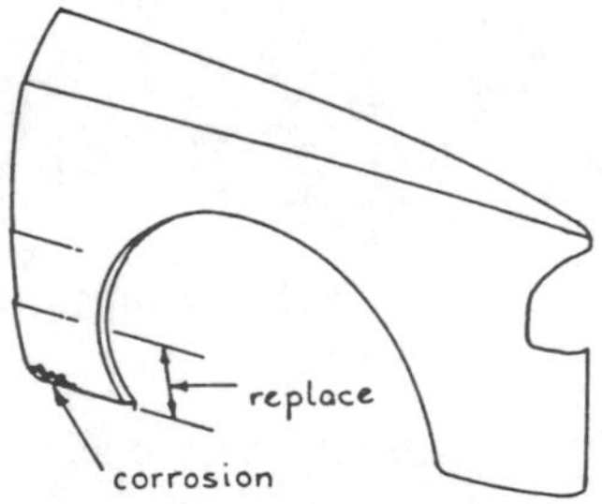

replace

corrosion

....

....

....

....

....

....

To enable the marking out on material such as mild steel to be seen clearly, the surface may be coated with some colouring. This may be

1. ....   or   2. ....

The circles shown on the sketch below are centre-punched.

What is the reason for this?

....

....

What is the main use of the centre punch?

....

The component below has been marked out prior to cutting out and making.

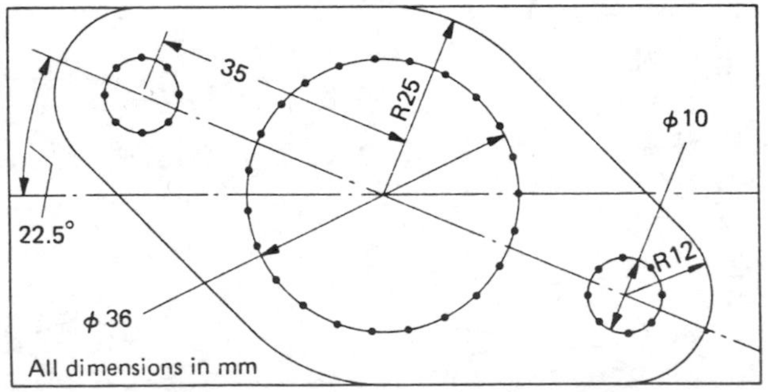

35
R25
φ10
22.5°
φ36
R12
All dimensions in mm

List the stages of marking out.

1.	
2.	
3.	
4.	
5.	
6.	
7.	
8.	

USE OF DATUM

Datum lines, datum points and centre lines are necessary to ensure that other lines, points, curves and angles can be placed in their correct relative positions.

Indicate two edges suitable for use as datum lines.

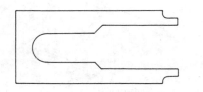

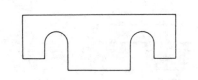

Sketch suitable centre lines required to mark out the components below:

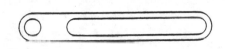

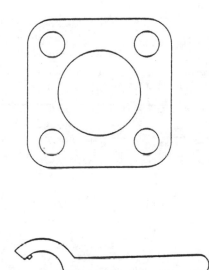

Indicate the datum line on the drawing below.

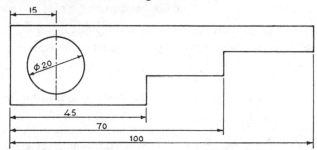

How are dimensional errors best avoided when marking out?

....

ECONOMIC USE OF MATERIAL

A template for the development of a fuel tank shield was used to cut out 18 pieces from a sheet 125 cm by 85 cm and so leave minimum waste. There are two possible ways to do this, show one on the blank rectangle below.

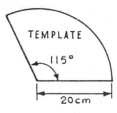

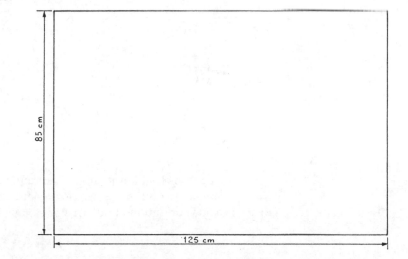

Identify these tools associated with measuring and gauging and state a typical motor-vehicle application for each one.

....

....

....

....

....

....

....

....

....

....

....

....

....

....

Which gauge would be particularly suitable for measuring wear in cylinder bores?

....

NOTE: These tools are covered in more detail in Chapter 6.

SAWING

The hacksaw is the most common type of saw used for cutting metals. The frame may be adjustable or non-adjustable.
Name the main parts of the hacksaws shown.

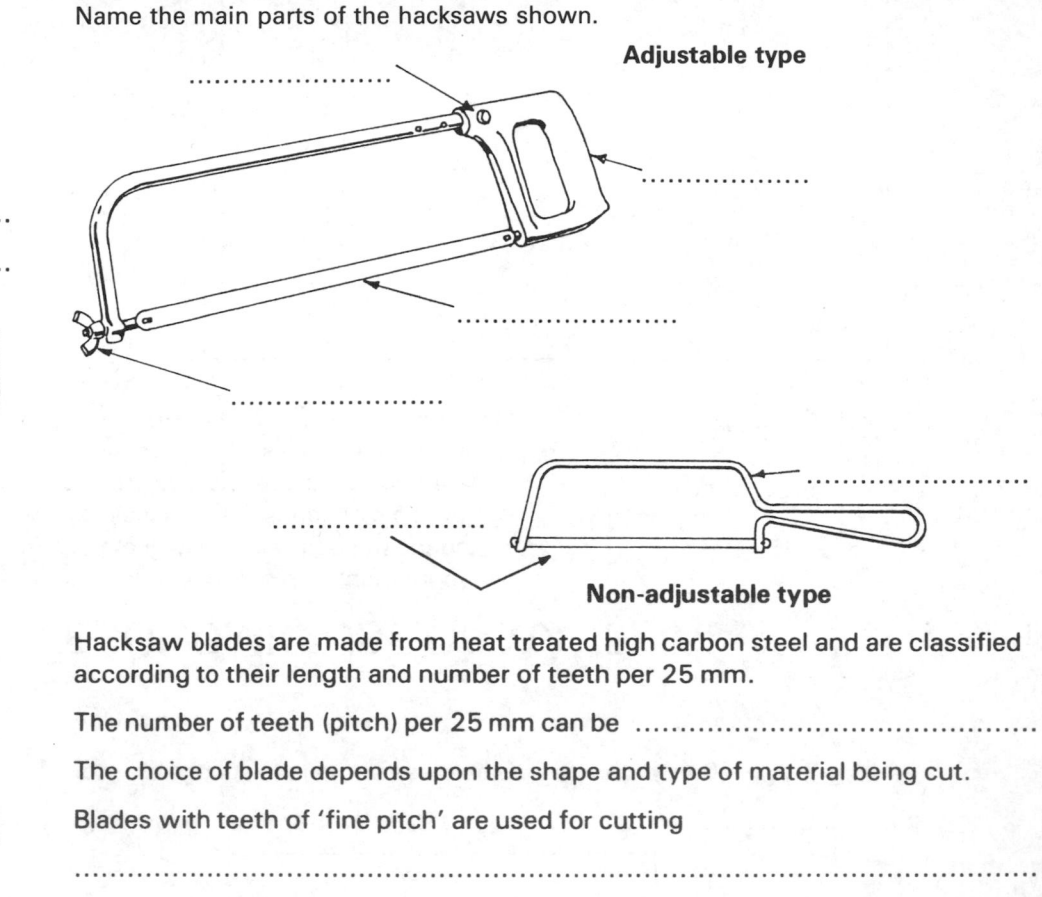

Adjustable type

....

....

....

....

Non-adjustable type

....

Hacksaw blades are made from heat treated high carbon steel and are classified according to their length and number of teeth per 25 mm.

The number of teeth (pitch) per 25 mm can be ....

The choice of blade depends upon the shape and type of material being cut.

Blades with teeth of 'fine pitch' are used for cutting

....

Saw blades with teeth of 'coarse pitch' are used for cutting

....

The individual teeth on a hacksaw blade form a pointed 'wedge' which digs into the metal and produces a 'shearing' action. The teeth on the blade are offset

from one another. This offsetting is called the ....
of the teeth.

Examine two types of hacksaw blade. How do they differ with regard to their shape or 'set' of teeth?

....
....
....

Complete the sketch below to show a hacksaw blade in the sawcut. Indicate clearly the set on the teeth and state, alongside the drawing, the purpose of the set.

....
....
....
....
....
....
....

Which way round should the blade be fitted into a hacksaw frame?

....

On which stroke does the cutting action occur?

....

Two types of hacksaw blade are available, one is considered flexible and the other non-flexible. How do these blades differ in use?

....
....
....
....
....
....

Give three causes of saw blade breakage.

1. ....

2. ....

3. ....

Describe the procedure for sawing off a 300 mm length from a strip of metal whose cross-section is 25 mm × 10 mm.

....
....
....
....
....
....
....
....
....

When cutting thin sheet it is good practice to have at least 3 teeth in contact with the metal.

Show the correct position of the blade for sawing.

(i) *Tubing*

(ii) *Thin sheet metal*

....
....

....
....

CUTTING and PUNCHING

9.3, 4

Hammers

The hammer is a very common tool in all trades. On a motor vehicle, different types are used for special jobs. Name the hammers shown and give an example of their use. The ball and cross-pein hammers are available in different (sizes) weights.

....
....

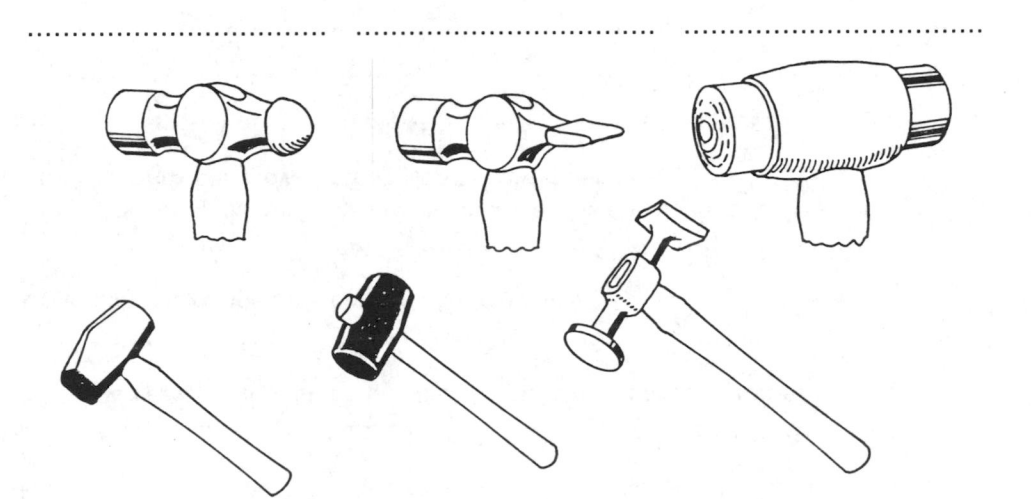

....
....

Describe how a gasket may be made using a small ball pein hammer.

....
....
....
....
....

Shears for cutting metal

Tin snips are commonly used for cutting thin sheet steel. The snips may be flat or curved-nosed. They are used very like a pair of scissors.
For cutting large sheets of metal (or metal too thick for snips) a guillotine or bench shears may be used.
Observe a demonstration cut with tin snips and say what happens to the narrow waste side of the metal.

....

Identify the items shown below.

....

....

Wire cutters

Below are shown two types of wire cutters. Name each type and describe its use.

1. ....   1. ....
....
....
2. ....   2. ....
....

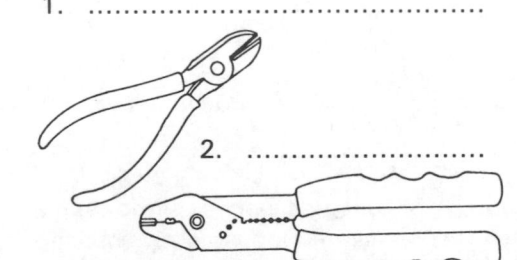

CHISELS

The cutting action of a chisel works on the principle of forcing a wedge into the material to shear off any unwanted material.

The drawing below shows the point of a chisel during cutting. Hammer blows cause the pointed 'wedge' to 'shear' through the metal. The depth of cut is maintained by holding the chisel at the correct angle (angle of inclination). Three other important factors that affect the efficiency of the cutting action are:

1. .... angle,   2. .... angle

and   3. ....   angle of the chisel.

Label the drawing.

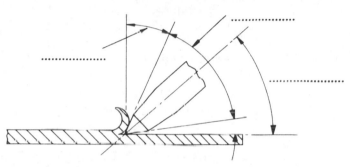

Chisels with point angles in the region of 55-65° are used for cutting relatively hard materials and the tool point is quite strong. For cutting softer materials the point angle is reduced.

Sketch chisel points for the materials named below, and state the approximate point angle.

Low carbon steel   Aluminium

The common engineering chisel is often called a COLD CHISEL. They are usually made from high carbon steel which is hardened only at the pointed end. Why is the head left soft?

....

....

Examine chisels of the types named below, and in the spaces provided make sketches of each type and give examples of use.

Flat chisel   Cross-cut chisel

....

....

Diamond point chisel   Half round (round nose) chisel

....

....

When chiselling and striking with the hammer, on what part of the work should the eyes be focused?

....

151

FILING

The cutting action of a file is similar to that of a chisel or hacksaw. Each tooth on a file is a tiny cutting blade. Files are classified according to: length, shape, grade of cut and type of cut.

Name the types of file shown below.

General utility file, cuts on both sides and edges

....

Parallel in width, used for roughing or finishing. One safe edge

....

One side flat, one curved

....

Circular section, tapering

....

Four equal sides, 90° angles

....

Three cutting sides at 60° angles

....

Very thin file

....

Fairly slim file. One safe edge

....

Flat faces but radiused edges

....

Relatively large, separate teeth. Used on soft materials

....

As can be seen, there is a shape of file to suit any work situation.

Complete the drawing below to show teeth on the files named. Indicate teeth angle in the second and third drawing.

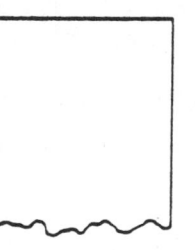

Rasp   *Single cut*   *Double cut*

Files are graded according to the number of teeth per centimetre, that is, their roughness or smoothness. Name four grades of file between the rasp and dead smooth files and state typical uses.

File grade	Typical use
....	....
....	....
....	....
....	....

State four hints for obtaining maximum life from a file.

1. ....

2. ....

3. ....

4. ....

DRILLING

The most common type of drill is the twist drill. It is supplied in three lengths: jobbers' series, these are normal length drills; long series; and stub (short) drills. Metric drill sizes range from 1 mm diameter to 20 mm diameter, the smaller sizes being available in 0.1 mm steps.

Name the main parts of the drills shown, including the different types of shank.

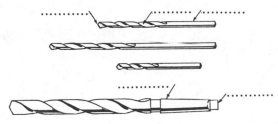

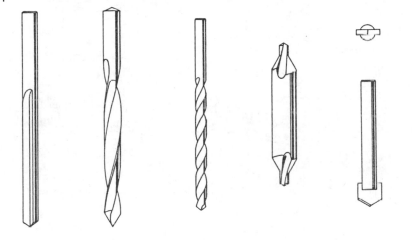

Other types of drills are shown below. Name and state suitable uses for them.

....

....

....

....

....

Twist drills remove metal by using two cutting edges rotating about a centre point.

Indicate the cutting edges and lands. Indicate included (point) angle. Show the direction of rotation.

The point angle necessary for general-purpose work is ....

State the purpose of the *land* on a twist drill.

....

....

When a drill is sharpened by grinding, it is essential to keep the cutting edges (lips) the same length and at the same angle to the drill axis. State how each drill below has been incorrectly sharpened.

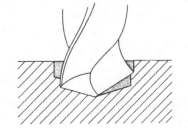
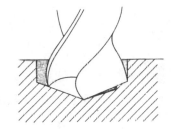

....

How is the hole affected by the faults shown above?

....

The above are causes of inaccurate drilling.
State TWO other causes.

....

....

When drilling different materials, what type of lubrication is required?

....

....

....

....

....

Name the types of drilling machines shown below.

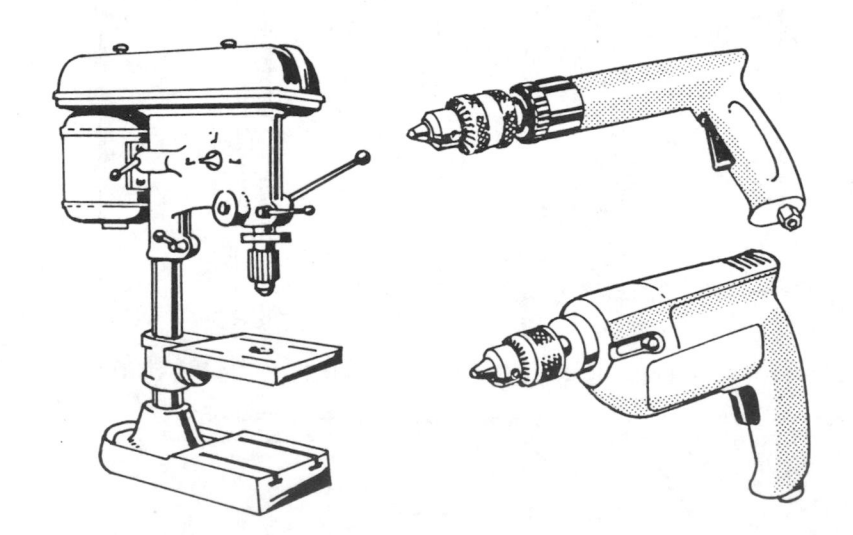

State how the drilling speed is varied on

Drill (1) ....

....

Drill (3) ....

....

What are common operating voltages for the electric drills shown?

....

Drill speeds and feeds

The *spindle speed* of a drill is the rotational speed at which the drill turns.

It is expressed in ....

The *linear cutting speed* of a drill is the speed at which the cutting edges pass

over the work. It is expressed in ....

What is meant by the *feed* on a drilling machine?

....

....

As a general guide, the feed increases as the drill size increases.

The spindle speed of a drill is set according to

1. ....

2. ....

State the linear cutting speed (using HSS drill) for:

1. Tool steel ....   2. Mild steel ....   3. Brass ....

....

....

....

....

It can be seen from the examples chosen that, when cutting soft material, the cutting speed is higher than that used for hard material. It is normal practice to refer to tables to obtain the correct spindle speed for a particular material and size of hole required.

Table of approximate drilling speeds (rev/min)

Drill diam.	Type of metal			
	Steel	Cast iron	Brass	Aluminium
4	1200	1900	6000	7200
6	800	1270	4000	4800
8	600	900	3000	3600
10	480	765	2400	2860
12	400	640	2000	2400

When drilling a hole what precautions could be taken to ensure accuracy of the operation?

....
....
....
....
....
....
....
....
....
....

Show on the hole where 'cut back' grooves should be positioned.

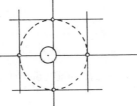

When cutting sheet metal, what precautions should be made to prevent damage to the work when using a conventional drill?

....
....
....

Name the alternative types of drill that can be used to cut sheet metal.

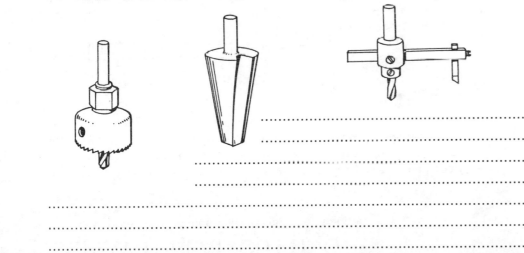

....
....
....
....

Other processes that can be carried out on a drilling machine are shown below. Describe the function of each operation.

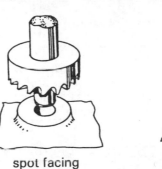

spot facing	counter boring	counter sinking

....
....
....
....

PUNCHES

Name the types of punches shown below.

Where would each type be used?

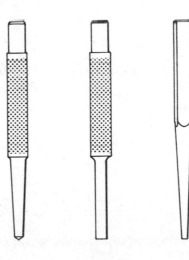

....
....
....
....
....
....
....
....
....
....
....
....
....

SCREW THREAD CUTTING

A screw thread is produced with the aid of a tap or die.

TAPS

The tap is an accurately made thread with a cutting edge formed on the thread. There are three types of tap. These are shown below. Name each type and identify the types of hand wrenches that can be used to operate the tap.

....

....

....

State the purpose of

The taper tap ....

The second tap ....

The plug tap ....

....

Describe the correct use of a tap when commencing to tap a drilled hole of the correct size.

....
....
....
....
....

What precautions should be taken when tapping a blind hole?

....
....
....

What is the purpose of the item shown below?

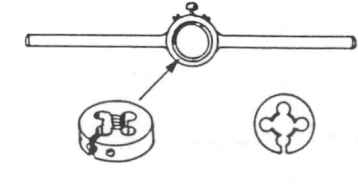

....
....
....
....
....

DIES

A die is a form of nut accurately made with a cutting edge formed on the thread. Why is the die either split or made up of two pieces?

....
....

Name the types of stocks and dies shown.

....

Describe the correct use of a die when commencing to cut a thread on a bar.

....
....
....
....

9.3.4 ISO METRIC SCREW THREAD

Screw threads may be external (male) — for example, bolts, studs, screws — or internal (female) — for example, nuts and threaded holes.

The metric thread is now used very extensively in motor-vehicle engineering. A coarse or fine pitch is used to suit the application.

Sketch below the profile of a metric screw thread.

Complete the labelling below to show the main terms used in describing screw threads.

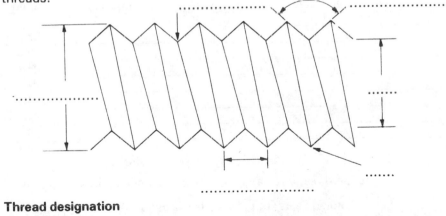

Thread designation

A thread designation such as M10 × 1.5 describes a metric thread, where

M = ... 10 = ... 1.5 = ...

ISO METRIC is an abbreviation for ....

Define the term *thread depth* ....

....

Define the term *lead* used in connection with screw threads.

....

....

Fine pitch and coarse pitch screw threads are shown below, label the drawings accordingly.

....

Complete these statements regarding coarse and fine threads such as those shown above.

(a) The thread having the greater pitch is the .... thread.

(b) The greater thread depth is on the .... thread.

(c) For one turn of the nut on the fine thread it will move a ....

   distance than would a nut on the .... thread.

   Its .... is less.

Why are coarse threads often used in soft alloys?

....

....

....

Why are fine threads very commonly used for most motor-vehicle applications?

....

....

157

TYPES OF SCREW THREAD

Although metric threads are normally used, there are still a large number of other screw thread forms found on motor vehicles.

The abbreviations for these are shown in the tables below.

Complete the table to show what the abbreviations represent.

BSW	British Standard Whitworth
BSF	
BSP	
BA	
UNC	
UNF	
ANF	
ANC	
APT	

The correct size of hole to be drilled for cutting a particular thread can be determined by referring to 'thread tables'.

Extract from iso metric coarse thread table

Screw or bar diam.	Screw designation (diam. × pitch)	Tapping drill diam.	Clearance drill diam.
4	M 4 × 0.70	3.30	4.8
6	M 6 × 1.00	5.00	7.0
8	M 8 × 1.25	6.80	9.0
10	M10 × 1.50	8.50	11.0
12	M12 × 1.75	10.20	13.0

Indicate each dimension on the sketch for a 10 M screw size.

State a workshop method, other than using tables, to determine

(a) The approximate drill size for cutting a thread ....

....

(b) The clearance hole diameter for a bolt to pass through ....

....

Name the items shown below and state how they would be used in the repair of vehicle components.

....
                                            ....
                                            ....
                                            ....
....
                                            ....
....
                                            ....
....

Describe how the last item shown above should be used in the situation shown below.

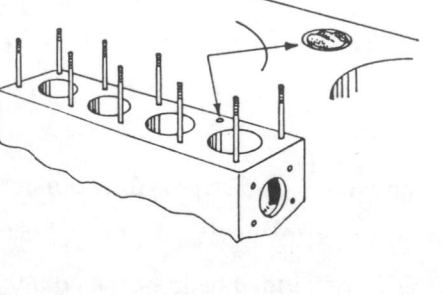

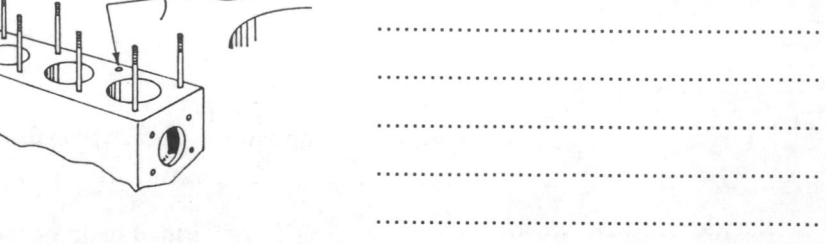

....

....

....

....

....

....

....

REAMING

If a very accurate hole size is required, then a reamer should be used to achieve this hole size. This is because an ordinary high speed drill may not drill with 100% accuracy. Name the type of reamers shown below.

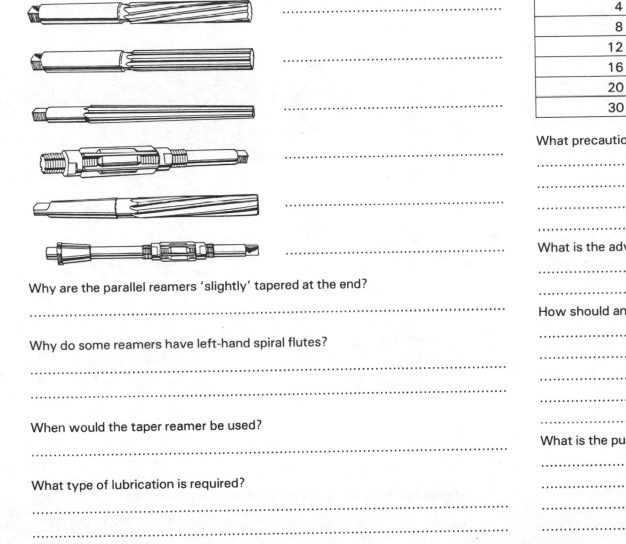

....

....

....

....

....

....

Why are the parallel reamers 'slightly' tapered at the end?

....

Why do some reamers have left-hand spiral flutes?

....

....

When would the taper reamer be used?

....

What type of lubrication is required?

....

....

When using a reamer, a hole of suitable size should have first been drilled. Depending on drill size, this hole is 0.2 to 0.5 mm less than the required hole finish size. Complete the table below to show drill size prior to reaming.

Diameter of hole finished size (mm)	Drill size before reaming (mm)	Reaming allowance (mm)
4		0.20
8		0.20
12		0.25
16		0.50
20		0.50
30		0.50

What precautions should be observed when hand reaming a hole?

....

....

....

....

What is the advantage of using adjustable reamers?

....

....

How should an adjustable reamer be set up?

....

....

....

....

....

What is the purpose of pilot reamers?

....

....

....

....

GRINDING

Most vehicle repair shops will possess some or all of the types of grinding machines shown below.
Name the types shown.

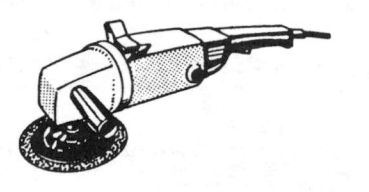

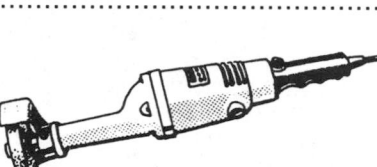

....

....

....

....

State PERSONAL PRECAUTIONS to be observed when using abrasive wheels.

....

....

....

....

Before commencing any grinding operation, a visual inspection of the grinding wheels and the machine's condition should be made.
List the important inspection points.

....

....

....

....

....

....

....

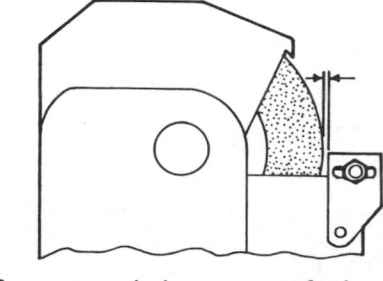

Dressing a wheel

Grinding speeds

Over-speeding is one cause of a grindstone wheel bursting.

Wheel bursting

This accounts for 12% of grindstone accidents, many of which are fatal.

Recommended exposure of wheel

It is important that the speed of abrasive wheels is not exceeded. Doubling the speed increases the centrifugal stress four times. What are the regulations concerning speed?

....

....

....

....

What is the main cause of over-speeding?

....

....

WORK HOLDING

The bench vice

Two types of vice are commonly found in motor-vehicle workshops. These are shown below. They look very similar but one is adjustable (quick release) and the other is non-adjustable.

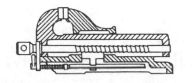

....

....

Both types can be supplied with a swivel base. The 'garage' vice shown below has a swivel base, hardened steel anvils, offset jaws to hold long and wide work vertically.
State other features that the vice possesses.

....

....

....

....

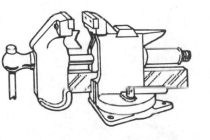

When machine drilling for light machine operations, a hand vice is commonly used while the drill is held in a chuck. Name the workholding clamps shown.

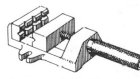

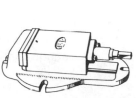

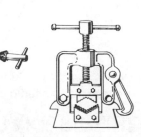

Clamps

For holding small work, hand clamps are suitable. Name the clamps shown.

....

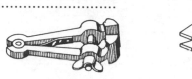 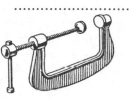

....

When drilling for absolute accuracy on a sensitive drilling machine, the material must be securely clamped. Name the jig clamps shown.

....

....

State the positions of the holding device when carrying out the following operations.

Cutting ....

Drilling ....

....

Grinding ....

....

Show how the blocks below could be held for drilling on a sensitive drilling machine, using suitable jig fixing.

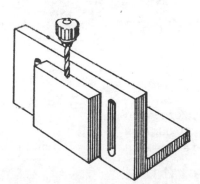

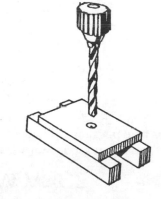

PIPE BENDING

For bending conduit and heavy copper pipe, bench-mounted bending machines are used.

Plumber's light gauge bender

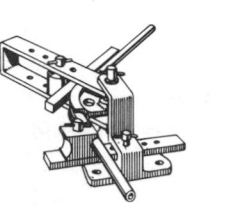

Small-diameter pipes can be bent using a block of wood that will rest on the floor and has a hole of suitable size at the top end. The pipe is put through the hole and pressed at both sides until it is bent to the shape required. How can bends and kinks be prevented when bending in this manner?

....
....
....
....

BRAKE PIPE BENDING

Two types of pipe or tubes which may require bending in a garage workshop are

....

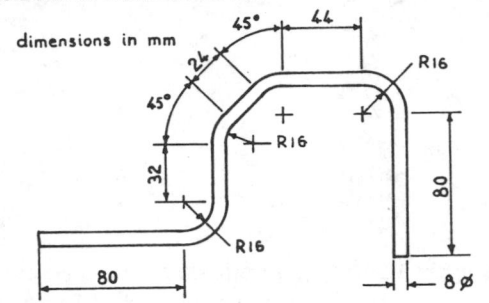

....
....
....

BEND ALLOWANCE

If pipes are bent without allowing for the metal shorting on the inner corners, the finished pipe will be undersize and difficult to fit.

dimensions in mm

Indicate on the drawing the radii used for calculating the curves.
Calculate the length of pipe required to make the shape shown.

....
....
....
....

CARE AND MAINTENANCE OF BENCH-FITTING TOOLS

Select TWO tools from examples such as files, drills, reamers, hacksaw, chisel; examine them and complete the table below by considering their care and maintenance.

Selected tools		
Protection		
Checking for truth		
Handling		
Sharpening		
Selection		
Safety		

9.6 COMMON FORMS of METAL SUPPLY

The metal stocked by garages is mostly in the form of finished products, e.g. engines, gearboxes, exhausts and body panels. For basic repair it may stock some sheet metal for body fabrication repair, and various flat and round bars or tubes. If you inspect your College engineering store you will find a much more comprehensive stock of basic metal sections. Name the standard shapes of bar shown below.

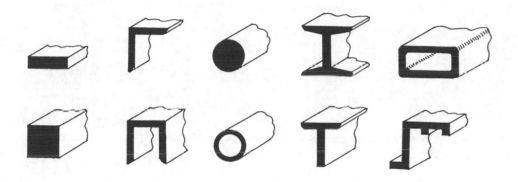

Colour coding

A store may stock many grades of metal which all look the same but have totally different properties and are required for different uses. In order to be able to identify these metals easily a colour code has been introduced and colours are painted on the different metals. State the colours for the metals stated in the table.

	Ferrous metal			Non-ferrous metal		
	BS Number	(1955 No.)	Colour	BS Number	Material	Colour
Steels	220M07	EN1A		2874	Brass	
	070M20	EN3		369	Bronze	
	080M30	EN6		1400	Lead bronze	
	401S45	EN52		1400	Monel	
	431S29	EN57		1474	Aluminium	
	Cast iron			—	Copper	

FERROUS AND NON-FERROUS METALS

Most of the main mechanical and structural components of a car are made from metal.

Metals may be split into two main groups:

Ferrous and non-ferrous metals

A ferrous metal is ....

....

A non-ferrous metal is ....

....

....

Name typical motor-vehicle components made from the materials below:

Ferrous metals	Components	Non-ferrous metals	Components
Low carbon (mild) steel		Aluminium alloy	
High-carbon steel		Copper	
Cast-iron		Copper-based alloys, brass and bronze	
Alloy steels		Lead-based alloys	
		Zinc-based alloys (diecasting)	

163

FERROUS METALS

Ferrous metals are defined by the amount of carbon contained in the metal.

....

....

....

....

State which metal will have the percentage carbon content shown opposite.

 Cast iron
 Mild steel
 High-carbon steel
 Wrought iron
 Medium-carbon steel

Material	% Carbon
	0.01
	0.25
	0.50
	1.20
	3.00

ALLOY STEELS

Alloy steels are used for most of the highly stressed components used in the modern car. What is meant by an alloy steel?

....

....

....

....

Most of the tools in a mechanic's tool box are made from alloy steel, for example, spanners, pliers, hammers, screwdrivers, chisels, hacksaw blades.

Examine a selection of spanners. From what alloy steel are they made?

Spanner	Type of alloy steel

Why are alloying elements such as those listed below added to steel?

....

....

Complete the table giving the reasons why each (or a combination) of the elements shown is used to improve the properties of a steel.

Elements	Properties improved
Nickel	
Chromium	
Nickel and chromium	
Chromium and vanadium	
Chromium and molybdenum	
Tungsten	
Manganese	
Cobalt	

List some typical steel motor-vehicle components and state the type of alloy steel from which they may be made.

Typical motor-vehicle components	Typical alloy steel material

NON-FERROUS METALS

Most of the pure non-ferrous metals are not used separately but are alloyed with other materials when used to produce motor-vehicle components.

The reason for this is ....

....

....

State the main properties of the non-ferrous metals shown below.

Material	Colour	Main properties
Aluminium		
Copper		
Tin		
Lead		
Zinc		

Aluminium and its alloys

Pure aluminium is not commonly used in a vehicle because it is too ductile and malleable. But, when small amounts of other materials are added, alloys can be produced that are much stronger, harder, able to retain strength at high temperatures and corrosion resistant.

....

....

....

....

....

....

Give reasons why the following non-ferrous metals are considered very suitable materials for the following components:

Component	Material	Reason for choice
Piston Some cylinder heads	Aluminium	
Radiator core (or stack)	Copper	
Electrical cables	Copper	
Fuel pumps, carburettors	Zinc-based aluminium alloy	
Small plain bearings	Bronze	
Radiator header tanks	Brass	
Bearings	Aluminium, tin, copper, lead	

The main alloys of copper are brass and bronze.

Brass is an alloy of copper and ....

Bronze is an alloy of copper and ....

165

PLASTICS

Plastics are a large group of man-made materials. They may be formed into any required shape under the application of heat and pressure.
There are two groups of plastics.

1. Thermosetting

....
....
....
....
....

2. Thermoplastic

....
....
....
....
....

State whether the following materials are thermoplastic or thermosetting:

Material	Type	Material	Type
Celluloid		Bakelite	
Formica		Polythene	
Polystyrene		PVC	
PTFE (Teflon)		Nylon	
Terylene		Epoxy resins	

Listed are three common plastics used on vehicles:
Complete the table as required.

Material	Properties	Vehicle applications
Nylon		
PTFE		
PVC		

Some body panels and one-piece car bodies are manufactured by using thermosetting plastics (polyester resins) to reinforce glass fibre.
State advantages of this type of body over an 'all-steel' body.

1. ....
2. ....
3. ....
4. ....

CERAMICS

A ceramic material is one that has been produced through a heating process and forms a pot-like substance that is very hard and brittle.

One of the few ceramic substances used on a vehicle is for

....
....

For adhesives, see Chapter 9.

9.7 IDENTIFICATION OF MATERIALS BY WORKSHOP METHODS

Complete the stated tests on the materials mentioned below.
Use bars of similar sizes which are stamped for identification.
Carry out each individual test on all the bars before stating results.

Type of metal	Appearance of metal colour and surface finish	Grinding, colour quantity and type of spark	Resistance to scratch, file saw or indentation	Sound when dropped on ground	Reaction to magnet
Mild steel	....	....	....		
Medium carbon steel	....	....	....		
Alloy steel (tool steel)	....	....	....		
Cast iron	....	....	....		
Aluminium	....	....	....		
Copper	....	....	....		

Identify the metal used in several motor-vehicle components using at least TWO of the tests shown above.

Component	Comparison test. State two methods used	Results	Metal identified
	1. .... 2.	....	
	1. .... 2.	....	
	1. .... 2.	....	

9.8 CHARACTERISTICS (OR PROPERTIES) OF MATERIALS

The selection of materials for a particular application is determined by their characteristics.
A material may possess one or more of these characteristics.
Define each characteristic and give an example of a motor-vehicle component which demonstrates this characteristic.

Characteristics	Description	Typical MV component
Hardness		
Strength		
Brittleness		
Toughness		
Ductility		
Malleability		
Elasticity		
Plasticity		
Softness		
Thermal conductivity		
Electrical conductivity		

MATERIAL SELECTION WITH REGARD TO ITS PROPERTIES

Low-carbon steel or mild steel

List the properties that make low carbon steel a very suitable material for car bodies.

....
....
....
....
....

Cast iron

List the properties that make iron a particularly suitable material from which to make such parts as engine cylinder heads and blocks, cylinder liners, piston rings, brake drums and clutch pressure-plates.

....
....
....
....
....

Using simple tests, determine how properties vary in different materials and may be changed by cold working.

1. Hardness

Use small metal plates of similar thickness. Place a ball bearing between plates and squeeze in a press or between the jaws of a vice.

Repeat on all materials. (Apply equal pressure each time.)

Material				
Diameter of indentation (mm)				

Rank the materials in order of their relative hardness (hardest first).

Material				

2. Ductility (cold forming)

Suspend long lengths of thin wire of different materials and gradually load each wire until it breaks.

Material	Original length (mm)	Total length after breakage	Extension (mm)

The most ductile material was the wire that .... the most;

this material was ....

3. Brittleness (bending)

Grip bars of different metals but a similar diameter and length securely in a vice. Place a long tube over each bar in turn and bend to and fro.

State most brittle material first.

Material				

How did you determine which was the most brittle metal?

....

4. Toughness

Using similar bars to (3) held upright in a vice, strike each a similar blow with a hammer.

State the toughest material first.

Material				

The toughest material was the one that ....

5. Elasticity and strength (stretching)

Use long thin bars of equal length and diameter. Grip each bar in turn horizontally in a vice.

Suspend a hanger on the end of each bar and load until the bar bends.

Note: (1) The amount of deflection each bar makes before bending.

(2) The mass on the hanger when each bar bends.

(3) Remove hanger to see if the bars return to their original positions.

Material				
Maximum deflection before bending (mm)				
Maximum load before bending				

The material that has the greatest elasticity will ....

....

The material having the greatest strength will ....

....

6. Malleability

Use thin sheets of metal and indent the centre with a ball-pein hammer or cupping machine until the metal fractures.

Material				
Depth of indentation before fracture (mm)				

State the material having the best malleability first and list others in relative order.

Material				

EFFECT OF HOT AND COLD WORKING

Almost all motor-vehicle components are manufactured by changing the shape of the material; this change is achieved by either cold or hot working. These methods not only change the shape of the material, they deform the grain structure and this modifies some of the properties of the materials.

COLD WORKING

This flattens the crystal structure making the metal harder and more brittle.

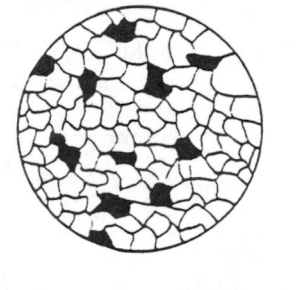

Normal structure of mild steel viewed under a microscope

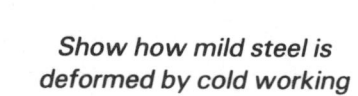

Show how mild steel is deformed by cold working

HOT WORKING

Hot working occurs when the temperature is high enough to allow the crystals to reform during the manufacturing process.

Hot forging strengthens the component by causing the grain to flow in the direction in which deformation takes place.

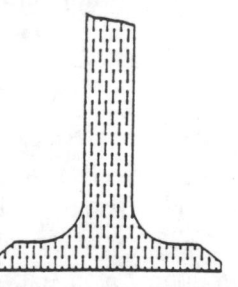

Shows grain flow if the valve were turned from a solid bar

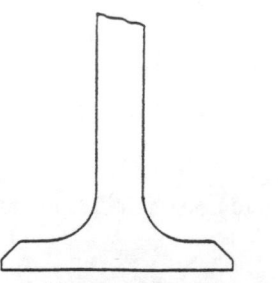

Shows the grain flow produced when the valve is forged

HEAT TREATMENT — EFFECTS OF HARDENING AND TEMPERING

Heat treatment affects the mechanical properties of steel.

Indicate the changes that occur during heat treatment and state how these affect the mechanical properties of the steels mentioned in the next column.

....
....
....
....
....
....
....
....
....
....
....
....
....
....
....
....
....

Examine fractured bars that have had various treatments and show how the grain structure varies in each case.

(a) *Untreated high-carbon steel*

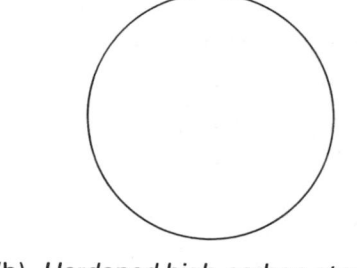

(b) *Hardened high-carbon steel*

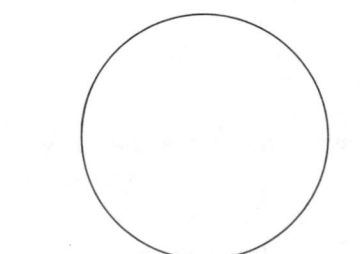

(c) *Hardened and tempered high-carbon steel*

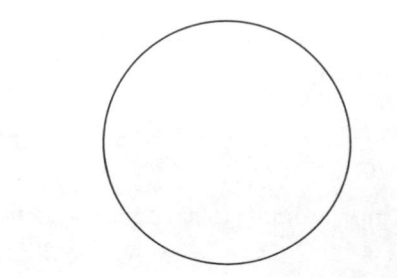

9.10 HARDENING, TEMPERING, NORMALISING, ANNEALING

Describe the process relative to each term and explain in respect of steel, how the undesirable effect of property changes can be eliminated or minimised.

Note – The hardening and tempering processes are used to harden and temper high carbon steels. These processes are not effective with low carbon steel.

Hardening

Process ....

....

Properties after heat treatment ....

....

Tempering

Process ....

....

Properties after heat treatment ....

....

Normalising

Process ....

....

Properties after heat treatment ....

....

Annealing

Process ....

....

Properties after heat treatment ....

....

The cooling medium used for both hardening and tempering is water or oil.

State the advantages of both types.

Water ....

....

....

Oil ....

....

....

State the effect of heat treatment on the characteristics of 'low-carbon' steel.

....

....

Give examples of motor-vehicle components which benefit from the following processes:

Process	Component	Reason for choice of process
Hardening	....	....
Tempering	....	....
Normalising	....	....
Annealing	....	....

171

CORROSION

Corrosion is the natural tendency of metals to return to their oxidised states.
Carbon steels are particularly vulnerable to corrosive attack.
State TWO common forms of corrosion.

1. ....

2. ....

Most metals are produced from the metallic oxide ores which are their natural
state. Oxidation or chemical corrosion is a natural process which allows oxygen
to combine with the surface of the metal and in the case of ferrous metals,
slowly to form flakes of rust.

What are the main causes of chemical corrosion?

....

....

Describe the effect chemical corrosion has on an unprotected vehicle chassis or
body.

....

....

....

....

....

....

....

When is the oxidation process considered to be an advantage?

....

....

....

....

....

Electro-chemical effect

When two different metals are in contact in damp conditions the moisture will
act as an electrolyte, similar to a battery cell, and the metal which has a negative
electrical potential to the other metal will be corroded away. Any unprotected
pair of different metals will corrode in this manner.

The table below shows the electrode
potential of different metals.

Metal	Electrode Potential (volts)
Aluminium	−1.68
Zinc	−0.76
Chromium	−0.56
Iron/steel	−0.44
Cadmium	−0.40
Nickel	−0.22
Tin	−0.14
Lead	−0.13
Copper	+0.40

Which material would corrode first if:

Steel were coated with zinc
(galvanising)?

....

Aluminium and steel were bolted
together?

....

Steel was plated with tin?

....

Sketch what occurs when moisture penetrates steel that has been coated with

(i) *Zinc*   (ii) *Tin*

....

State FIVE effects of corrosion on a modern vehicle.

....

....

....

....

....

9.12 SURFACE PROTECTION

Surfaces are given various types of protective coatings. Sometimes these coatings are also decorative, for example, body paintwork.

What are the basic reasons for providing 'surface' protection?

....

....

....

One method of protecting materials is by coating the material with a thin layer of non-corrosive material. Some examples of this are shown below. State any motor-vehicle component protected by the processes named.

Protection process	Motor-vehicle component
Galvanising	
Tin plating	
Anodising	
Cadmium plating	
Chromium plating	

Spare parts which may be stored for a long time are protected with various substances. Examine some such components.

State how or what material is used to protect their surfaces.

Component	Type of protection

The vehicle body may be protected by various painting processes. With each process, different types of paint materials are applied to the surface.

What is the object of

(a) The first surface primer-coat? ....

....

....

....

(b) Various layers of undercoat? ....

....

....

....

....

(c) Final high-gloss coat? ....

....

The underside of a vehicle is usually given extra protection.
Name and very briefly describe three types of protection that may be used.

1. ....

2. ....

3. ....

List the main causes of corrosion on a vehicle.

1. ....

2. ....

3. ....

4. ....

5. ....

CLEANING OF VEHICLES, UNITS AND COMPONENTS

Car valeting systems

Many modern filling stations provide carwash and valeting services.

State the type of washing/cleaning facilities available in a variety of price ranges.

1. ....
2. ....
3. ....
4. ....
5. ....
6. ....
7. ....

State some common cleaning agents used for

Car valeting ....
....

Steam cleaning ....
....

Parts cleaning ....
....

Steam and high-pressure cleaners

These types of cleaners are common in all modern garages. They may be separate units or combined as one compact unit. State TWO basic functions of a

1. Steam cleaner

....
....
....

2. High-pressure washer

....
....
....

Hot, steam automatic pressure washer

Cleaning tanks

All garages must have some method of cleaning the mechanical parts removed from the vehicle.
State the types of tanks that may be used:

....
....
....

Abrasive cleaners

The most common abrasive cleaner used in vehicle workshops is a spark plug cleaner.
What type of abrasive is used?

....

In engine reconditioning workshops it is common to find either a 'shot blaster' or a 'glass bead blaster' cleaner. What are the advantages of using these types of cleaners?

....
....
....

Glass bead blaster machine

List safety precautions to be observed using cleaning machines.

1. ....
....
2. ....
3. ....
4. ....
....

Chapter 9

Joining

JOINING of MATERIALS and COMPONENTS

The proper joining of parts or materials is essential in the construction of a modern motor-vehicle. The parts may be fabrications such as vehicle bodies, assembled units of engines and gearboxes etc. The choice of joining will be by the best and most economical method possible. TEN methods are listed below.
Give motor-vehicle examples of where such joining occurs.

Soft and hard soldering	**Nuts, bolts and screw joints**
....	....
....	....
....	....
Brazing and braze welding	**Adhesive bonding**
....	....
....	....
....	....
Oxy-fuel-gas welding	**Shrinking**
....	....
....	....
....	....
Manual metal arc welding	**Compression pressing**
....	....
....	....
....	....
Riveting	**Use of dowels and keys**
....	....
....	....
....	....

SOFT SOLDERING

Soft soldering is a low-temperature metal-joining process used for joints which are relatively lightly loaded and not subjected to severe heating. It is also used for securing electrical cable connections and some pipe unions.

List FOUR metals that can be joined by soft soldering.

....

Soft soldering involves:

1. Preparing the surfaces to be joined.
2. Applying flux.
3. Applying sufficient heat for 'tinning' and running the molten solder into the joint.

How are the joint surfaces prepared?

1. ....

2. ....

3. ....

Why is this preparation necessary?

....

....

....

....

State the purpose of 'tinning' a soldering iron.

....

....

....

....

The heat required to warm the irons may be supplied in four ways.

1. .... 2. ....

3. .... 4. ....

Complete the drawing below to show an electrical soldering iron soldering the connection between a stator lead and diode wire in the alternator's rectifier pack.

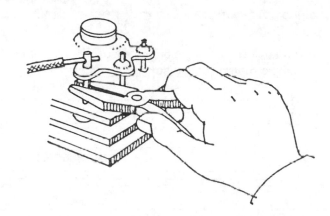

Complete the drawing below to show a soldering iron being held to the work at approximately the correct angle to create capillary action to sweat the joint.

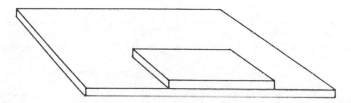

177

SOLDER

Soft solders are *lead-tin* alloys which may contain a small percentage of *antimony*. The percentage of lead and tin in a solder is varied to suit the application. As the percentage of lead in the solder is increased, the melting temperature range between initial melting and fully molten becomes greater, that is, the solder remains 'plastic' or 'pasty' over a wide temperature range. At what temperature does ordinary solder *begin* to melt?

....

Complete the table below.

% Lead	% Tin	Temperature range while solder is in a plastic state	Typical use
40	60		
50	50		
70	30		

50/50 solder is commonly called ....

40/60 lead-tin solder is commonly called ....

70/30 lead-tin solder is commonly called ....

State the advantage of 'tinmans' solder.

....

....

....

What benefit is to be gained by using a solder which has a prolonged 'pasty' stage when solidifying?

....

....

....

FLUXES

State the purpose of a soldering flux.

....

....

....

The type of flux must be chosen to suit the application. Two types of flux are in general use.

State materials for which the following fluxes are best suited.

Corrosive	
Hydrochloric acid	
Zinc chloride (killed spirit)	

Non-corrosive	
Tallow	
Resin	

Corrosive fluxes are .... fluxes which prevent oxidation taking place, thereby protecting the joint surfaces during soldering. These fluxes also help to clean the joint surfaces.

Non-corrosive fluxes are .... fluxes which protect the 'cleaned' surface during the soldering process.

What precautions should be taken when using corrosive fluxes?

....

....

....

SOLDERING A JOINT

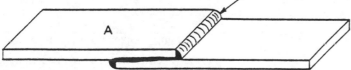

The joint shown above is a .... joint.

Outline the procedure for soldering this joint.

(a) ....

(b) ....

(c) ....

This soldering process is known as ....

It may be necessary to apply a little solder at 'B'. If this is done, the solder will flow into the joint formed between the faces; this is known as the
.... action of the solder.

Heat loss can be a problem when soldering. How can this be minimised?

....
....

Another probem associated with soldering is the damaging effect of heat flow to certain parts of a component being soldered. How can heat flow to special regions be limited during the soldering process?

....
....
....

List THREE common soldering faults.

....
....
....

HARD SOLDERING

With any soldering process, the metal used for joining melts at a lower temperature than does the parent metal. In this connection brazing is a hard soldering process. Another hard soldering process is 'silver soldering'.

What are the essential similarities/differences of hard and soft soldering?

Similarities ....
....
....

Differences ....
....
....
....

What are the basic ingredients of 'silver solder' and how is the silver soldering process carried out?

Ingredients ....

Process: ....
....
....

Give three reasons for joining metals by silver soldering.

1. ....
....

2. ....
....

3. ....

BRONZE — BRAZE — WELDING

The difference between bronze welding and fusion welding is that the metals being joined are not actually melted but heated to a red heat. The filler rods used are a brass alloy, the alloying constituents of which are designed to suit the metals being joined. It is also necessary to use a flux.

Describe the technique of braze welding as applied to a lap joint in steel.

....

....

....

....

....

....

BRAZING

This is a similar process to bronze welding, i.e. the metals to be joined are heated to a red heat and the filler rod (brazing spelter), having been suitably fluxed, is melted by the temperature of the joint area and flows into the joining gap. The filler rod must not be directly heated by the torch flame.

State the reason why brazing would be used in preference to fusion welding.

....

....

....

....

What is the most common brazing fault?

....

....

....

OXYACETYLENE WELDING

This form of welding is still widely used in general repair work, but more specialised applications demand more modern types of welding equipment. During welding the metals being formed are actually melted so that they flow together.

Acetylene is a hydrocarbon fuel; it reacts with oxygen to liberate heat at high temperatures.

Oxygen: A stable gas, contained at high pressures of about 200 bar (3000 lbf/in²), in black-painted cylinders.

Acetylene: An unstable gas, contained at medium pressures of about 15.5 bar (225 lbf/in²) in cylinders packed with kapok, or kapok and charcoal. Acetylene cylinders are painted maroon.

Complete the drawing below, showing a typical oxyacetylene welding set. Name the parts and state the colour of the bottles.

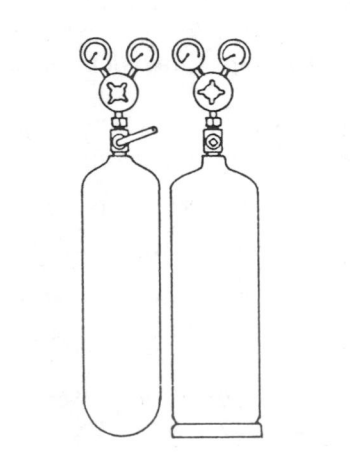

State THREE faults common in this type of welding.

....

....

....

MANUAL METAL ARC WELDING

An electric arc is a sustained spark caused by current jumping across the gap between two terminals in an electrical circuit. In metallic arc welding, the arc is formed between the metal to be welded and an electrode. The arc creates intense heat in a small area. This melts the metal and the tip of the electrode; molten metal from the electrode then transfers across the arc to act as filler.

Equipment

The power source that supplies the current for metal arc welding may be either a.c. (alternating current) or d.c. (direct current). With a.c. the energy is supplied from an a.c. welding transformer set. The basic equipment for d.c. comprises a generator which may be driven by an electric motor or an internal combustion engine.

Name the parts indicated on the sketch.

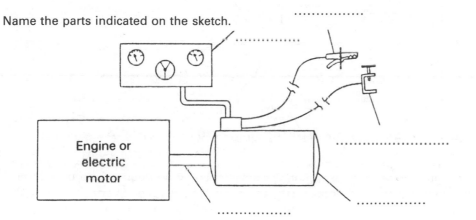

A direct current (d.c.) welding set

What are the particular advantages and disadvantages of manual metal arc welding as used in the vehicle-repair trade?

....

....

....

....

RESISTANCE WELDING

Resistance welding is a process in which the welding heat is generated by the resistance offered to the passage of an electric current through the parts being welded.

The form of resistance welding widely used on motor vehicles is known as 'spot welding'. This is a process where the two metal sheets being joined are clamped between two large copper electrodes which pass the welding current through the plates.

Name the main parts of the spot welder shown below.

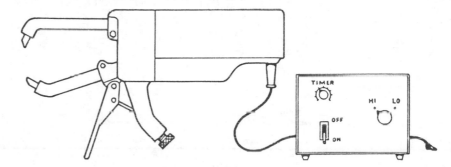

State the advantages of this method of joining metals.

....

....

Three forms of resistance welding are spot, seam and protrusion (projection). Seam uses rollers and produces a watertight joint.
Protrusion presses on projections which collapse during welding (securing clips are spot welded by this process).

Investigation

Examine a modern vehicle and state TWO places where each resistance weld is used.

Spot	Seam	Protrusion
1.	1.	1. ....
2.	2.	2. ....

SHIELDED ARC PROCESS

With the metallic arc process already described, oxidisation is prevented by slag-forming fluxes in the electrode coating. An alternative method of preventing oxidisation is to shield the arc and molten metal from the atmosphere by shrouding the area with an inert gas, i.e. a gas that will not combine with heated metals. The two gases most widely used for this purpose in the UK are argon and carbon dioxide (CO_2).

Argon arc (TIG)

The heat for welding is supplied by an arc struck between a 'non-consumable' tungsten electrode and the joint to be welded. The argon gas shield is supplied through a nozzle concentric with the electrode tip. Most joints require the use of a filler rod.

The diagram below shows the layout of the tungsten argon arc welding plant; label the diagram.

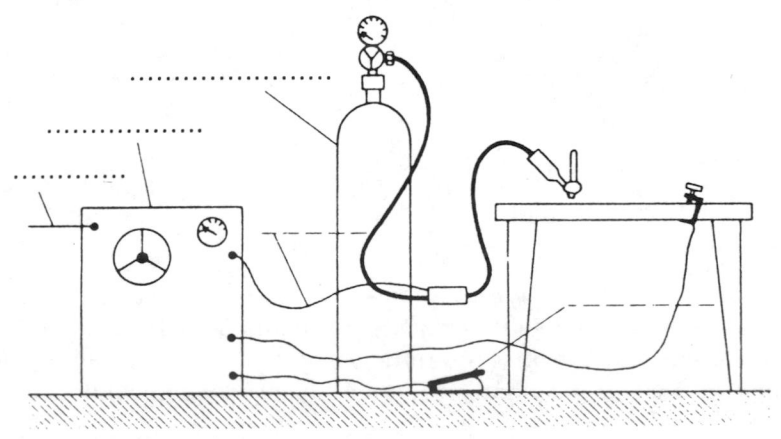

State three advantages of the TIG system.

1. ....
   ....
2. ....
   ....
3. ....

CO_2 process (MIG)

In this process a 'consumable' electrode in the form of a wire is fed automatically from a reel into the arc, the weld area being shrouded with CO_2 gas.

The equipment for CO_2 welding comprises the following essential parts: a d.c. power unit, a CO_2 gas supply, a gun or torch to which the filler wire, current and gas are fed, and a control unit for the reel of filler wire.

Complete the diagram below to show the layout of equipment for CO_2 welding.

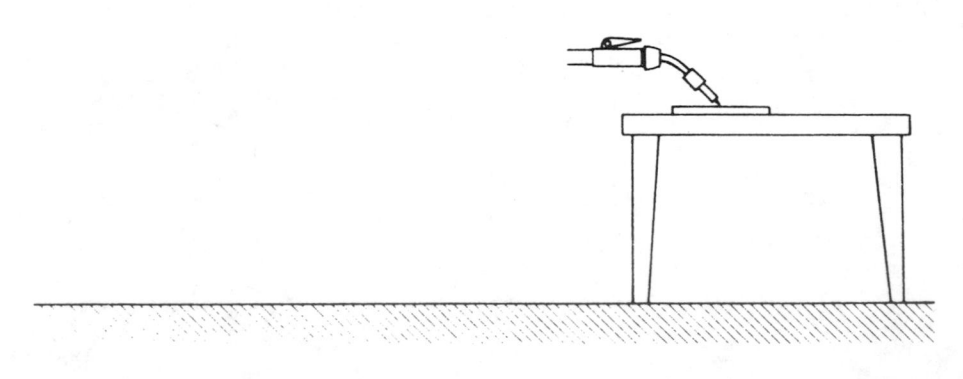

State the advantages of the MIG system when compared with other forms of welding.

....
....
....
....

RIVETING

Riveting is one form of mechanical fastening which makes a permanent joint between two or more materials such as chassis frames, body fabrications, metal to fabric.

State FOUR materials from which rivets are commonly made.

....

A solid rivet is shown below. Make sketches above each title to show the types of rivets named.

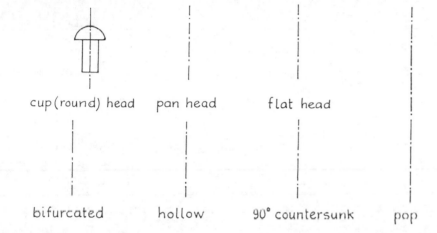

cup (round) head   pan head   flat head

bifurcated   hollow   90° countersunk   pop

The sketch at A below shows a double riveted lap joint and includes the general dimensional spacing that should be used when positioning and marking out items to be joined.

Complete the other named joints and apply similar dimensioning.

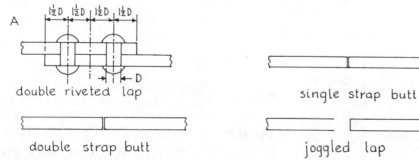

double riveted lap   single strap butt

double strap butt   joggled lap

The riveted joint is closed by forming a head on the projecting part of the shank. The tools required for cold riveting small soft metal rivets or hot riveting small steel rivets are a support dolly, a drawing up tool, a ball pein hammer and a rivet snap.

Complete the drawing below to show the correct rivet size and the tools used in the riveting process.

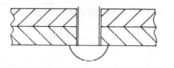   

Indicate the correct length of rivet required to form a cup head.

Show use of support dolly and drawing up tool.

   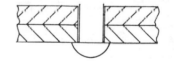

Show use of ball pein hammer to swell and form rivet head.

Show use of rivet snap.

What factors govern the size and type of rivet used for a particular job?

....

....

When drilling holes for riveting, what size of drill relative to the rivet shank should be selected?

....

Riveting faults

If the riveting is incorrectly carried out, then the strength of the joint will be severely reduced.

Opposite is shown a typical riveting fault.
Complete the four drawings below to show the faults stated.

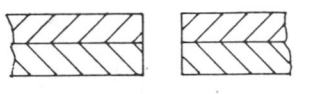

Rivet not drawn up

Rivet too long

Rivet too short

Hole too large

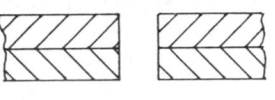

Rivet struck off centre

How could most riveting faults be prevented?

....

....

....

....

POP RIVETS

Pop rivets are hollow rivets which are supplied already threaded on to a mandrel. They are closed by gripping the mandrel in a riveting tool and pulling it so that it forms a head on the remote end of the rivet and then breaks off.

What are the main advantages of pop rivets?

....

....

....

....

The sketch at A below shows the pop rivet and the riveting tool in position before the rivet is closed. Complete the sketch at B to show the action of the tool and the shape of the rivet after closing.

A

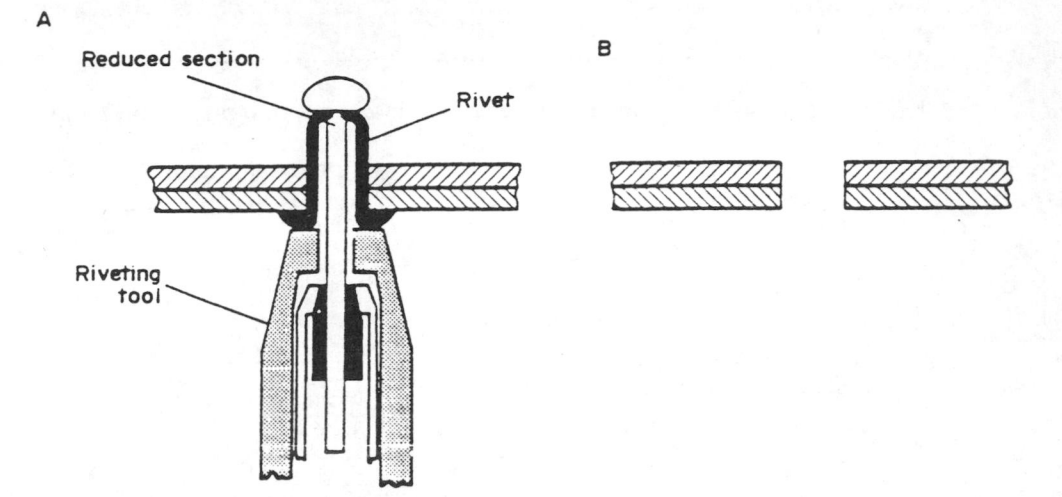

Reduced section

Rivet

Riveting tool

B

Some pop rivets have a specially shaped head which remains trapped in the formed head. Such a rivet is shown below; why are these used?

....

What type of rivets are used for attaching brake and clutch linings to the relative faces, and what is the reason for their use?

....

....

....

....

....

JOINING BY NUT AND BOLT OR SCREW

The nut and bolt is the most common method of joining two detachable components together. Name the parts of the nut and bolt shown.

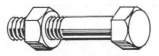

Bolts normally have a hexagon or allan socket type of head while the screw thread is usually of a Vee type. A screw has a screwdriver type of head fitment and a thread similar to a bolt, or a faster thread similar to a woodscrew or self-tapping screw.

Bolts, screws and nuts are supplied in many forms and sizes for motor-vehicle use, and may be identified by one or more of the headings below.
State reasons why each of the fixtures is important.

Shank diameter ....

Screw length ....

Material ....

Shape of head ....

Screw thread ....

For types of screw thread, see Chapter 8.

Types of screw heads

Name the types of screw heads shown below.

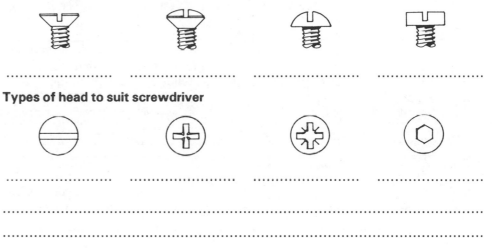

Types of head to suit screwdriver

....

Clearance in bolt holes

All bolt and stud holes must be given a correct amount of clearance to ensure that a joint on a component can be easily separated. Why may it be difficult, after some time, to separate a joint that has been securely tightened?

....

Complete the drawings below to show this clearance.

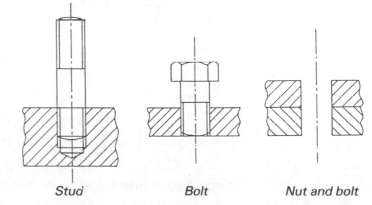

Stud   *Bolt*   *Nut and bolt*

LOCKING DEVICES

Most of the nuts and bolts used on motor vehicles are fitted with locking devices. This is to counteract the loosening effect caused by strain and vibration.

Name the types of locking device shown below and give an example of where each may be used on a motor vehicle.

Insert

Which of the locking devices shown opposite are Positive locking devices? ....
....

Frictional locking devices? ....

....

Describe an alternative method of locking nuts and bolts that is very often used in engine assembly.

....

....

Both 'left-' and 'right'-hand screw threads are used on motor vehicles. However in most cases it is the right-hand thread which is used.

State which of these represents left- and right-hand threads.

....

State two places on a motor vehicle where left-hand threads are used and give the reasons for using them.

(1) ....

....

(2) ....

....

When tightening nuts and bolts, care must be taken to ensure that they are not left slack or overtightened. What tool should be used to ensure a correct tightness is applied?

....

What problems are associated with the overtightening of nuts or bolts?

....

USE OF ADHESIVES

A considerable range of adhesives are used in the automotive industry today. They have a large variety of applications and in many instances are replacing joints previously riveted or welded.

Requirements

The requirements of an adhesive are that it will 'wet' and adhere to the surfaces being bonded and that the film in between the surfaces will have a high cohesive strength.

Adhesive types

Thermo-hardening adhesives
Thermo-hardening adhesives will form a strong heat-resistant joint between a wide variety of materials. The adhesive is made up from two parts — a resin and a hardener (catalyst curing agent) — which when mixed transform into a hard solid. These adhesives, which contain epoxy resin, require heat to effect a 'cure'.

State the meaning of the following terms as applied to adhesives.

Structural adhesives ....
....

Thermo-plastic ....
....

Impact type ....
....

Hot set ....
....

Cold set ....
....

There are many advantages of adhesives, three of which are listed below. State three more advantages and three disadvantages.

Advantages

1. *They give stress distribution over the whole bond area.*

2. *They can be used to join a wide variety of materials.*

3. *Ideal for joining fragile materials.*

4. ....

5. ....

6. ....

Disadvantages

1. ....
....

2. ....
....

3. ....
....

State the meaning of the term 'wetting the surface' in relation to adhesives.

....
....
....

To what part of the joining operation does the word 'cure' relate?

....
....

187

It is extremely important when using epoxy resins that the correct procedure is adopted. What factors must be considered before and when making a joint so as to avoid faults?

(a) ....

(b) ....

(c) ....

(d) ....

(e) ....

Give THREE examples of the use of epoxy resins in the construction or repair of automobiles.

1. ....

2. ....

3. ....

Joining process – thermo hardening adhesive

Outline the sequence of operations for making a joint between mild steel and aluminium, using any suitable adhesive.

Type of joint ....

Adhesive trade name ....

....

....

....

....

....

....

Joining process – impact adhesive

Impact adhesives contain a solvent which, when exposed to air, evaporates.

The surfaces being joined, having been suitably prepared, are coated with the adhesive and after a period of time (stipulated by the manufacturer) are brought into contact and pressure applied. These adhesives, which are often supplied in tape form, are generally less rigid and weaker than thermo-hardening types.

Give six examples of the use of impact adhesives in the construction or repair of automobiles.

1. ....   2. ....

3. ....   4. ....

5. ....   6. ....

Name four popular impact adhesives which are used in the motor trade and state a typical use for each.

1. ....

2. ....

3. ....

4. ....

The cyanoacrylate adhesives are impact adhesives. These are very quick acting adhesives and are known as ....

Safety precautions when using adhesives

State the safety precautions to be observed when using adhesives.

....

....

....

....

FITTING PARTS BY SHRINKING

The component to be fitted is first either heated and expands or is cooled and contracts before fitting. In all cases the components must be machined very accurately to the correct sizes.

Hot shrink

The part is usually an external gear or collar and has a smaller internal diameter than the diameter on to which it is to be fitted. The most common example of a hot shrunk component on a vehicle is the ring-gear fitted to the engine flywheel.
Complete the table to show the ring-gear internal diameter.

Heating process	Ring-gear internal diameter	Flywheel external diameter
Before heating		320 mm
Ring gear heated to 300°		320 mm
When fitted and cooled		320 mm

Describe how a worn ring-gear can be removed from the flywheel.

....

....

....

What is the correct heating procedure to fit a new ring-gear?

....

....

....

What technique should be applied when fitting the ring-gear to the flywheel?

....

....

....

Cold shrunk

The component is usually an internally fitted part which is larger than the hole into which it is to be located. An engine valve seat insert is a common motor-vehicle example.

Sketch a valve seat insert about to be fitted into an engine cylinder head.

The shrinkage process is more commonly carried out by the manufacturers who have the equipment capable of cooling to temperatures of − 190°.
How can a component be cooled in a motor-vehicle workshop?

....

....

....

....

....

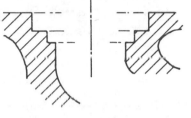

What are the advantages of hot or cold shrinking a component?

....

....

....

....

What faults may occur during the hot shrinking, cold shrinking or the fitting process?

....

....

....

FITTING PARTS BY COMPRESSION PRESSING

A compression joint is a joint requiring an interference fit which requires assembly by some form of pressure.

The fit is not as tight as a shrunk fit but is sufficiently tight. Show how the bush may be simply pressed into the casing.

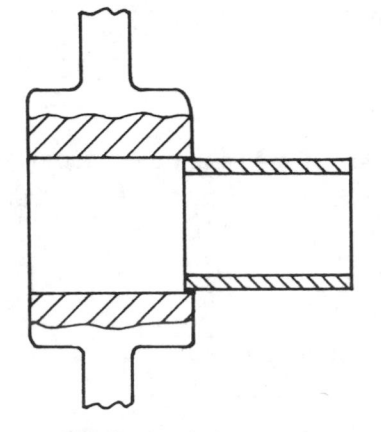

Explain how the tool is extracting the bush from the assembly.

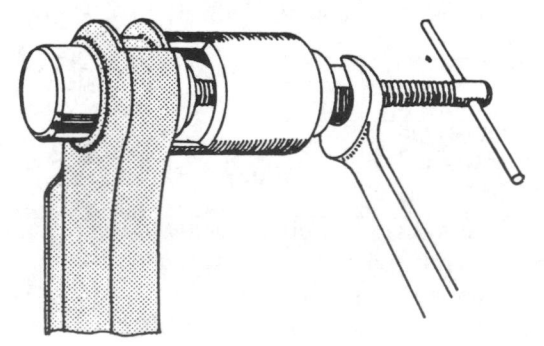

....
....
....
....

All compression joints have a centring edge.
What does this mean and what is the edges function?

....
....
....
....

Before applying pressure to the joint, what preliminary procedures should be made?

....
....
....
....

What are the most common faults that occur when fitting components by compression pressing?

....
....
....
....

The five drawings below show a wheel hub assembly. State in each case what compression pressing procedure is occurring.

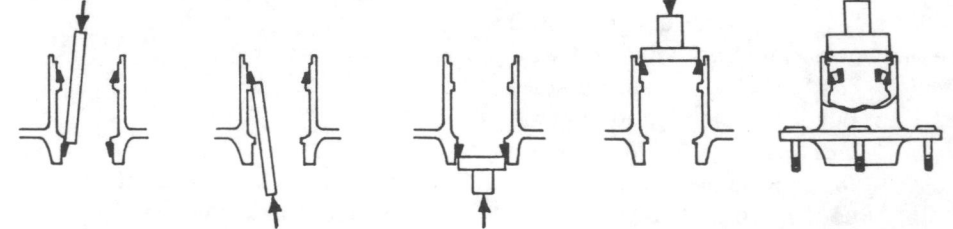

....
....
....

USE OF PINS AND KEYS

All types of pins and keys are items which locate parts before securely fixing them, preventing excessive movement or completely locking two parts together.

PINS

Identify the types of pin shown below.

....

A dowel is a short parallel shank pin which fits into a precisely reamed hole.
What are the functions of the dowels shown below?

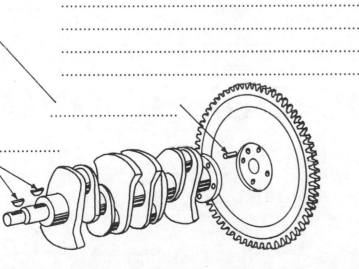

....
....
....
....
....
....
....
....
....

Taper and parallel pins

Taper pins fit into holes of similar taper. Parallel pins, including split pins, allow easy dismantling.
What are the advantages of using taper pins?

....
....

What is the main problem encountered when fitting pins?

....
....

The pin shown below is called a
It has a nut at one end to secure the
pin in position.
Give TWO examples of where on a
motor-vehicle such a pin may be
used.

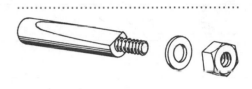

1. ....   2. ....

KEYS

Keys prevent pulleys and gears on shafts from turning.
Identify the keys shown below.

....

The first key is the one most commonly found on motor-vehicles.
Describe how the two keys positioned to fit in the crankshaft opposite should be correctly assembled together with the timing chain pulley and crankshaft pulley.

....
....
....
....
....
....

UNIT 05

ROAD VEHICLE SCIENCE BACKGROUND

INCLUDES

ELEMENT 11.   VEHICLE SCIENCE   193

Chapter 10

Road Vehicle Background Science

THE SI SYSTEM

The SI system is a system of measurements adopted by all the European and many other countries. It allows us to solve problems that are simple or, depending on our requirements, very complicated.

In the SI system there are SEVEN basic units. In motor-vehicle science you will use and become familiar with the first FIVE units in the table below.

Complete the table stating the quantity represented by each unit and its base symbol.

Basic Unit	Quantity	Unit Symbol
Metre	....	....
Kilogram	....	....
Second	....	....
Ampere	....	....
Kelvin	....	....
Candela	....	....
Mole	....	....

Why are these units called basic units? ....

....

Forms of measurement

Measurement is the comparison of a quantity with a standard unit, e.g. consider a car:

(i)   Its length is 3 m. The quantity is ...., the unit is ....

(ii) It has a mass of 1000 kg. The quantity is ...., the unit is ....

(iii) It can attain its maximum speed in 20 s. The quantity is ...., the unit is ....

From the above it can be seen that QUANTITY = ...

State the quantity, number and unit expressed in the statements below	Quantity	Number	Unit
1. An engine has a mass of one hundred kilograms			
2. A car ramp is five metres long			
3. A vehicle was brought to an emergency stop in twelve seconds			

Many units are derived by multiplying or dividing quantities of the basic units.

Derived units of length

If we consider the quantity length, then to find the area or volume of a component we must multiply quantities of length. Consider the diagrams:

AREA =

      =

      =

Therefore, the derived unit for area = ...

VOLUME =

         =

         =

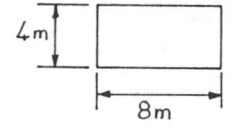

Therefore the derived unit for volume = ...

Mixing basic units

If the units of length, time and mass are suitably mixed, values for speed, acceleration, and force can be obtained.

Example — speed (velocity)

If a car travels 400 m in 20 s, what is its speed?

The speed of a car is determined by the distance it covers in a specific time.

Therefore SPEED = ...   From example, SPEED = ...

Example — acceleration

A car is travelling at 4 m/s. It then accelerates to 16 m/s in 8 s. What is its acceleration?

Acceleration is the change in speed measured in a specified time.

Therefore ACCELERATION = ...

From example, ACCELERATION = ...

FORCE is defined as ....   Therefore FORCE = ...

Since force is a very common feature in science and the derived unit is very awkward, it has been simplified and called the

....

SYMBOLS OF BASIC QUANTITIES IN THE SI SYSTEM

All the names of quantities commonly used in motor-vehicle science are given abbreviated symbols. This is so that the full name of the quantity need not be written out each time it is used. The symbols for the units have already been used on the previous page. When shown in books the symbols for units are printed in ordinary print and the symbols for quantities are printed in italics, e.g. (metre = m) (mass = m).

Complete the symbols of the quantities and units shown.

Quantity	Quantity symbol	Unit of measurement	Unit symbol
Length	....	....	....
Mass	....	....	....
Time	....	....	....
Area	....	....	....
Volume	....	....	....
Speed (velocity)	....	....	....
Acceleration	....	....	....
Force	....	....	....

MULTIPLES and SUB-MULTIPLES of SI

In the SI system, prefixes are used in front of the basic unit to eliminate the need of writing many noughts on large or small numbers.

Complete the table below which shows those prefixes.

Prefix	Symbol	Factor	Value written in full
giga	....	....	....
mega	....	....	....
kilo	....	....	....
hecto	....	....	....
deca	....	....	....
	basic unit		
deci	....	....	....
centi	....	....	....
milli	....	....	....
micro	....	....	....
nano	....	....	....

It is preferred that numbers are expressed in units between 0 and 999, e.g.

$$50 \text{ m} = 50 \text{ m}$$
$$50000 \text{ m} = 50 \times 10^3 \text{ m} = 50 \text{ km}$$
$$0.05 \text{ m} = 50 \times 10^{-3} \text{ m} = 50 \text{ mm}$$

In practice the basic unit and the milli, kilo and mega units are very commonly used.

The values centi, deci, deca and hecto are only used when dealing with areas and volumes where it may be more convenient to use them because square and cubic millimetres become awkward to use, e.g.

$$1 \text{ m}^3 = 1\,000\,000\,000 \text{ mm}^3 = 10^9 \text{ mm}$$

Complete the following statements.

The number of metres in a kilometre is ....

The number of millimetres in a kilometre is ....

The number of newtons in a meganewton is ....

The number of milligrams in a gram is ....

The number of watts in a gigawatt is ....

Change each of the following values to its preferred value.

1. 7800 m
....

2. 0.006 m
....

3. 0.000 06 m
....

4. 22 000 g
....

5. 5 200 000 g
....

6. 200 000 N
....

7. 9 673 000 N
....

8. 3600 MW
....

9. 430 cm
....

10. 0.0087 A
....

INDICES

3×3 can be written as 3^2 (three squared or three to the 'power' of two).

Similarly $3 \times 3 \times 3 \times 3$ is 3^4 (three raised to the power four). The figure placed above the 3 in the examples above is the

....

When multiplying and dividing numbers which are the same, their indices can be added or subtracted. The same rule applies to letters used instead of numbers. For example

$a^2 \times a^3$ becomes $a^{2+3} = a^5$

or

$a \times a \times a \times a \times a = a^5$

$\dfrac{a^6}{a^2} = $ is $\dfrac{a \times a \times a \times a \times a \times a}{a \times a} = a^4$

When multiplying, ... the indices. When dividing, ... the indices.

Simplify the following:

(a) $y^2 \times y^3 \times y^5 = $

(b) $\dfrac{a^2 \times a^4 \times a^7}{a^3 \times a^2} = $

(c) $a^2 \times b^3 \times a^3 \times b^2 = $

When dealing with expressions like ab^2, only the b is squared.

That is $ab^2 = a \times b \times b$

But $(ab)^2 = $

A value can be stated by using the base number 10 raised to a certain power. For Example

$$100 = 10^2$$

Instead of writing 100 we write 10^2, it has the same value. This method can be convenient when large numbers are involved or when fractions of 10 are involved.

Express the following by using base 10 raised to a power.

1000	=
10000	=
100000	=
1000000	=
10000000	=
100	=
10	=
1	=

Fractions of 10

0.1	=
0.01	=
0.001	=
0.0001	=
0.00001	=
0.000001	=

When multiplying decimal fractions by the base 10 raised to a power, the decimal point is moved right or left according to the value of the index.

If the index is 'positive', the decimal point moves to the

....

If the index is 'negative', the decimal point moves to the

....

Examples

12.47×10^2	=
1003×10^2	=
1.5684×10^3	=
138.51×10^5	=
5000.35×10^1	=
542×10^{-2}	=

368.76×10^{-3} =
15768.62×10^{-6} =

Multiples and sub-multiples of SI

Using the 'power ten' method, numbers can be expressed in a shorter form. For example

10500 can be expressed as

10.5×10^3

Express the following numbers using this method. Express in powers of 10^9, 10^6, 10^3, 10^{-3}, 10^{-6} or 10^{-9}.

6575000	=
49500000	=
85650	=
682543981	=
7246	=
7240000000	=
0.0000013	=
0.001	=
0.000354	=
0.07	=
0.00631	=
0.000000085	=

AREAS OF REGULAR FIGURES

The figure shown below is a square. That is length and breadth are equal.

The shading represents the area of the square.

Area   a

a

To calculate the area, we square the length of one side.

area $= a \times a = a^2$

Rectangle

Area   b

l

The area of a rectangle as shown above is found by multiplying the length and breadth.

area $= l \times b$

State the SI derived units used to express area ....

....

Perimeter

How is the perimeter of a square rectangle calculated?

....

....

Examples

1. Calculate the area of a square whose sides are 3 m in length

   Area $= 3 \times 3 = 9\,m^2$

2. Calculate the area of the rectangle shown below.

35 mm

150 mm

   Area $= 150 \times 35 = 5250\,mm^2$

3. A workshop is 12 m square. The floor area is therefore:

   (a) $12\,m^2$ (b) $24\,m^2$

   (c) $144\,m^2$ (d) $240\,m^2$

   Answer (   )

4. A workshop has 4 work benches each measuring 1 m × 2½ m. The floor area covered by the benches is therefore (a) $4\,m^2$, (b) $5\,m^2$, (c) $2½\,m^2$, (d) $10\,m^2$.

   Answer (   )

5. A motor-lorry platform measures 10 m × 2 m. How many boxes whose bases measure 0.5 m × 0.5 m would it take to cover the platform?

   ....

   ....

   ....

   ....

   ....

6. The figure shown below represents the workshop floor and pit area. Calculate

   (a) the area of the pit, and

   (b) the area of the remaining floor space.

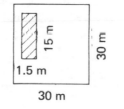

1.5 m

30 m

   ....

   ....

   ....

   ....

   ....

   ....

   ....

7. Determine the area and perimeter of the following shapes.

   (a)

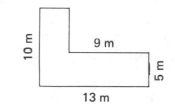

10 m   9 m

5 m

13 m

   (b)

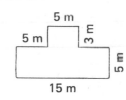

5 m   5 m   3 m

5 m

15 m

8. Complete the following table, in respect of rectangles.

Length	Breadth	Area
4.5 m	3 m	
150 mm	100 mm	
8 m		16 m²
	3.5 m	21 m²
25 mm	200 mm	

11.1 Triangles

All triangles have an area which is half that of a rectangle whose length and breadth is equal to the base and perpendicular height of the triangle. For example.

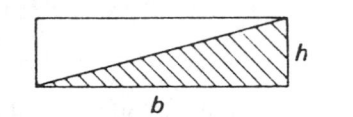

Therefore the area of a triangle would be

$$\text{Area} = \frac{\text{base} \times \text{perpendicular height}}{2}$$

This holds good for any triangle provided the height used is the perpendicular height.

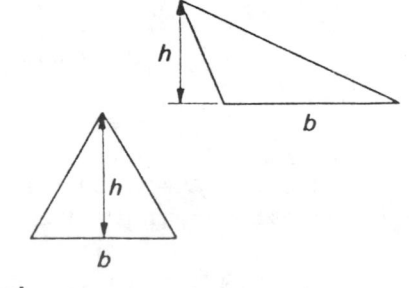

Circle

To calculate the area of a circle the following formula can be used:

$$\text{Area} = \pi r^2 \quad \text{or} \quad \frac{\pi d^2}{4}$$

Where

$$\pi = \frac{22}{7} \quad \text{or} \quad 3.142$$

r = radius and d = diameter

π (the greek letter pi) is the symbol for the ratio

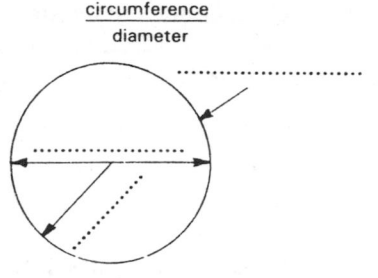

$$\frac{\text{circumference}}{\text{diameter}}$$

The 'perimeter' of a circle is the

.... State the formula to calculate the circumference of a circle.

Examples

1. Calculate the area of a circle which has a diameter of 40 mm.

$$\text{Area} = \pi r^2$$

$$\begin{aligned}\text{Area} &= 3.142 \times 20 \times 20 \\ &= 1256.8 \text{ mm}^2 \\ &= 12.568 \text{ cm}^2\end{aligned}$$

2. Calculate the area of the triangle shown below.

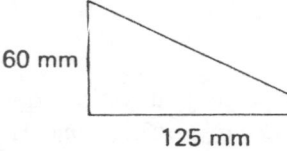

$$\text{Area} = \frac{b \times h}{2}$$

$$\begin{aligned}\text{Area} &= \frac{125 \times 60}{2} = 3750 \text{ mm}^2 \\ &= 37.50 \text{ cm}^2\end{aligned}$$

---

3. Calculate the area of a triangle which has a base of 20 cm and a perpendicular height of 45 cm.

4. A brake master-cylinder has a bore diameter of 25 mm. What is the area of the bore?

5. Determine the area of the shape

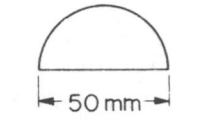

---

6. Determine the area and perimeter of the following shapes.

(a)

(b)

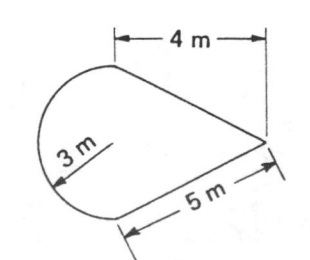

VOLUME OF REGULAR FIGURES

The volume of any regularly shaped object can be found by multiplying the area of the end by the length.
Examples of regularly shaped objects are:

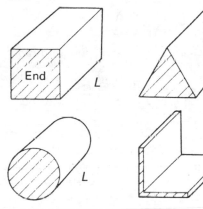

State three SI derived units commonly used to express volume.

....

....

....

If a figure is described as being regular shaped or of 'uniform' cross-section, what do these terms mean?

....

....

....

....

....

Examples

1. Determine the volume of the rectangular prism shown below.

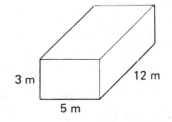

Volume = area of end × length
        = 3 × 5 × 12
        = 180 m³

2. If the cross-sectional area of a metal bar of uniform section is 0.0025 m² and its length is 4 m, the volume of metal would be

(a) 0.005 m³   (b) 0.01 m³

(c) 125 mm³   (d) 150 mm³

Answer (   )

3. If a cube has sides measuring 5 mm × 5 mm × 5 mm, its volume would be

(a) 25 mm³   (b) 50 mm³

(c) 125 mm³   (d) 150 mm³

Answer (   )

4. Calculate the volume of the rectangular prism shown below.

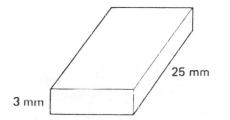

....

....

....

....

5. Calculate the volume of the section of angle iron shown below.

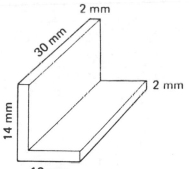

....

....

....

....

6. Determine the volume of the wedge shown below.

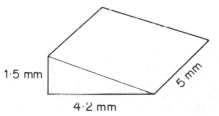

....

....

....

7. Calculate the volume of the compressor mounting block shown below.

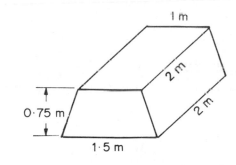

....

....

....

....

11.1 CYLINDER VOLUME

The volume of an engine cylinder is found by multiplying the area of the cylinder by the distance moved by the piston (stroke).

$$\text{Area of cylinder} = \frac{\pi d^2}{4} \text{ or } \pi r^2$$

Where d = cylinder bore.

Swept = volume

Insert the appropriate dimension abbreviations on the drawing. For example, calculate the swept volume of an engine cylinder having a bore diameter of 84 mm and a stroke of 90 mm.

Take π as $\frac{22}{7}$

(Since engine capacity is often quoted in cubic centimetres (cm^3), sometimes written as cc, the basic dimensions should be first converted to cm.)

Therefore bore 84 mm = 8.4 cm and r = 4.2 cm
stroke 90 mm = 9.0 cm

$$\text{Swept volume} = \pi r^2 \times \text{stroke}$$

$$= \frac{22}{7} \times 4.2 \times 4.2 \times 9$$

$$= \frac{22}{1} \times 0.6 \times 4.2 \times 9$$

$$= 498.96 \text{ cm}^3$$

If this cylinder was from a four cylinder engine it would be a .... litre engine.

1. Calculate the swept volume of an engine cylinder having a bore diameter of 70 mm and a stroke of 100 mm.

2. Calculate the swept volume of an engine cylinder having a bore diameter of 80 mm and a stroke of 70 mm.

3. Calculate the capacity of a four-cylinder engine whose bore and stroke are both 90 mm.

4. What is the volume of fuel contained in a cylindrical fuel tank 600 mm diameter and 900 mm long, when (a) it is completely full and, (b) two-thirds of the fuel has been used?

EVALUATION OF FORMULAE

If the values for the symbols in a formula are known, the calculation can be completed by substituting numbers for the symbols in the formula. For example, the length l of a rectangle is 5 m and the breadth b is 2 m. Calculate the area A

State basic formula: $A = l \times b$
Substitute values: $A = 5 \times 2$
Answer: $A = 10\,m^2$

Evaluate the following formulae.

No.	Formula	Given	Calculation
1	$V = I \times R$	$I = 0.8, R = 15$	
2	$u = \frac{P}{W}$	$P = 24, W = 96$	
3	$A = \pi r^2$	$\pi = \frac{22}{7}, r = 14$	
4	$P = 2\pi NT$	$\pi = \frac{22}{7}, N = 50, T = 110$	
5	$V = blh$	$b = 4, l = 10, h = 25$	
6	$c = \pi d$	$\pi = \frac{22}{7}, d = 28$	
7	$B = GH + y$	$G = 12, H = 8, y = 4$	
8	$V_2 = V_1 + at$	$V_1 = 5, a = 6, t = 8$	

1. The compression ratio (CR) of an engine is given by the formula

$$CR = \frac{V_s + V_c}{V_c}$$

if $V_s = 250\ cm^3$ and $V_c = 40\ cm^3$, CR is

(a) 250:1

(b) 6.25:1

(c) 7.25:1

(d) 10:1

Answer (   )

2. In an electrical circuit $V = IR$, where V is the pressure in volts I is the current in amperes and R is the resistance in ohms. If $I = 1.5$ A and $R = 8$ ohms, the voltage would be

(a) 9.5 V   (c) 24 V

(b) 12 V   (d) 10 V

Answer (   )

3. If $H = \dfrac{2y - 5t}{V}$ calculate H when $y = 15$, $t = 4$ and $V = 2.5$.

The value of H will be

(a) 4

(b) 8

(c) 60

(d) 5

Answer (   )

For additional similar problems, see Chapter 11.

4. The volume of an engine cylinder is given by the formula $V = \pi r^2 h$.

If $\pi = \frac{22}{7}$, $r = 30$ mm and $h = 65$ mm, calculate the volume of the cylinder.

....

....

....

....

....

....

....

5. The torque transmitted by a friction clutch is given by the formula

$$torque = F\left(\frac{r_1 + r_2}{2}\right)n$$

If the frictional force $F = 680$ N, $r_1 = 75$ mm, $r_2 = 112$ mm and the number of pairs of frictional faces (n) is 2, calculate the torque transmitted by the clutch.

....

....

....

....

....

....

TRANSPOSITION OF FORMULAE

Transposition of formulae means changing the formula round in order to make a new subject.

$$A = B - C$$

This is a formula in which A is the subject. When this formula is rearranged as follows:

$$A + C = B$$

B becomes the subject.

It is necessary to transpose a formula when the 'unknown quantity' is not the subject. For example:

If a rectangle 100 mm long has an area of 5000 mm², what is its breadth?

This may be called the given formula: $A = l \times b$

Transposed this becomes: $\dfrac{A}{l} = b$

$\therefore$ Breadth $= \dfrac{5000}{100} = 50$

$\therefore$ Breadth $= 50$ mm

Change the subject in the following formulae.

No.	Formula	Subject	Result
1	$V = lbh$	b	
2	$c = \pi d$	d	
3	$A = \frac{bh}{2}$	h	
4	$P = 2\pi NT$	T	
5	$CR = \dfrac{V_s + V_c}{V_c}$	V_s	
6	$A = \pi r^2$	r^2	
7	$V = \frac{4}{3}\pi r^3$	r	

Problems

1. To find voltage (V) in an electrical circuit we use the formula

   $$V = I \times R$$

   The formula to calculate resistance (R) would be:

   (a) $R = \dfrac{V}{I}$ (b) $R = V \times I$

   (c) $R = \dfrac{I}{V}$ (d) $R = V - I$

   Answer (   )

2. If $A = \dfrac{B + C}{2}$, transposing to make

   B the subject will give

   (a) $B = A - C \times 2$

   (b) $B = \dfrac{A}{2} \times C$

   (c) $B = (A \times 2) - C$

   (d) $B = \dfrac{A \times 2}{C}$

   Answer (   )

3. The volume of a hemispherical combustion chamber is given by the formula

   $V = \dfrac{2}{3}\pi r^3$. The subject r^3 is

   (a) $r^3 = \dfrac{2V}{3}\pi$ (b) $r^3 = \dfrac{V - \pi}{2 + 3}$

   (c) $r^3 = \dfrac{3V}{2\pi}$ (d) $r^3 = \dfrac{2V}{3\pi}$

   Answer (   )

4. A mechanic applies a force of 60 N at the end of a spanner when he is tightening a bolt. If the torque exerted on the bolt is 18 N m, calculate the length of the spanner.

   (torque = force × radius)

   ....
   ....
   ....
   ....
   ....
   ....
   ....
   ....

5. Calculate the length of an engine cylinder which has a volume of 198 cm³ and a diameter of 6 cm.

   (Cyl. vol. $= \pi r^2 \times$ length)

   ....
   ....
   ....
   ....
   ....
   ....
   ....
   ....

MASS

All substances consist of matter or molecules packed together to form a material, be it made of steel, wood, glass, plastic etc.

Mass is defined as ....

The SI unit of mass is the ....

FORCE

Force cannot be seen or touched but its effects can be observed, that is, if a force applied to a stationary object causes that object to move it would move in the ....

The effect that a force has on an object will depend upon:

1. ....   2. ....   3. ....

....

If a force is applied to a moving object the object will either:

1. ....   2. ....   3. ....

FORCE AS A VECTOR QUANTITY

A force can be represented by a line having a starting point and an arrowhead to show direction. The amount of force is indicated by the length of the line. (See also page 210.)

Show a vector line indicating
1. A force of 80 N horizontally to the right.
2. A force of 1000 N horizontally to the left.

Indicate the scales used.

ACCELERATION

Velocity is the distance travelled in a unit time, for example, the number of metres travelled in one second (m/s).
When an object moves and steadily increases its velocity, for example, when a car drives away from rest, the object is said to have ....

Acceleration is ....

The SI unit of acceleration is ....

The relationship between force, mass and acceleration is found directly from the effects that a force produces.

....

....

....

WEIGHT — MASS AND GRAVITY

The Earth's gravity attempts to pull everything on the Earth towards the centre of the Earth. The force of gravity, its weight, is proportional to ....

Any component or mass has a potential force if it falls. This force is called its

....

The same mass would weigh

.... times less on the Moon than it does on Earth.

If a car fell over a cliff it would accelerate at approximately

....

this is actually

....

Now since 1 N is required to accelerate 1 kg at 1 m/s², then .... N

are required to accelerate 1 kg at ....

Therefore the effect of the Earth's gravity causes

....

The SI unit of mass (m) is the ....
The SI unit of force (F) is the ....
The SI unit of weight (W) is the ....

PROBLEMS

1. A mass of 10 kg would create a force of ....

2. A load of 981 N would form a mass of ....

3. A car when placed on a weigh-bridge registered 950 kg. What downward acting force would this produce?

   ....

   ....

   ....

4. An engine having a mass of 50 kg is suspended by a sling. What is its potential force?

   ....

   ....

   ....

5. A balance weight of 90 g is lost from a wheel. What is the wheel's static out-of-balance force?

   ....

   ....

   ....

6. When the driver of a vehicle sits in the car the downward acting force of the vehicle increases by 800 N. What is the weight or mass of the driver?

   ....

   ....

7. A car positioned at the top of a hill has a potential force of 10 kN. The vehicle's mass must therefore be

   ....

   ....

   ....

8. The downward acting force of a fully loaded car was 15 kN. When unloaded it was 9.114 kN. What mass was removed from the car?

   ....

   ....

   ....

One of the effects of force is that to every action there is an equal and opposite reaction. Name some vehicle applications that obviously show this effect.

1. ....   3. ....

2. ....   4. ....

CAPACITY

The capacity of a container or tank is the cubic content or volume that it will hold. When stating the capacity of a tank in connection with a quantity of liquid, the units are .... Capacity is determined by calculating the volume and converting the cubic measurement into litres.

$$1 \text{ litre} = 1000 \text{ cm}^3 \qquad \text{or} \qquad 1 \text{ litre} = 0.001 \text{ m}^3$$

1. The volume of a tank is 1 m^3, its capacity in litres is therefore

   (a) 1   (b) 100   (c) 1000   (d) 10 000

2. Calculate the capacity of the fuel tank shown below (ignore capacity of filler neck and the rounded corners of the tank).

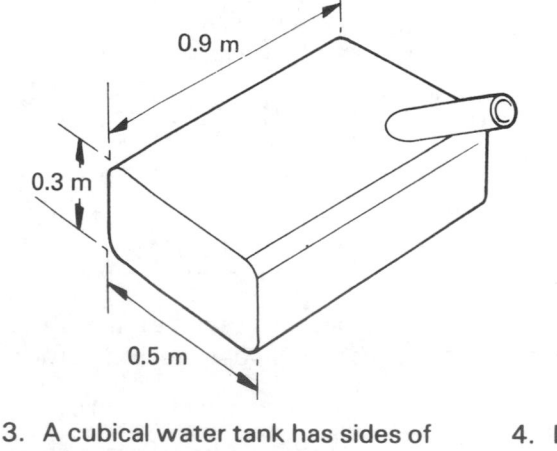

0.9 m

0.3 m

0.5 m

3. A cubical water tank has sides of 0.4 m, its storage capacity is therefore

   (a) 4 litres   (b) 12 litres

   (c) 64 litres   (d) 640 litres

4. During a journey a vehicle uses 30 litres of fuel from a tank. If the fuel tank has a volume of 0.045 m^3, the amount of fuel left in the tank is

   (a) 15 litres   (b) 30 litres

   (c) 45 litres   (d) 90 litres

MASS

The mass of a quantity of liquid or of a solid object depends on the *amount of matter* it contains.

For the purpose of calculation, 1 litre of water has a mass of ....

The kilogram is the base unit of mass (*m*).
State its common multiples and sub-multiples.

....

....

....

VOLUME

The volume of a material or the capacity of a tank uses a basic SI-derived unit of m^2. State its common sub-multiples which may be used.

....

....

....

DENSITY

Density is the mass per unit volume of a substance. For example, the density of water is .... If, therefore the volume and density of a liquid are known, the total mass can be calculated.

The SI derived unit for density is kg/m^3.
State its common sub-multiples which may be used.

....

Density (ρ) = $\dfrac{\text{Mass} \quad (m)}{\text{Volume} \quad (V)}$ or Mass =

Substance	Density (kg/m³)	Substance	Density (kg/m³)
Petrol	....	Steel	....
Water	....	Copper	....
Aluminium	....	Lead	....

1. Given that paraffin has a density of 800 kg/m³, calculate the mass of the contents of a tank when full if the volume of the tank is 4 m³.

....

....

....

....

3. Calculate the mass of petrol contained in the tank shown below when the tank is half full. The density of the petrol is 720 kg/m³. Ignore filler neck and rounded corners.

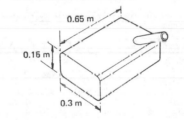

....

....

....

....

....

....

....

....

....

2. A diesel fuel tank contains 200 litres of fuel. What is the mass of the fuel if its density is 850 kg/m³?

....

....

....

....

4. A cylindrical oil storage tank is 0.75 m in diameter and 1.2 m long. How many litres of oil will the tank hold when it is full?

....

....

....

....

....

5. A cylindrical petrol storage tank is 2 m in diameter and 3 m long. How many tonnes of fuel does the tank contain when full if the density of petrol is 720 kg/m³ (1 tonne = 1000 kg)?

....

....

....

....

....

....

....

....

11.4 ELECTRICAL CIRCUITS

To allow an electrical current to flow an electric circuit must consist of:

(a) A source of supply.

(b) A device that will use the supply to do useful work.

(c) Electrical conducting materials that will transfer the electric current from the power source to the consuming device, and then return it to the supply source.

On a motor vehicle TWO sources of electrical power are

1. ....

2. ....

Name FIVE different types of device that consume current:

1. ....

2. ....

3. ....

4. ....

5. ....

What is meant by the term *electrical conductor*?

....

....

What is meant by the term *electrical insulator*?

....

....

EFFECTS OF AN ELECTRICAL CURRENT

The flow of current in an electrical circuit can produce three main effects. State these effects and give examples found on motor vehicles.

1. ....

2. ....

3. ....

For an electric current to flow there must be a complete electrical circuit. Basically this consists of a power source, for example, a battery; a resistance through which the current will do useful work, for example, a light bulb; and supply lines to make the circuit complete.

Will each bulb light?   (*NOTE:* These are pictorial views — NOT symbols).

(a) .... (b) .... (c) ....

State which circuit could be called an

'earth-return circuit' .... ; 'insulated return circuit' ....

SYMBOLS USED IN CIRCUIT DIAGRAMS

Connect the following components to build an electrical circuit:

battery, ammeter, switch, light bulb

Using conventional symbols, draw the circuit diagram. Indicate, using arrows, the conventionally accepted direction of current flow.

State the amount of current flowing in the circuit ....

(For conventional symbols, see Chapter 1.4i.)

SERIES AND PARALLEL CIRCUITS

Investigation

Build two electrical circuits as shown

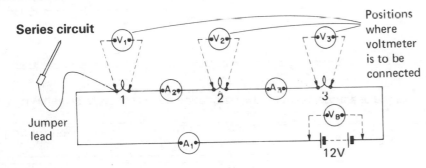

Series circuit

Jumper lead

Positions where voltmeter is to be connected

Connect all bulbs in circuit and note readings.

Voltage

V₁	V₂	V₃	Total	V_B

Current flow

A₁	A₂	A₃

Why are the bulbs dim? ....

Remove bulb 1, what happens? ....

Why does this occur? ....

Place prod of jumper lead to bulb 2, take readings:

Voltage

V₂	V₃	Total	V_B

Current flow

A₁	A₃

What differences have now occurred and why?

....

Remove bulb 2, connect prod of jumper lead to bulb 3, take readings.

Voltage

V₃	V_B

Current flow

A₁

Parallel circuit

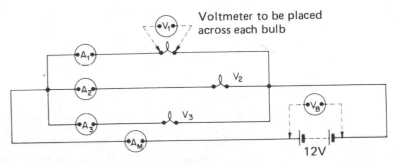

Voltmeter to be placed across each bulb

Connect all bulbs in circuit and note readings.

Voltage

V₁	V₂	V₃	V_B

Current flow

A₁	A₂	A₃	Total	A_M

When three bulbs are connected, compared with the series circuit what differences occur with regard to the following? Give reasons.

Voltage ....

....

Current flow ....

....

Light intensity ....

....

Note current flow when bulbs are removed.

	A₁	A₂	A₃	Total	A_M
One bulb removed					
Two bulbs removed					

Why did not the same thing occur as in the series circuit?

....

BUILDING VARIOUS ELECTRICAL CIRCUITS

Investigation

Equipment:

    various types of resistances; switches; cables; ammeter; voltmeter; battery

Assemble the circuits described below; include in each circuit an ammeter, switch and battery.
In at least TWO circuits show the correct connection of an ammeter.

You may be provided with *either*

    (a) motor-vehicle components   or   (b) a peg board   or   (c) a construction kit.

Sketch the circuit diagrams and state the total current flow in each case.

In a series circuit, the bulbs or resistances are connected:

....

....

....

....

In a parallel circuit, the bulbs or resistances are connected:

....

....

---

1. Two resistances connected in parallel	2. Four resistances connected in series	3. Six resistances connected in parallel
Current flow	Current flow	Current flow ....

---

4. Two resistances in series connected with one resistance in parallel

5. Two resistances in parallel connected to one resistance in series. Repeat this layout using three *additional* resistances and connect *both layouts* in parallel with one another.

Current flow ....

Current flow ....

CURRENT, VOLTAGE, RESISTANCE — OHM'S LAW

Ohm's Law is the expression that relates voltage, current and resistance to each other.

State what these electrical terms mean, and state the units in which they are measured.

Voltage ....

....

Current ....

....

Resistance ....

....

One of the relationships defining Ohm's Law states that, provided the resistance is kept constant, the current will double if the voltage is doubled. Expressed more mathematically this could be stated as

....

....

Expressed as a formula using electric symbols

$$I = \frac{E}{R}$$

Where I = ...

R = ...

E = ...

(NOTE: The symbol V may be used instead of E.)

The formula may be transposed to state

E = ... and R = ...

Example

Calculate the current flowing in a circuit when a pressure of 12 V is applied across a 3-ohm resistance.

....

....

....

SIMPLE OHM'S LAW PROBLEMS

1. Calculate the current flowing in a coil of resistance 4 ohms when the electrical pressure is 12 V.

....

....

....

....

....

....

2. Calculate the voltage required to force a current of 2.5 amps through a resistance of 5 ohms.

....

....

....

....

....

3. 'A dynamo produces a current of 35 A when the voltage is 14 V. What is the resistance of the dynamo?

....

....

....

....

....

4. What voltage will be required to cause a current flow of 3 A through a bulb having a filament resistance of 4.2 ohms?

....

....

....

....

....

....

5. What will be the total resistance offered by a lighting circuit if a current of 11 A flows under a pressure of 13 V?

....

....

....

....

....

....

6. Two 12 V headlamp bulbs each have a resistance of 2.4 ohms. Calculate the current flowing in each bulb and the total current flowing in the circuit.

....

....

....

....

FORCES

A force applied to a body can

(a) cause movement

(b) ....

(c) ....

(d) ....

To REPRESENT a force, the following characteristics of the force must be known:

(1) size or magnitude

(2) ....

(3) ....

Representation

The characteristics of a force can be represented by a single line.

The arrowhead indicates the .... of a force.

The length of the line represents the .... of the force.

The letter 'o' represents the ....
.... of the force.

To represent the magnitude of the force, the line is drawn to scale, e.g. if 1 mm = 10 N, a line 50 mm long would therefore represent a force of .... and the arrow shows direction.

This known as a VECTOR QUANTITY or VECTOR.

RESULTANT FORCE

A RESULTANT FORCE is a force which can replace two or more forces.

At (a), two or more forces act along the same line of action. The scale chosen to represent MAGNITUDE is 1 cm = 20 N; add the resultant and indicate its magnitude.

(a) 40 N ⟶   60 N ⟶

The forces shown at (a) are acting in the same direction, add the resultant to the drawing at (b) using the scale for (a).

(b) 60 N ⟶   ⟵ 40 N

EQUILIBRANT FORCE

The EQUILIBRANT FORCE cancels out or balances other forces; it is a reactive force which produces EQUILIBRIUM in a system of forces.

Equilibrium allows a body to remain at rest or to
....

The EQUILIBRANT force is equal to and opposite in direction to the ....
.... Add the equilibrant forces to 1, 2 and 3 below.

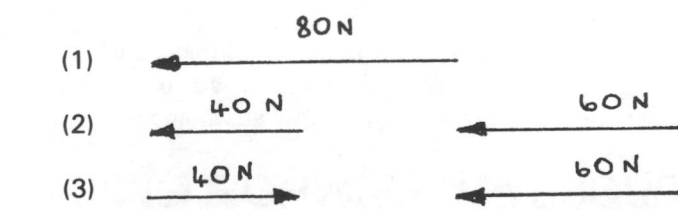

(1) 80 N ⟵

(2) ⟵ 40 N   ⟵ 60 N

(3) 40 N ⟶   ⟵ 60 N

Two or more forces can have the same point of application and act along different lines of action, that is, their lines of action intersect.

The RESULTANTS of the forces at (a) and (b) opposite are represented by the DIAGONAL in each case. At (a), where the forces are acting at 90° to each other, the resultant is obtained by completing the square or rectangle to obtain the diagonal and hence the resultant.

The resultant at (b) is obtained by completing ....

This is known as the ....

Measure the diagonals and indicate the magnitude of the resultants at (a) and (b). Add also the EQUILIBRANT vectors to each system.

RESOLUTION OF A FORCE

One force can be divided into two forces or COMPONENTS. Resolve the vector 'R' shown at (c) opposite into its vertical and horizontal components.

You can see the relationship between the equilibrant force, forces F1 and F2 and the angle formed between F_1 and F_2 at (a) and (b). Why is knowledge of this relationship important when, say, using a chain sling to lift an engine?

....

....

....

....

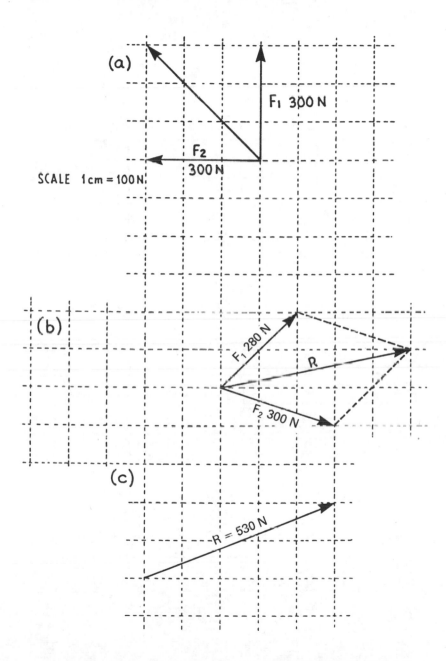

(a)

F_1 300 N

F_2 300 N

SCALE 1cm = 100 N

(b)

F_1 280 N

R

F_2 300 N

(c)

R = 530 N

TRIANGLE OF FORCES

When the direction and layout of a number of forces whose lines of action intersect is known, unknown forces can be determined by accurately drawing to scale (or constructing graphically) a TRIANGLE whose sides represent the DIRECTION and MAGNITUDE of the forces.

The vectors AB, BC and CA represent forces R, P and Q in the layout at (a) opposite.

The lettering in between the forces on the SPACE DIAGRAM is known as

....

Construct a triangle of forces for the vector diagram shown at (a). Use the same scale.

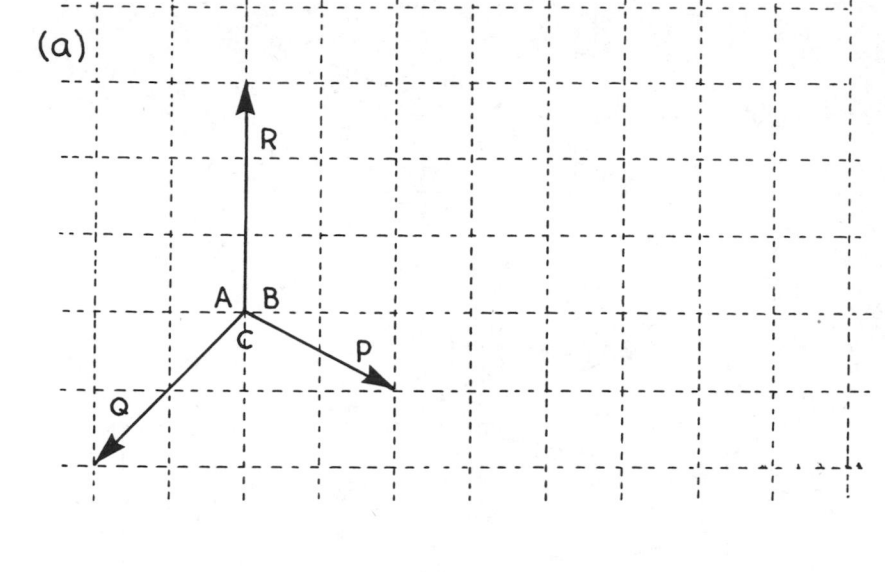

POLYGON OF FORCES

When more than three forces are involved, a POLYGON OF FORCES can be constructed to determine the magnitude and direction of an unknown force. Construct a polygon for the forces shown at (b) opposite.

The triangle and polygon shown opposite are complete or 'closed'.
What does this mean for the force systems shown?

....

If, for example, the polygon does not 'close', the vector which joins the open ends represents the direction and magnitude of the

....

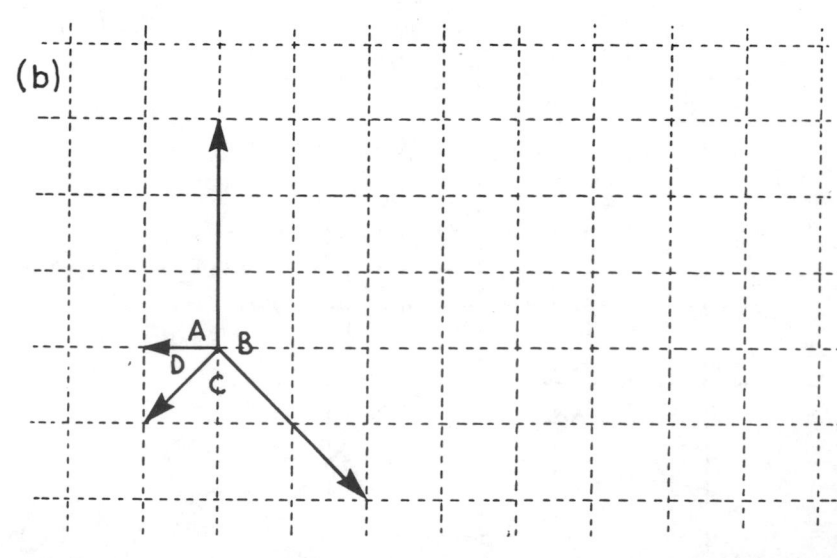

The drawing at (a) represents a bogged-down vehicle being recovered by two other vehicles. The vectors (x) and (y) on the scale 1 mm = 2 kN represent the magnitude and direction of the forces in the tow ropes, which act at the same point on the stranded vehicle. Determine the force required (Resultant) to move the vehicle. At (b) the tow ropes are acting at different points on the vehicle but their lines of action intersect.
How does this affect the forces in the ropes?

....

....

....

The force required to raise the engine is 1 kN. Construct triangle of forces diagrams to determine the forces in the sling chains when the angle between them is: (a) 120°
(b) 60°

....

....

....

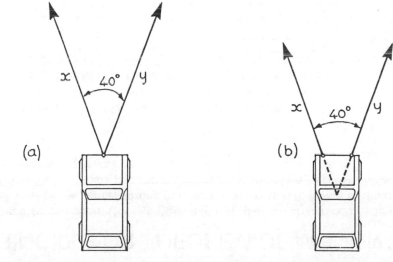

(a)

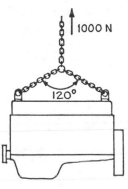

(b)

PRINCIPLE OR THEOREM OF MOMENTS

Using a simple beam (for example, a metre rule) which can be pivoted on a stand as shown below, apply forces of different value to either side of the pivot. Position the forces by the use of 'cord loops' to obtain a state of balance, as shown in the diagram.

NOTE:

Sum of the forces horizontally $\Sigma\ F_x$ must equal   0
Sum of the forces vertically $\Sigma\ F_y$ must equal   0
Sum of the moments both sides $\Sigma\ M$ must equal   0

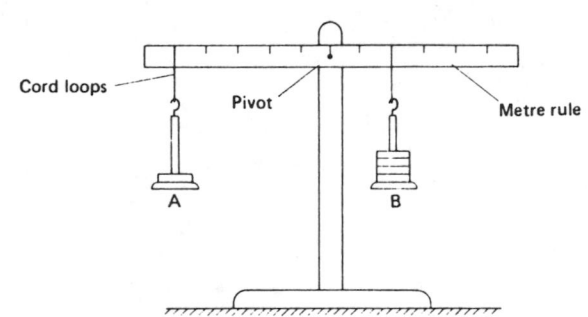

Cord loops   Pivot   Metre rule

A   B

Add the information as required below:

force A = ...   force B = ...

perpendicular distance from pivot force A = ...

perpendicular distance from pivot force B = ...

Each force will produce a moment about the pivot

that is, a moment = ...

force B will produce a clockwise moment =

force A will produce an .... =

The product of both these moments is ....

It can be seen therefore that to obtain a state of balance (equilibrium)

....

There are considered to be three types of levers, all using the principle of moments in their operation.
The lever may be considered to be the simplest form of machine.

Type 1 has a force at one end while the resisting load is at the other.   (1)

The fulcrum being somewhere along the lever.

F Mass

Fulcrum

Type 2 .... (2)
....

Mass

....

Fulcrum

....

Type 3 ....

F

.... (3)

....

....

....

....

....

....

Show by simple sketches one motor vehicle or garage application of each of the types of levers shown above.

11.8 Problems

1. Determine *F* needed to balance the beam.

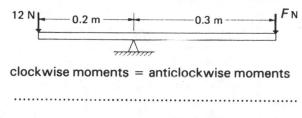

clockwise moments = anticlockwise moments

....

....

....

2. Determine *F* needed to balance the beam.

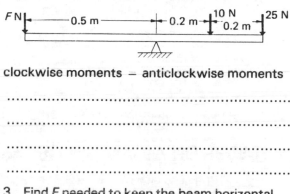

clockwise moments – anticlockwise moments

....

....

....

....

3. Find *F* needed to keep the beam horizontal.

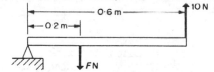

clockwise moments = anticlockwise moments

....

....

....

4. Determine the force *F*.

Handbrake lever

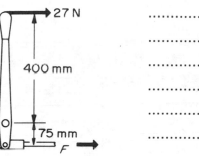

....

....

....

....

....

....

....

5. Determine the force *F*.

Brake pedal

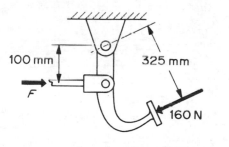

....

....

....

6. Complete the table below by adding values that will maintain equilibrium in the lever shown for the situations indicated.

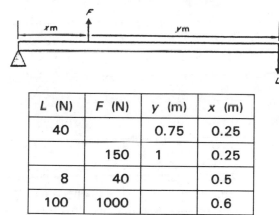

L (N)	F (N)	y (m)	x (m)
40		0.75	0.25
	150	1	0.25
8	40		0.5
100	1000		0.6

....

....

....

....

7. Determine *F* needed to maintain equilibrium.

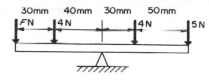

....

....

....

....

BEAMS

A beam has two vertical supports and the total downward force on the beam is equal to the reaction forces in the supports.

Use a pair of spring balances and a beam with weights set up as shown to prove that the sum of the vertical forces = 0.

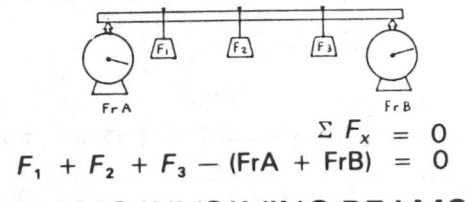

$$\Sigma F_x = 0$$
$$F_1 + F_2 + F_3 - (FrA + FrB) = 0$$

PROBLEMS INVOLVING BEAMS

Example
Calculate the reaction forces at A and B.

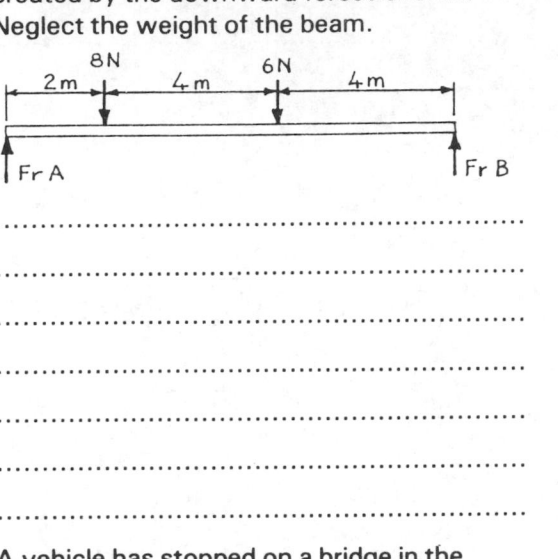

$$\Sigma M = 0$$
$$CWM - ACWM = 0$$
Therefore, $CWM = ACWM$

Take moments about FrA:

$$(3 \times 1) + (2 \times 2) + (3 \times 3) = FrB \times 4$$
$$3 + 4 + 9 = FrB \times 4$$
$$16 = FrB \times 4$$
$$\frac{16}{4} = FrB$$

Therefore FrB $= \underline{4 \ N}$

$$\Sigma F_y = 0$$

Upward force − Downward force = 0

Therefore Upward force = Downward force
$$FrA + FrB = F_1 + F_2 + F_3$$
$$FrA + 4 = 3 + 3 + 2$$
$$FrA = 8 - 4$$
$$FrA = \underline{4 \ N}$$

---

1. Calculate the vertical reaction forces created by the downward forces shown. Neglect the weight of the beam.

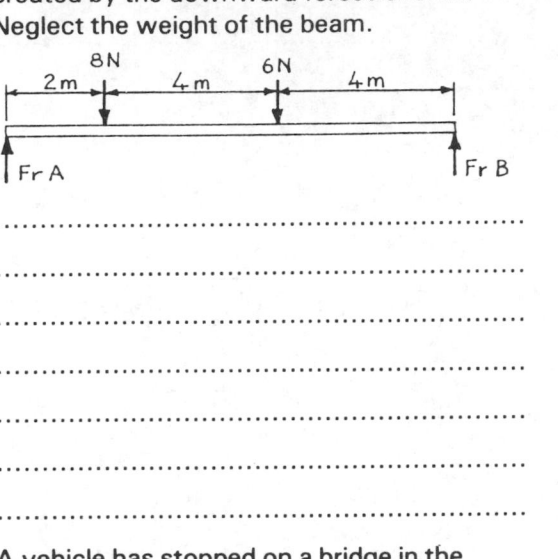

....
....
....
....
....
....
....
....

2. A vehicle has stopped on a bridge in the position shown. Calculate the reaction forces in the bridge supports created by the car.

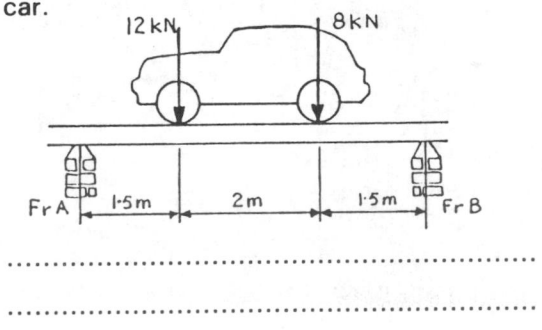

....
....
....
....
....
....
....
....

The direction of a moment of force determines whether it may be considered to be positive or negative.

A clockwise moment is ....

An anti-clockwise moment is ....

The forces on the beam below which are:

(i) positive are ....

(ii) negative are ....

When considering the above drawing, the theorem of moments states that the sum of moments of a number of forces about any point is equal to the moment of the resultant force about that same point,
i.e. resultant moment $M_R = M_1 + M_2 + M_3$

Calculate the (i) resultant moment, (ii) resultant force, (iii) resultant force's distance from the pivot. Indicate this position on the sketch.

....
....
....
....
....
....
....

CENTRE OF GRAVITY

The weight of an object is the downward force of gravity on its mass. The centre of gravity or centre of mass of an object can be imagined as the point at which all the weight or force is concentrated, i.e. we can assume that the weight of the object acts through the centre of gravity.

With a regular shaped object the centre of gravity is at the geometric centre. Theoretically, such an object would balance on a point in line with the centre of gravity.

....
....
....
....
....

With a plate of uniform thickness, the centre of gravity will be at mid-thickness in line with the centre of area of the plate.

Mark the centre of area (centroid) of the following shapes:

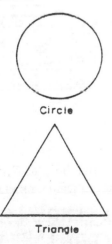

Circle

Square

Rectangle

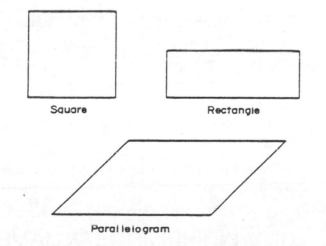

Triangle

Parallelogram

Experiment

To determine the centre of gravity of a connecting rod.

1. Using two spring balances, suspend a connecting rod as shown below and note the spring balance readings.

   Spring balance reading; big end ....

   Spring balance reading; small end ....

2. Measure the rod between bearing centres:

   Connecting rod length between centres = ...

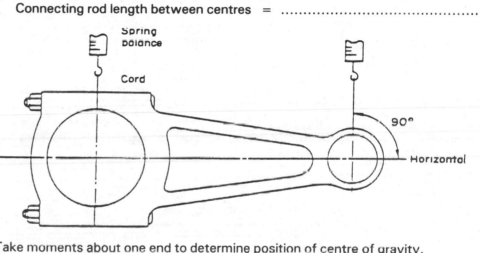

Take moments about one end to determine position of centre of gravity.

....
....
....
....
....
....

Indicate on the drawing the approximate position of the centre of gravity.

11.10 CENTRE OF GRAVITY, EQUILIBRIUM AND STABILITY

On the vehicle shown below the cross marks the *centre of gravity*. With a front engine, front wheel drive vehicle the C of G would be nearer to the front.

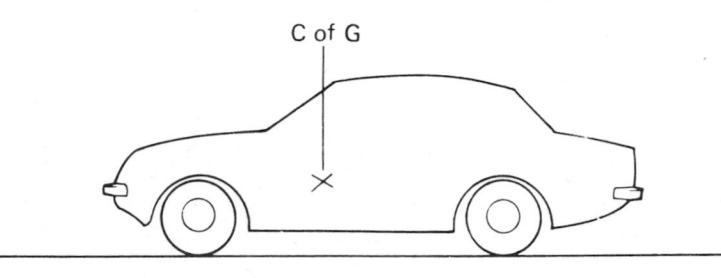

C of G

In the space below, sketch a vehicle that would have its C of G towards the rear, and indicate its approximate position.

The stability of a vehicle when cornering or braking is greatly affected by the actual position of the vehicle's C of G.

Give examples of vehicle types which have:

1. Low C of G ....

2. High C of G ....

Consider the vehicle shown below. During braking the force *F* due to the inertia of the vehicle acting at the C of G tends to tilt the vehicle about the front wheels, thus putting more load on to the front wheels, and reducing the load on the rear wheels. 'Load transfer' takes place.

C of G

F

Wheelbase

The degree of load transfer is dependent upon a number of factors. How do the following affect load transfer during braking?

1. Height of centre of gravity

....

....

2. Wheelbase

....

....

3. Rate of retardation

....

....

4. Ratio of C of G height to wheelbase

....

....

CALCULATIONS

1. Centre of gravity

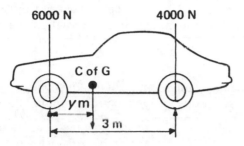

6000 N   4000 N
C of G
y m
3 m

Theoretically the point of balance of the vehicle would be on a pivot at the C of G. To find the position of the C of G relative to the front wheels:

Take moments about the front wheels.

Clockwise moments	=	Anti-clockwise moments
$10\ 000 \times y$	=	4000×3

Distance of C of G from front wheels =

Why is the distance y multiplied by 10 000?

....

....

Load on wheels

Similarly, when the position of the centre of gravity, wheelbase and vehicle weight are known, the load on the wheels can be calculated, that is, the load distribution.

2. Calculate the loads on the front and rear axles for the vehicle shown top opposite.

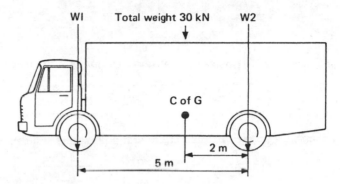

W1   Total weight 30 kN   W2
C of G
2 m
5 m

To calculate the load on front wheels:

Take moments about rear wheels

Clockwise moments = Anti-clockwise moments

....

....

....

....

3.

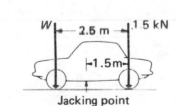

W   2.5 m   1 5 kN
1.5 m
Jacking point

The jacking point shown is at the centre of balance. Determine the weight W on the front wheels.

....

....

....

....

....

4. A car has a wheelbase of 2.5 m. If the load on the front axle is 4500 N and the load on the rear axle is 3000 N, calculate the distance of the C of G behind the front axle.

Let y = distance of C of G from the front axle

....

....

....

....

219

FRICTION

Friction is the resistance to motion, or reactive force, produced when two surfaces in contact are made to slide over each other.

Other effects of friction are:

(a) ....

(b) ....

The force *F* required to move the block over the surface shown below must be sufficient to overcome the frictional resistance. It is known as the *force of friction.* It is reactive force and the law of .... applies.

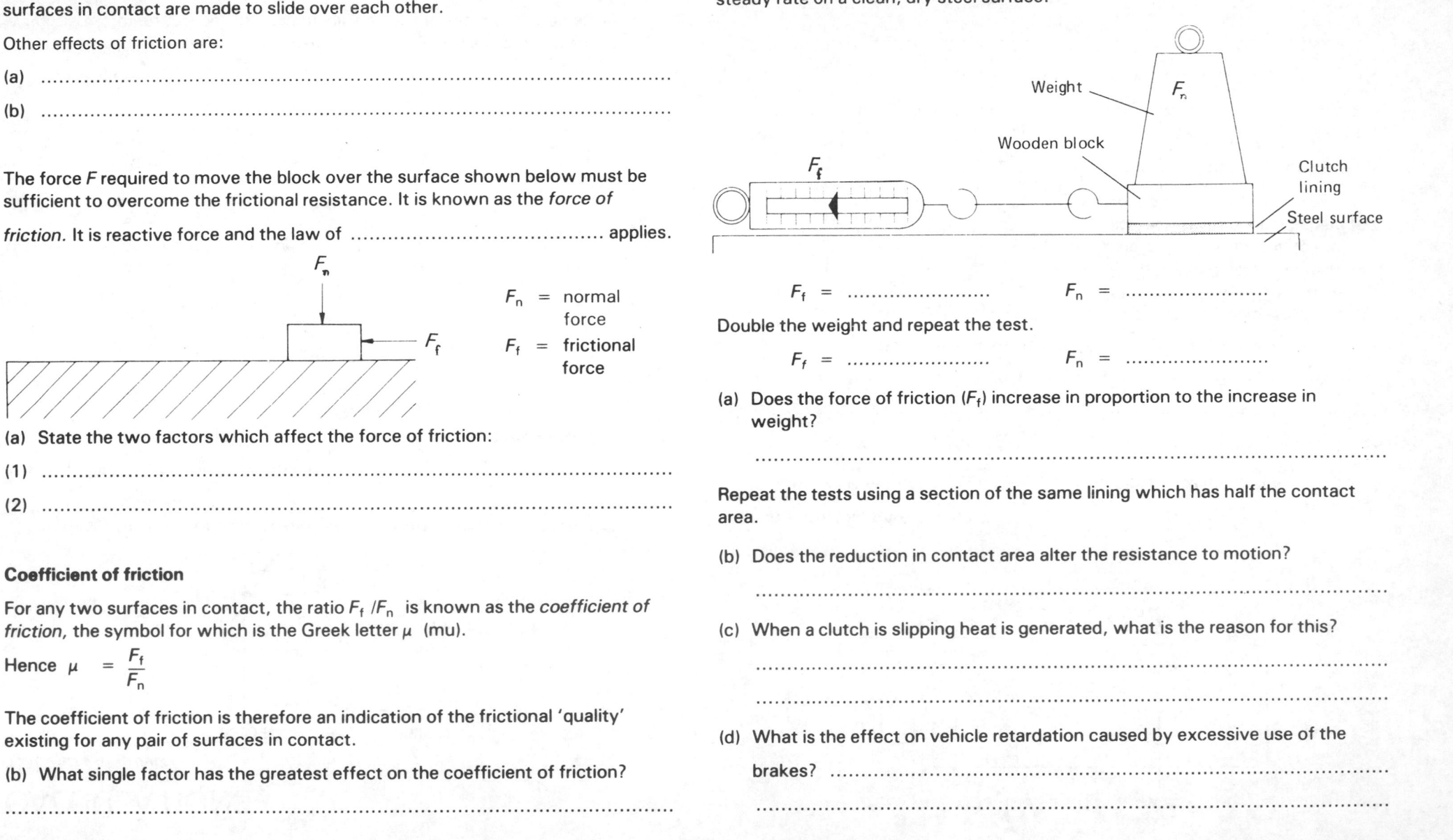

F_n = normal force

F_f = frictional force

(a) State the two factors which affect the force of friction:

(1) ....

(2) ....

Coefficient of friction

For any two surfaces in contact, the ratio F_f / F_n is known as the *coefficient of friction*, the symbol for which is the Greek letter μ (mu).

Hence $\mu = \dfrac{F_f}{F_n}$

The coefficient of friction is therefore an indication of the frictional 'quality' existing for any pair of surfaces in contact.

(b) What single factor has the greatest effect on the coefficient of friction?

....

Investigation

Find the force required to move a loaded section of clutch or bake lining at a steady rate on a clean, dry steel surface.

F_f = ...

F_n = ...

Double the weight and repeat the test.

F_f = ...

F_n = ...

(a) Does the force of friction (F_f) increase in proportion to the increase in weight?

....

Repeat the tests using a section of the same lining which has half the contact area.

(b) Does the reduction in contact area alter the resistance to motion?

....

(c) When a clutch is slipping heat is generated, what is the reason for this?

....

....

(d) What is the effect on vehicle retardation caused by excessive use of the brakes? ....

....

11.11 REDUCTION OF FRICTION BY LUBRICATION

When examined under a microscope, even apparently flat, smooth surfaces look like mountain ranges. For example, this even applies to a newly ground big end journal and its new shell bearings. The sketch below shows how two surfaces interlock with one another when they are dry.

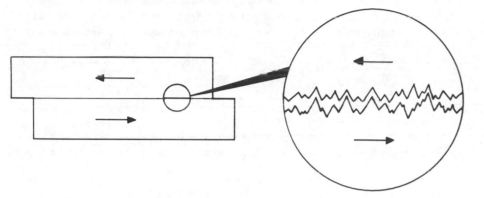

Complete the sketch to show the effect of lubrication.

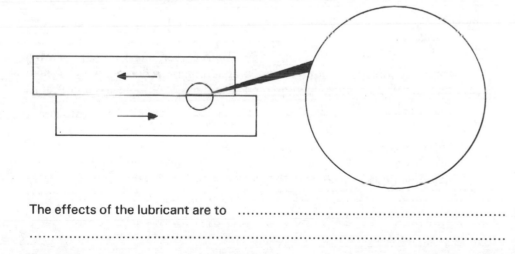

The effects of the lubricant are to ....

....

....

Friction can be an advantage or a disadvantage depending upon the situation. For example, it is essential to prevent the driver's foot slipping off the brake pedal, but is highly undesirable in engine bearings.

Name FOUR vehicle parts where friction is an

Advantage	Disadvantage
1.	1. ....
2.	2. ....
3.	3. ....
4.	4. ....

FRICTION BETWEEN A ROLLER AND A FLAT SURFACE

The driving force required to roll a wheel over a flat surface is called

....

The coefficient of friction is found in the normal way.

Therefore $\mu =$

BEARINGS

There are two main types of bearing:

(a) plain bearings in which .... is produced by the relative movement of the bearing surfaces.

(b) ball or roller bearings in which .... is produced by the relative movement of the bearing surfaces.

Which type of friction, 'sliding' or 'rolling' offers the least resistance to motion?

....

11.11 State TWO factors that can affect the coefficient of friction between a roller and flat surface.

1. ....

2. ....

Note – When calculating, all mass values (kg) must be converted to force or weight values (N).

Problems

What force will be required to pull a spare parts packing case, which has a total mass of 50 kg, along a horizontal garage floor if the coefficient of friction between the case and floor is 0.5.

$$\mu = \frac{F}{W}$$

$$\therefore \quad F = \mu \times W$$

$$F = 0.5 \times (50 \times 9.81) \text{ N}$$

$$F = 245.25 \text{ N } Ans.$$

1. If the parts, which have a mass of 40 kg, are now removed, calculate the force required to pull the now empty packing case.

....

....

....

2. A vehicle exerts a downward load of 10 kN. If the coefficient of friction between the tyres and road is 0.55, the maximum retarding force which could be applied by the brakes would be

    (a) 5.5 kN   (c) 0.55 kN

    (b) 100 kN   (d) 55 kN

                       Ans. (   )

3. The retarding force produced by the braking system of a vehicle when locking all four wheels is 6 kN. If the vehicle has a mass of 1000 kg, calculate the coefficient of friction between the tyres and the road.

....

....

....

....

....

....

....

4. A steel block has a mass of 80 kg. If the force necessary to slide the block at a uniform rate along a horizontal surface is 200 N, calculate the coefficient of friction between the surfaces.

....

....

....

....

....

....

5. What weight must be added to the block in the previous question to increase the force of friction by 50 N?

....

....

....

....

....

....

PRESSURE

An excellent example of pressure and change in pressure is in an engine cylinder. The mixture, which is a form of gas is drawn into the cylinder and as the piston rises, the pressure is ....

The mixture is then ignited and the pressure is further ....

In the first case a reduction in .... caused the pressure to

.... while in the second case an increase in

.... caused the .... in pressure.

The intensity of pressure may be defined as 'the applied force per unit area acting at right angles'.

or Pressure = _____

The SI unit of pressure is the Pascal (Pa).

1 Pa = , 1 kPa = , 1 MPa = or

When dealing with forces and areas, it is more usual to use the force/area units and then covert them to Pascals.

Examples

1. Calculate the pressure acting on a piston when a total force of 16 kN is applied to the piston crown whose cross-sectional area is 0.004 m².

....
....
....
....
....
....

2. Calculate the pressure in a brake cylinder when a force of 450 N is applied to the piston whose cross-sectional area is 150 mm².

....
....
....
....
....
....

Investigation

To show that gases exert pressure and are compressible.

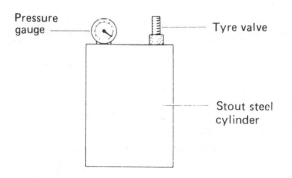

Pressure gauge

Tyre valve

Stout steel cylinder

1. Use a pump or compressed air to pressurise the container. Note the reading. ....
   Release the pressure.

2. Stand apparatus in hot water or in water being heated.

Results and observations

Pressure reading when cold ....

Pressure reading when hot ....

Conclusion ....

....

3. Calculate the pressure acting on a radiator cap when the spring force is 24 N and the cap area resisting force is 6 cm² (0.0006 m²).

....
....
....
....
....
....

4. Calculate the force acting on a piston when the average pressure is 900 kPa and the cross-sectional area of the piston is 0.008 m².

....
....
....
....
....
....

PRESSURE

The SI unit of pressure is the ....

Pressure may also be expressed in two forms.

....

What is meant by gauge pressure? ....
....

What is meant by the term *vacuum*?

....
....

Give an example where such a gauge would indicate:

a positive reading ....

a negative reading ....

What is meant by absolute pressure? ....
....

The air pressure on Earth is known as................................

and is equal to ....

This means that air presses with a force of 100 kN on every square metre of the Earth's surface.
Thus pressure may be expressed as the 'bar', barometer reading.

1 bar = ... or .... 1 mbar = ...

When considering pressure, the Pascal (N/m^2) may be expressed in N/cm^2 or in bar.

1 Pa = 1 N/m^2 = ... N/cm^2 = ... bar = ... mbar

---

When an ordinary pressure gauge reads '0', the absolute pressure is ....

Therefore to convert gauge pressure to absolute pressure:

Absolute pressure =

1. An oil pressure gauge gave a reading of 350 kPa.

   The absolute pressure would be

   ....
   ....
   ....

2. An oil pressure relief valve opened at a gauge pressure of 30 N/cm^2.

   Express this as kPa and calculate the absolute pressure.

   ....
   ....
   ....
   ....

3. When testing cylinder compressions the following readings were obtained:

   Cyl. 1. 675 kN/m^2 2. 680 kN/m^2 3. 678 kN/m^2 4. 676 kN/m^2

   State the absolute pressures

   Cyl. 1. .... 2. .... 3. .... 4. ....

4. The inlet manifold depression when idling was found to be -69 kPa.
   The absolute pressure would be

   ....
   ....
   ....
   ....

5. The absolute pressure in an engine cylinder was 824 kPa. What would the gauge pressure reading be?

   ....
   ....
   ....
   ....

PRESSURE ON LIQUIDS — PASCAL'S LAW

Pascal's Law is applied when any hydraulic equipment on a vehicle is used.
State Pascal's Law and, using arrows, indicate its effect on the hydraulic system shown below.

....

....

....

....

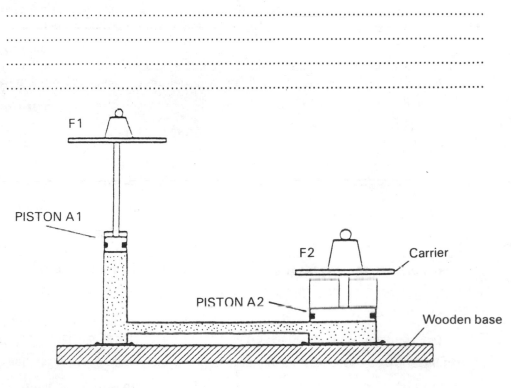

F1

PISTON A1

F2   Carrier

PISTON A2

Wooden base

If the load F1 on the small piston A1 is 20 N and the area of that piston is 400 mm², calculate the pressure in the system.

....

....

....

....

If the area of the piston A2 is 1200 mm², what is the force of the weight F2?

....

....

....

....

HYDRAULIC PRESSURE

When cylinders of different diameters are used, the fluid pressure on the smaller piston is the same as the fluid pressure on the larger piston.

So the pressure $P = \dfrac{F1}{A1} = \dfrac{F2}{A2}$

1. Consider the arrangement shown below:

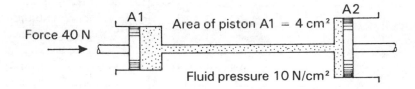

A1   Area of piston A1 = 4 cm²   A2

Force 40 N

Fluid pressure 10 N/cm²

What will be the force on piston A_2 above, if its area is 8 cm²?

2. If the hydraulic pressure in the arrangement below is 30 N/cm², A1 = 50 cm² and A2 = 400 cm², what are the values of F1 and F2?

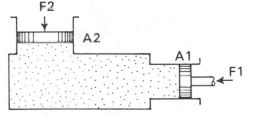

F2

A2

A1

F1

3. A force of 60 N is applied to the small piston. If the area ratio of the pistons is 16:1, calculate
   (i) reaction force at the large piston;
   (ii) area of the large piston if the small piston area is 18 cm²;
   (iii) fluid pressure.

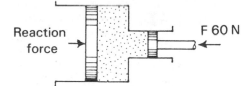

Reaction force

F 60 N

HEAT AND TEMPERATURE

Heat is a form of energy ....

....

....

The SI unit for measuring heat is the ....

Common multiples of this unit are ....

Sub-multiples of this unit are ....

Heat losses occur when heat transfers from hot substances to cold substances.

Give examples of where on a vehicle heat transfer occurs to advantage and disadvantage.

Advantageous heat transfer	Disadvantageous heat transfer
....	....
....	....

Investigation

Heat a motor vehicle component (for example, in a gas flame) until it is very hot. Then place the component in a container holding sufficient water to submerge the component.

Note the temperature of the water before and after submersion. Explain what happens to the flow of heat.

Temp. of water	Before	°C
	After	°C

....

....

Investigation

Fill two beakers with water and heat as shown in the sketch.

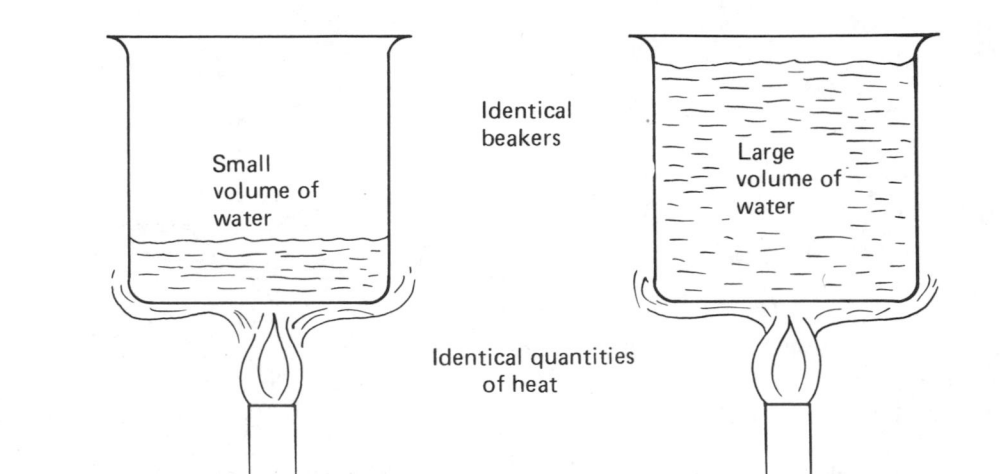

Small volume of water

Identical beakers

Large volume of water

Identical quantities of heat

Note the temperature rise in both beakers at half-minute intervals until the water in the small beaker boils.

Time (min)	0	0.5	1.0	1.5	2.0	2.5
Temperature (°C) small volume	20					
Temperature (°C) large volume	20					

These results show the basic differences between heat and temperature.

Temperature does not measure heat; it is ....

....

TEMPERATURE

The instrument commonly used to measure temperature is called a ....

The common temperature scale is the .... scale.

This may also be known (although not recommended in science) as the

.... scale.

This scale has .... divisions between two fixed points.

Indicate these on the sketch opposite.

The temperature scale used to measure absolute temperature is called the

.... scale. Although the divisions are the same as the

.... scale, its zero point is at a temperature so cold that all
molecular or atomic vibration ceases, that is, there is no heat.

This occurs at a temperature of .... °C.

Indicate the fixed points on this scale and write in the
absolute zero temperature on both scales.

To convert from Celsius to Kelvin add ....

NOTE: the symbol for Celsius is ....

       while the symbol for Kelvin is ....

Examples

1. Convert 27°C to Kelvin

    ....

    ....

    ....

2. Convert 833 K to degrees Celsius.

    ....

    ....

    ....

3. The temperatures of gas in an engine cylinder at the
commencement and end of compression were 30°C
and 580°C. Express these temperatures in Kelvin.

    ....

    ....

4. The temperature of air in a tyre during running
increased from 290 K to 327 K. State these
temperatures in °C and calculate the temperature
increase in °C and in K.

    ....

    ....

    ....

    ....

Upper fixed point

Lower fixed point

Celsius   Kelvin

Absolute zero ——

HEAT TRANSFER

Three methods by which heat is transferred are:

1. From the hotter to the colder part of a material by travelling within the actual

   material; this is known as ....

2. Through the atmosphere by means of rays; this is known as

   ....

3. By the movement of liquids or gases; this is known as ....

   ....

In many instances heat is dissipated from the heat source by more than one method at a time.

How is the heat dissipated from the friction surfaces in a drum brake assembly?

....

....

Heat will flow in one direction only ....

....

Give examples of materials which are

Good conductors of heat	**Poor conductors of heat**
....	....
....	....
....	....

Conduction

Pistons (and some cylinder heads and blocks) are made of aluminium alloy, instead of cast iron or steel. There are two reasons for the choice of this material. One is that it is lighter, the other is

....

This leads to the fact that the rate of conduction varies

....

....

Convection

Convection currents occur because of the difference in density between cold and hot water. In practical terms water density varies little through its complete

liquid state, but cold water does have .... density than warm water.

What occurs to a quantity of water as its temperature rises? ....

....

....

The changes in density therefore directly produce ....

....

Radiation

Metal will lose heat at different rates according to:

1. ....

....

2. ....

....

3. ....

....

CONDUCTION

The amount of heat a material can transfer determines whether it is a good or bad conductor.

Investigations

Several types of equipment are available to demonstrate the relative heat conductivity of various materials. One is shown below. Conduct your test and list the order of heat (or thermal) conductivity of the rods. Show the position of the collars when the first one drops off.

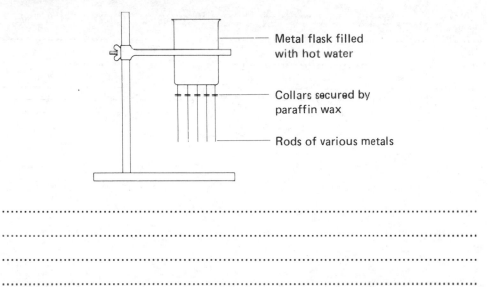

Metal flask filled with hot water

Collars secured by paraffin wax

Rods of various metals

....
....
....
....

Order of conductivity	Material	Where could this material be used on a vehicle
1.		
2.		
3.		
4.		
5.		

Water is a poor conductor of heat. To verify this, hold at its lower end a fairly long narrow test tube filled with water. Heat the open end by means of a bunsen burner. Explain briefly your method and the results.

....
....
....
....
....

Make a sketch to show the equipment used to carry out the experiment.

What ensures the water in a vehicle's cooling system does not have this effect?

....
....

CONVECTION

Give two examples of heat transfer by convection relating to a vehicle:

1. ....

2. ....

Investigation

Sketch a piece of simple apparatus by which it is possible to see the movement of a liquid when heated. Carry out the experiment and report on your observations.

....

....

....

....

....

Give FOUR examples of good heat

Conductors	Insulators
1.	1. ....
2.	2. ....
3.	3. ....
4.	4. ....

RADIATION

Give two examples of heat transfer by radiation relating to a vehicle.

1. ....

2. ....

Investigation

The effect of colour on the transfer of heat by radiation.

Thermometers

Equal-sized metal containers filled with hot water.

Matt black finish

Polished finish

Gloss white finish

Heat insulator

Take readings over a period of 15 minutes. List the order of relative heat (thermal) radiation of the canisters, the best first.

1. ....

2 ....

3. ....

Some motorists like to polish radiator header-tanks.

Explain why this is bad practice ....

....

In the interests of heat dissipation, what would be the best colour for a vehicle radiator? ....

EXPANSION

When metals are heated they expand and as they cool they contract. Many uses are made of this principle in a motor vehicle and in repair work.

Name two instances on a vehicle where clearance is allowed for expansion due to heat:

1. ....

2. ....

Describe what principle is used when a flywheel ring gear is fitted.

....

....

....

Type of expansion

When expansion is considered in terms of length only, it is called .... expansion. This type of expansion is most important.

A common example in a car engine is ....

It follows that if an expansion has taken place in length it must also expand in width. This is most important when dealing with items made from flat plate or sheets. The measurement of an expansion of an area is called

.... expansion.

A motor vehicle example would be ....

The expansion of a cube (or other three-dimensional object) must be in three (or all) directions at once. This is known as

.... expansion.

It can easily be shown using a metal ball passing through a ring. A motor-vehicle

example would be a ....

COEFFICIENT OF LINEAR EXPANSION

This is a decimal number representing the increase in unit length of a material per degree of temperature rise.

Material	Coefficient of linear expansion per °C
Aluminium	
Brass	
Steel	
Cast iron	

Bi-metal strips are a good example where practical use can be made of the expansion of solids. State typical metals that may be used and show by dotted lines the shape the strip shown below would assume when heated.

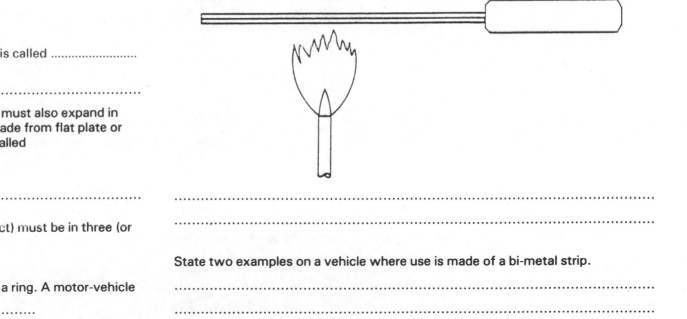

....

....

State two examples on a vehicle where use is made of a bi-metal strip.

....

....

231

CHANGE OF STATE

Certain materials, depending upon their temperature, may be in one of three states. These are:

1. .... 2. .... 3. ....

....

....

....

....

Water provides the most common example of changes of state, i.e. from ice to water, and water to steam.

The graph below shows these changes of state.

Identify each heating state.

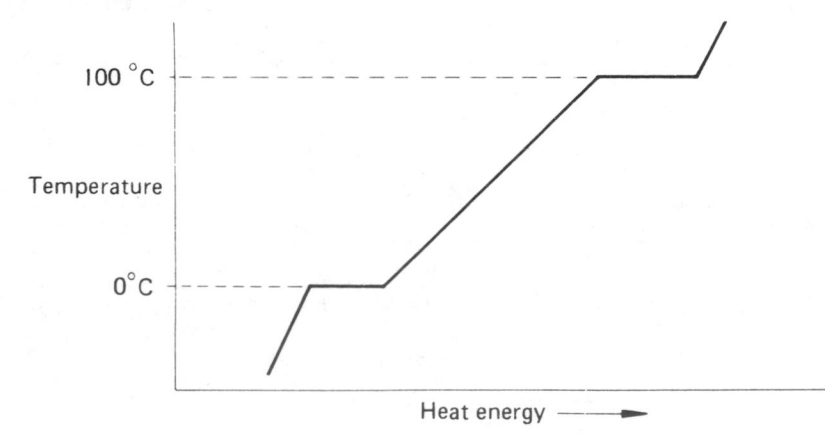

Explain the heating process during a change of state.

....

....

....

....

Investigation

A good example of changes of state which can be illustrated uses ice, water and steam.

Show sketches of the apparatus used. Tabulate the time and temperature required for the change of state to occur and comment on the results obtained; plot a temperature/time graph to indicate the rate of cooling.

Time (min)									
Temp. (°C)									

....

....

232

SENSIBLE HEAT and LATENT HEAT

In a similar way to the previous page, this graph shows the changes of state processes as a substance is heated.

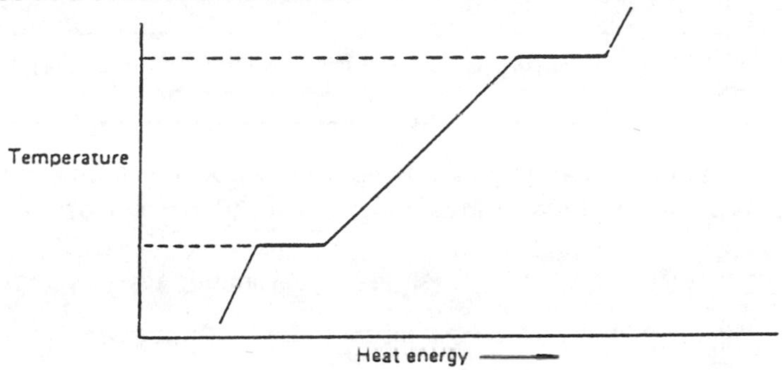

State what is meant by the following terms and indicate them on the graph.

A. Sensible heat (SI unit symbol .... and quantity symbol ....)

....

....

B. Specific latent heat of fusion (SI unit symbol .... and quantity symbol ....)

....

....

C. Specific latent heat of vaporisation (SI unit symbol ...... and quantity symbol .....)

....

....

Define the following terms used when heating or cooling.

Melting   ....

Solidifying   ....

Boiling   ....

Condensation   ....

Complete the following table of melting points (i.e. positions on temperature scale where a change of state occurs).

Material	Melting point or solidifying point (°C)
Aluminium	
Lead	
Tinman's solder	
Steel	
Copper	
Water	

Complete the following table to show latent heat values.

Material	Latent heat	
	Fusion (melting) kJ/kg	Vaporisation kJ/kg
Alcohol		
Aluminium		
Copper		
Lead		
Petroleum		
Steel		
Tin		
Water		

233

SPECIFIC HEAT CAPACITY

Investigation

Heat equal quantities of water and oil in beakers over a standard setting on two identical bunsen burners. Use tripods and a gauze for each. Measure temperature rise at regular intervals.

Water		Oil	
Time	Temperature	Time	Temperature
....	....	....	....
....	....	....	....
....	....	....	....
....	....	....	....

Which liquid gained temperature the faster? ....

When heated at the same rate 1 kg of oil will increase its temperature at a

.... rate than 1 kg of water.

Which will have the lower specific heat capacity? ....

The heat required to raise 1 kg of water 1°C is ....

∴ The specific heat capacity of water is ....

Different materials accept (or lose) heat at different rates and therefore for a similar mass they will increase (or decrease) their temperature at different rates.

Substance	Specific heat capacity (kJ/kg) K	Substance	Specific heat capacity (kJ/kg) K
Water		Steel	
Lubricating oil		Brass	
Aluminium		Lead	

The heat supplied to or lost from a material can be calculated if its rate of accepting heat (specific heat capacity), mass and temperature changes are known.

Heat lost or gained = mass × specific heat capacity × temperature
                              of substance   change

$$Q = m \times c \times \Delta t$$

For example, a cooling system contains 15 kg of water. Calculate the quantity of heat gained by the water if its temperature rises from 12°C to 88°C.

Heat gained $= m \times c \times \Delta t$

$= 15 \times 4.187 \times 76$

$= \underline{4.773\,kJ}$

1. A pump circulates 150 litres of water through a cooling system in 2 minutes. The temperature at the top of the radiator is 90°C and at the bottom 70°C. Calculate the heat energy radiated per minute. Take 1 litre of water as a mass of 1 kg.

   ....

   ....

   ....

2. Express the heat required to raise the temperature of a thermostat from 10°C to 80°C. The mass of the thermostat is 0.125 kg and its specific heat capacity is 0.4 kJ/kg K.

   ....

3. Calculate the quantity of heat which must be passed by the exhaust system to the inlet manifold in order to raise the temperature of the 'hot spot' from 12°C to 145°C. The non-ferrous inlet manifold has a mass of 0.25 kg and a specific heat capacity of 0.88 kJ/kg K.

   ....

   ....

   ....

   ....

4. An engine sump contains 560 kg of oil and undergoes a temperature change from 10°C to 90°C. Calculate the quantity of heat absorbed by the oil when its specific heat capacity is 2.22 kJ/kg K.

   ....

   ....

   ....

   ....

   ....

ENERGY

Energy is obtained in many forms. It cannot be created or destroyed. It can only be converted from one form to another.

List the four basic forms of energy found in a car.

1. .... 2. .... 3. .... 4. ....

The engine converts the chemical energy contained in the fuel to mechanical energy which is used to propel the vehicle.

How does this energy conversion take place?

....
....
....
....

The battery-charging system uses the four basic forms of energy. Explain how the energy is converted from one form to another.

....
....
....
....
....
....
....
....

When solving simple mechanical and heating problems:

Energy can be defined as ....

The SI unit of energy is the ....

WORK

The two factors which govern the amount of work done are

....

Work done is defined as ....
....
....

Force is expressed in ....

Distance is expressed in ....

These two values would produce ....

But the unit used to measure work is the ....

and one .... = one ....

Consider the situation below.

Work done by the man in moving the vehicle will be: $320 \times 20 = 6400$ N m

This is ....

Problems

1. A hydraulic lift exerts a force of 7000 N to raise a vehicle to a height of 2 m. Calculate the work done.

   ....
   ....
   ....

2. If the force required to tow a vehicle is 800 N how much work is done if the vehicle is towed for one kilometre?

   ....
   ....
   ....

(continued on next page)

3. Find the work done when an engine having a mass of 200 kg is lifted a vertical distance of 1.5 m.

....
....
....
....
....
....

5. The work done in dragging a metal box a distance of 6 m along a workshop floor is 726 N m. Calculate the force required to pull the box.

....
....
....
....

7. The work done in propelling a car 300 m was 72 kJ. What was the car's total resistance to motion?

....
....
....
....

4. Calculate the work done to drive a car 250 m if there is a rolling resistance of 50 N and a constant gradient resistance of 150 N.

....
....
....
....
....
....

6. The work done in raising the front end of a vehicle was 320 N m. If the force exerted by the lifting jack is 3200 N, to what height was the vehicle raised?

....
....
....
....
....

8. The work done by a press to push a bearing on to a shaft was 200 J. If the applied force was 10 kN, how far was the bearing pushed on to the shaft?

....
....
....
....

TORQUE

When a spanner is placed on a bolt and an effort is made to turn the bolt, the applied force is said to have created a turning moment or torque.

Define what is meant by torque ....
....

To calculate torque the following formula is used:

Torque =

Where the force is usually expressed in .... and the radius in ....

The SI unit for torque is ....

Complete the following exercise:

(a) 0.3 m, 125 N — Torque = ...

(b) 0.2 m, 125 N — Torque = ...

(c) 250 mm, 200 N — Torque = ...

(d) 150 mm, 0.3 kN — Torque = ...

(e) Wheelbrace, Crank radius 130 mm, 25 N — Torque = ...

(f) Tap wrench, 12 N, 12 N, 0.3 m — Torque = ...

WORK DONE BY A TORQUE

When using a spanner to tighten a bolt, the force applied at the end of the spanner will, in one revolution of the bolt, move through a distance which is, in fact, the circumference of a circle whose radius is the 'effective length' of the spanner.

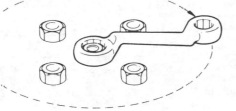

The work done per rev. = ...

Circumference = $2\pi r$ where r = radius.

Therefore work done per rev. = ...

but force × radius = ...

∴ work done per rev. = ... × 2π

If more than 1 rev. was involved then this would be multiplied by N (number of revs).

∴ work done by a torque = ...

NOTE: π may be expressed as 3.142 or $\frac{22}{7}$.

Example

When tightening a bolt a mechanic applies a force of 8 N at the end of a spanner 150 mm long.

Calculate the work done during 6 turns of the bolt.

Work done = $2\pi NT$ where number of revolutions $N = 6$
radius $r = 150$ mm = 0.15 m
torque $T = Fr$
But $F = 8$ N and $T = 0.15$ m, so $T = 8 \times 0.15$ Nm
= 1.2 Nm
Thus work done = $2 \times 3.142 \times 6 \times 1.2$ J
= 45.25 J

Problems

1. A man using a starting handle rotates an engine twice. If the torque required to do this is 35 N m, what is the work done by the man?

....

....

....

....

....

....

....

2. The force applied at the end of a spanner 100 mm long is 28 N. Calculate the work done during three revolutions of the spanner.

....

....

....

....

....

....

3. The force applied at the end of a vice handle of 0.3 m radius during a quarter of a turn is 80 N. Calculate the work done.

....

....

....

....

....

....

....

....

....

4. When propelling a vehicle, the torque in each halfshaft is 1200 N m. If the effective tyre radius is 0.25 m, calculate the work done in propelling the vehicle 25 m.

....

....

....

....

....

....

....

....

MECHANICAL ENERGY

Mechanical energy can be considered in two main forms: potential energy and kinetic energy. Both are a measure of energy which has a capacity to do work.

POTENTIAL AND KINETIC ENERGY

1. The sketch shows an example of ....

This energy can be described as the ....

....

....

....

Calculate the amount of energy possessed by the car.

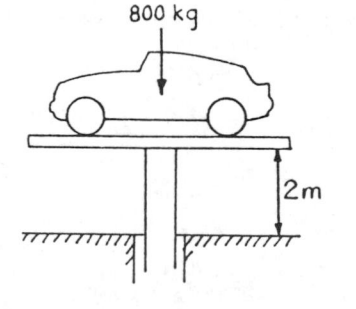

2. The sketch shows an example of ....

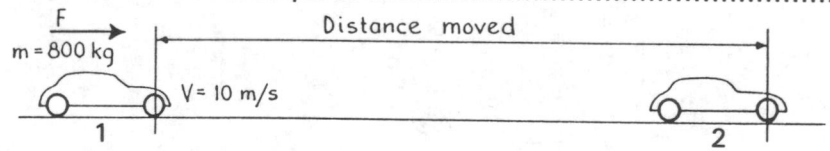

This energy can be described as the ....

....

....

Calculate the amount of energy possessed by the car at 2.

....

CONSERVATION OF ENERGY

The principle of conservation of energy states that

....

....

Mechanical energy can change from potential to kinetic to heat, due to friction, and then convert into heat energy.

Chemical energy can convert into heat energy and electrical energy can convert into mechanical energy.

If a car freewheels down a hill describe, in conservation of energy terms, the form of energy changes the vehicle will possess between points (1) and (3) in the drawing below.

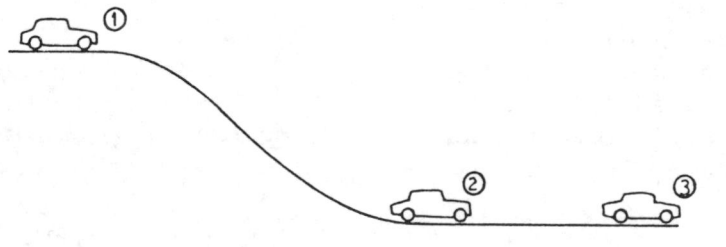

....

....

....

....

....

State how a modern car is designed to make use of the energy it consumes in more efficient and less harmful ways.

....

....

....

....

TOOLS USING LEVER PRINCIPLE

Many garage tools are based on the principle of levers. Study the illustrations below, name each one, indicate the position of the fulcrum and show the direction of movement of the effort and the load.

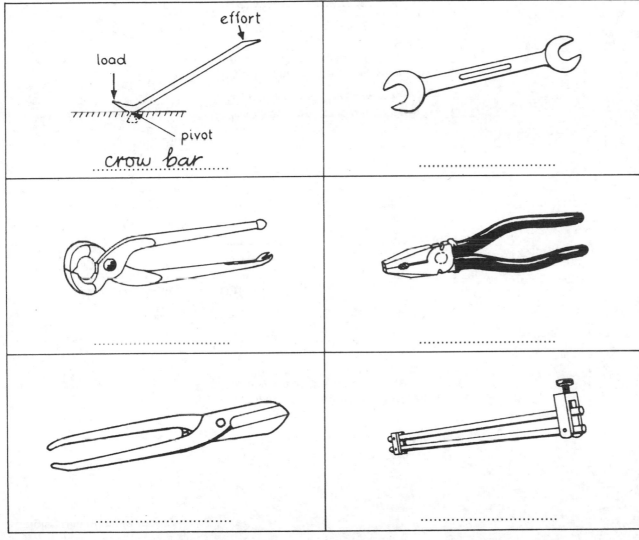

effort

load

pivot

crow bar

....

....

....

....

....

NOTE: see page 215 for calculations on moments.

WINCH

lifting drum

handle

gears

R

r

load

How does the winch shown above use the principle of levers to gain a mechanical advantage (i.e. a small effort will raise a heavy load)?

....

....

....

....

....

....

The lifting capacity of the winch could be increased by:

(a) ....

(b) ....

(c) ....

PULLEY SYSTEMS

Single pulley (single rope)

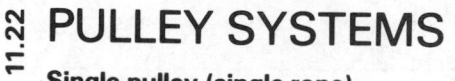

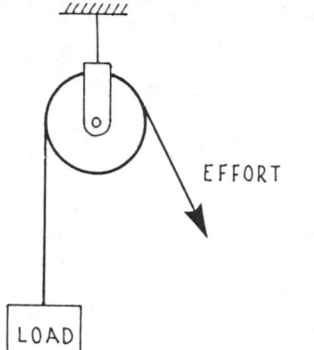

EFFORT

LOAD

With this single pulley system the only benefit is in the convenience of lifting a load.

Neglecting friction, the effort required is the same as the load.

The REACTIVE FORCE is equal to the ACTIVE FORCE.

ACTIVE FORCE = LOAD + ...

Two-pulley system (two rope)

If more than one pulley is used the system will multiply the input effort, thus it is possible to raise a greater load.

LOAD

In this system the lower pulley is FIXED TO THE LOAD and travels with it.

Neglecting friction, how does the effort compare with the load?

....
....
....
....
....

Three-pulley system (three rope)

1 2

3

In this system there are three ropes between the pulleys. Pulleys 1 and 2 rotate independently on the same shaft.

Calculate the effort required to raise a load of 600 N.

....
....
....
....
....
....

Four-pulley system (four rope)

LOAD

Add the ropes to the four pulley system shown.

From the pulley systems shown you can see that the FORCE RATIO is equal to the number of pulleys or the number of ropes between the pulleys. Therefore for a pulley system:

$$\text{EFFORT} = \frac{\text{LOAD}}{}$$

DIFFERENTIAL PULLEY BLOCKS

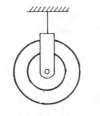

This pulley system is usually operated by chain (chain-block and tackle) and gives a high force ratio. It is very popular in garage workshops for lifting engines etc. Examine a block and tackle system and complete the drawing left to show the chain arrangement.

How does this system differ from the other pulley systems?

....

....

....

....

....

What is the SAFE WORKING LOAD for the system you have examined?

SWL = ...

INCLINED PLANE

Compared with lifting a load vertically, the EFFORT needed to move the same load up an INCLINED PLANE (or RAMP) will be .... Thus the inclined plane, in one form or another, is widely used in motor-vehicle applications.

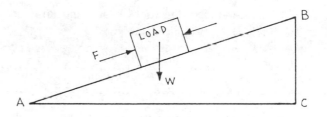

WORK DONE = FORCE × DISTANCE

The WORK DONE in moving the load from A to B is

....

The WORK DONE in moving the load from C to B is

....

Notice the fact that distance CB is less than distance AB. Thus the force *F* acting along the ramp must be less than the vertical force *W*.

How does the angle of the ramp affect the force acting along it?

....

....

....

....

A SCREWTHREAD as utilised in a car screwjack is a form

of .... arranged in a spiral
rather than a straight line.

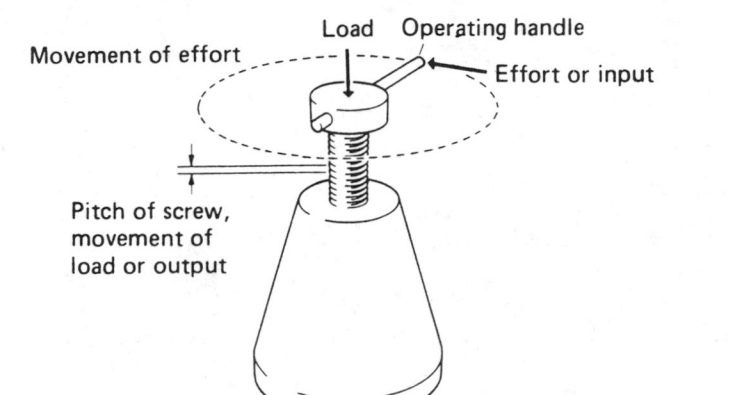

Movement of effort
Load   Operating handle
Effort or input

Pitch of screw,
movement of
load or output

For one rotation of the screw, the load is raised a distance equivalent to the
screw PITCH. Make a sketch below to illustrate screw pitch.

HYDRAULICS

The transmission of force through liquid in a system is another means by which a
mechanical advantage can be achieved. Give two examples of the use of
hydraulic systems.

1. ....

2. ....

The force on the liquid in the
container shown causes an increase

in ....

within the liquid.

What does PASCAL'S LAW say about pressure?

....
....
....
....

The factors which determine the amount of pressure are:

(a) ....

(b) ....

PRESSURE = ——————————————

STRESS

Engineering materials are designed to withstand the external forces and pressures placed upon them. The strength of a material is determined by its ability to resist loads without breaking.

The internal reaction that is set up in a material when force is applied is known as STRESS and the (often small) deformation that takes place when stress occurs is known as STRAIN.

Name the types of stress induced in the components shown at (a), (b), (c) and (d) by the application of the forces illustrated.

(a)

(b)

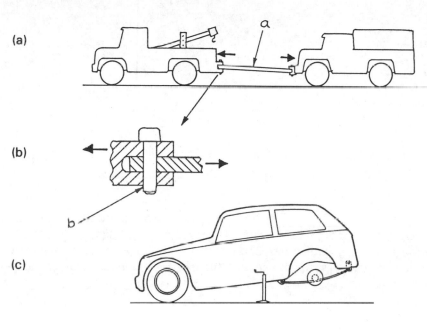

(c)

(d)

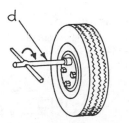

State the type of stress to which the following motor-vehicle components are mainly subjected:

Component	Type of stress
Cylinder head bolt	
Connecting rod	
Clutch disc rivets	
Handbrake rods	
Coil spring	
Cylinder head gasket	
Gudgeon pin	
Propeller shaft	

Stress is directly proportional to the force applied.

$$\text{STRESS} \ = \ \underline{\hspace{6cm}}$$

TENSION

When a tensile force is applied to a material, the material will stretch and will be in tension. As the force increases, the material will continue to stretch or elongate until it breaks.

The ease with which a material stretches, the amount of elongation before breakage and the force it can withstand before breakage, all depend on the type of material.

TESTING AND MATERIAL CHARACTERISTICS

To study the effects of stress in a material, tests are carried out using special machines and test pieces of the material. The material is then subjected to progressively applied loading (tensile, compressive or shear) and the results carefully observed.

TENSILE TESTING

A tensile test machine will gradually increase the tensile load on a material and the elongation of the material in proportion to the applied load is observed. A typical LOAD/ELONGATION graph is shown below; label the graph to indicate the significant points as arrowed.

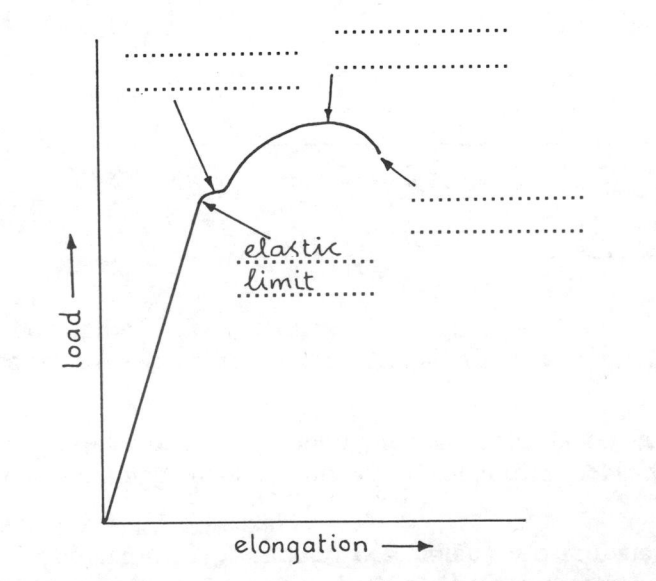

Give a brief explanation of the following:

ELASTIC LIMIT

....

....

....

YIELD POINT

....

....

....

ULTIMATE TENSILE STRESS (UTS)

....

....

....

FRACTURE POINT

....

....

....

SAFETY FACTOR

It is usual to divide the UTS by a FACTOR OF SAFETY to determine the practical SAFE WORKING STRESS. The safety factor chosen depends on a number of factors, e.g.

(a) the material

(b) the way in which it is loaded, and

(c) the type of job the material must perform.

If the UTS for a material is 500 N/mm² and the safety factor chosen for a particular application is 5, the SAFE WORKING STRESS is

Formula

SAFE WORKING TENSILE STRESS = ──────────────────────

SAFE WORKING TENSILE STRESS = ───────── = ... N/mm

Use a test specimen of one of the following materials and carry out a tensile test:

steel, aluminium, cast iron or copper

From data obtained from the test, plot the Load/Extension graph for the material.

Typical test piece

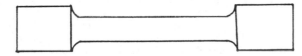

Sketch the test piece after testing to show the effect on the material.

LOAD/EXTENSION GRAPH

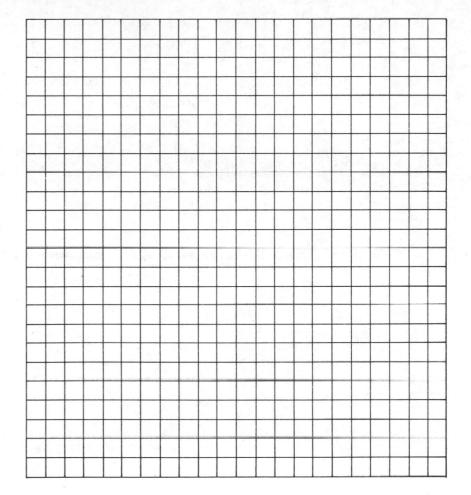

Results:

Material ....

UTS ....

Percentage elongation ....

COMPRESSION

Compressive forces act in the opposite direction to tensile forces, that is, they tend to reduce the length of a bar rather than increase it.

A compressive test would subject a material to an increasing compressive load until it gave way.

How does the compressive strength of a material compare with its tensile strength?

....

....

....

....

....

....

....

Sketch two motor-vehicle components subjected to compressive stress.

SHEAR STRESS

Shear stress occurs when a material is subjected to forces which tend to cut (or slice) through it.

The action of tin snips cutting metal is a shearing action.

In a shear test the specimen is loaded as shown below until breakage occurs. The specimen shown is in DOUBLE SHEAR and

SHEAR STRESS = ─────────────

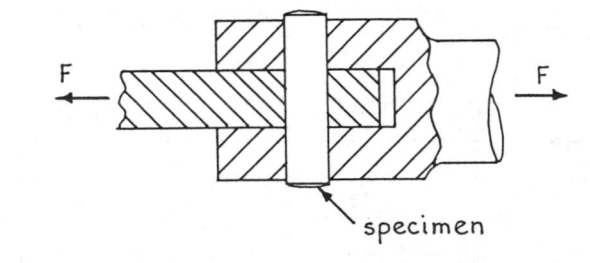

specimen

Sketch two motor-vehicle components subjected to shear stress.

ELECTROCHEMISTRY

Electrochemistry is concerned with the transfer of electrons (ions) through chemicals when plates of different potentials (voltages) are connected in an electrical circuit, or when an electric current is passed through a chemical cell.

What is meant by the term *electrolyte*?

....

....

....

What is the electrolyte used in a car battery?

....

Electrodes are the plates, rods or wires which are submerged in the electrolyte and act as conductors.

The *cathode* is the ....

The *anode* is the ....

What is meant by *electrolysis*?

....

....

....

....

....

....

....

....

Where is electrolysis industrially applied?

....

....

....

The drawing shows the construction of a primary cell in its simplest form. Name the electrolyte and materials from which the plates could be made, and show how they could be connected, to produce an electric current.

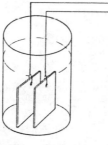

Describe what occurs in the above cell when the circuit is closed and an electric current flows.

....

....

....

....

....

....

....

....

For what, in its common form, is the primary cell used?

....

What is the cell's main disadvantage?

....

How does a secondary cell differ from a primary cell?

....

....

....

....

....

....

Where is a battery of secondary cells commonly used?

....

....

ELECTROCHEMICAL SERIES

The electrochemical series is a list of metals arranged in the order of the ability of an electrode to transmit current when it forms part of a simple cell.

The most reactive is at the top of the list; such metals form the anode and erode away.

Metal	Electrode Potential
Sodium	
Magnesium	
Aluminium	
Zinc	
Iron	
Tin	
Copper	
Silver	
Gold	

The electrode potential is a measure of the electrode's metal to enter the cell solution as positive ions.

FERROUS METALS

What is defined as a ferrous metal? ....

....

....

Ferrous metals are divided into two groups:

Wrought steel (wrought iron and all the steels), these contain up to .... %
carbon, and *cast irons* which contain amounts above this up to .... % carbon.

State the properties of the ferrous metals named below.

Metal	% Carbon Content	Properties	Typical use
Wrought iron			
Low-carbon (mild steel)			
Cast iron			

COMPOSITION AND STRUCTURE OF FERROUS METALS

Wrought iron

How is wrought iron produced from the smelted iron ore (pig iron)?

....

....

....

....

Low-carbon steel

Low-carbon steel is almost pure iron (0.25% carbon) consisting of ferrite grains
which are soft and easy to work.

How does increasing the percentage of carbon alter the structure of the steel?

....

....

....

....

Cast iron

How does cast iron differ from wrought iron and steel?

....

....

....

wrought iron   low carbon steel   cast iron

GRAIN STRUCTURE

During the manufacture of cast iron, elements are added to improve the
production process. Some if used to excess may have an undesirable effect on
the finished assembly. What may be the undesirable effect of adding the
following elements?

Sulphur (0.1% max.) ....

....

Phosphorus (0.1% max.) ....

....

NOTE: for examples of ferrous metals, improved properties of alloy steels and effects of heat treatment see Chapter 8.

CORROSION

Corrosion causes damage to metals by attack from acids and salts in air and water.

FORMS OF CORROSION

The most common form of corrosion is by electrochemical reaction. Iron, being higher in the electrochemical series than either oxygen or hydrogen, becomes the reducing agent (anode) and oxidises (rusts). The acids in the air accelerate the process (see also chapter 8).

Corrosion can also occur by other processes, define the forms of corrosion named below.

Corrosion by differential aeration

....
....
....
....

Bacterial corrosion

....
....
....

Stress corrosion

....
....
....

Galvanic corrosion

....
....
....

Formation of galvanic corrosion cells

....
....
....
....

METHODS OF PREVENTING CORROSION

What is a corrosion inhibitor?

....
....

Below are listed THREE ways in which corrosion may be prevented or reduced, describe and give examples of each type.

Inhibitors

....
....
....
....
....
....

Corrosion-resistant metals/alloys

....
....
....
....

Mechanical barriers

....
....
....
....
....

Chapter 11

Basic Workshop and Vehicle Calculations

This chapter is included in order to help students become familiar with the simple, everyday type of calculations that they are likely to use in connection with motor-vehicle work and leisure interests. It also gives further experience relative to syllabus section 11.1.

FRACTIONS

Addition

$$2\frac{3}{4} + 1\frac{5}{6} \longleftarrow \text{mixed number}$$

$$= 3\frac{9 + 10}{12} \longleftarrow \text{lowest common denominator}$$

$$= 3\frac{19}{12} = 4\frac{7}{12}$$

Improper fraction

Subtraction

$$3\frac{4}{5} - \frac{5}{9}$$

$$= 3\frac{36 - 25}{45} \longleftarrow \text{subtract}$$
$$\longleftarrow \text{l.c.d}$$

$$= 3\frac{11}{45}$$

Multiplication

$$3\frac{4}{7} \times \frac{4}{15} \times \frac{2}{3}$$

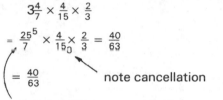

$$= \frac{25^{5}}{7} \times \frac{4}{15_{0}} \times \frac{2}{3} = \frac{40}{63}$$

$$= \frac{40}{63} \qquad \text{note cancellation}$$

converted to improper fraction

Division

$$\frac{7}{8} \div \frac{2}{3}$$

$$= \frac{7}{8} \times \frac{3}{2} = \frac{21}{16} = 1\frac{5}{16}$$

$$1\frac{5}{16}$$

turn upside down and multiply

Find the l.c.d. of the following groups:

$$\frac{2}{3}, \frac{3}{4} = (12) \quad \frac{3}{4}, \frac{1}{2}, \frac{2}{5} = (\quad) \quad \frac{2}{7}, \frac{3}{8} = (\quad) \quad \frac{5}{9}, \frac{2}{3}, \frac{7}{12} = (\quad) \quad \frac{3}{4}, \frac{2}{5}, \frac{1}{6} = (\quad)$$

Reduce the following to their lowest terms:

$$\frac{9}{24} = \left(\frac{3}{8}\right) \quad \frac{12}{36} = (\quad) \quad \frac{22}{46} = (\quad) \quad \frac{15}{27} = (\quad) \quad \frac{63}{84} = (\quad) \quad \frac{176}{256} = (\quad)$$

Convert the following to improper fractions:

$$2\frac{5}{8} = \left(\frac{21}{8}\right) \quad 3\frac{3}{4} = (\quad) \quad 8\frac{9}{16} = (\quad) \quad 5\frac{4}{11} = (\quad) \quad 3\frac{18}{23} = (\quad) \quad 7\frac{19}{33} = (\quad)$$

....

....

....

....

....

Problems

1. The oil capacity of an engine is $3\frac{3}{4}$ litre. When the oil level was checked, $1\frac{1}{3}$ litres of oil was needed. How much oil did the engine contain?

....

....

....

....

....

2. If a vehicle weights 912 kg and $\frac{5}{8}$ of the weight is on the rear wheels, what is the weight on the front wheels?

....

....

....

....

3. A vehicle travels 11½ km on 1 litre of fuel. If the fuel-tank capacity is 40 litres, how far will the vehicle travel on a full tank of fuel?

....

....

....

....

4. $\frac{1}{3}$ of a bar of steel is used on one day, $\frac{1}{6}$ on the next, and $\frac{1}{4}$ on the third day. How much is left?

....

....

....

....

....

5. Work out the following:

$$1\frac{1}{6} - 1\frac{2}{5} + \frac{7}{15}$$

....

....

....

....

....

6. Work out the following:

$$\frac{1\frac{5}{8} \times 3\frac{11}{13} \times 5\frac{2}{3}}{2\frac{7}{9}}$$

....

....

....

....

....

DECIMALS

Addition

```
    53.00
+    4.85
+    0.36
+    0.002
   58.212
```

NOTE: the decimal points must be under one another

Subtraction

```
  47.97
- 35.60
  12.37
```

NOTE: the decimal points must be under one another

Multiplication

```
    67.89
×    8.56
   40734
  339450
 5431200
 581.1384
```

Four figures on the right of the point

Therefore count four figures from the right in the answer

Division

$276.56 \div 35.4$

```
          7.8
354)  2765.6
      2478
      2876
      2832
        44
```

This answer is correct to one decimal place

The divisor is made into a whole number by moving the decimal point to the right. The point must also be moved the same number of places in the number being divided.

Treat as whole numbers to multiply then position point as indicated

Multiplying and dividing decimals by 10 and multiples of 10

Multiplying

56.42×10	$= 564.2$
56.42×1000	$=$
$56.42 \times 10\ 000$	$=$
56.42×100	$=$

Dividing

$56.42 \div 100$	$= 0.5642$
$56.42 \div 10$	$=$
$56.42 \div 1000$	$=$
$56.42 \div 100\ 000$	$=$

Problems

Solve the following:

```
  36.96          287.6
+  3.7         + 58.67
```

```
+  1.037        300.6
+  0.36       + 28.683
```

Find the thickness of metal in the pipe shown.

The circumference of a tyre is 1.25 m. How many revolutions will it make in travelling 20 m?

Solve the following:

```
  80.26          356.1
- 33.1        - 253.23
```

```
 961.35          87.38
- 298.2        -  6.29
```

What is the overall length of the metal plate shown?

The stroke of an engine is 6.58 cm. Calculate the linear distance travelled by the piston in 1 s when the engine speed is 1200 rev/min.

The answer to a problem may be correct to a number of decimal places, or correct to a number of significant figures, depending upon the accuracy required.

Decimal places

The following have been corrected to two decimal places.

(a) 21.632 is 21.63

(b) 184.676 is 184.68

(c) 3.5601 is 3.56

(d) 27.067 is 27.07

(e) 0.079 is 0.08

State the following to the number of decimal places shown.

Number	Decimal places	Answer
35.78	1	
276.14	1	
2.0676	3	
896.073	2	
1.8725	1	

Solve the following to two significant figures.

(1)	9.8	(2)	4.7	(3)	24.52	(4)	3.578
	× 4		× 8		× 3		× 12

Significant figures

The following have been corrected to three significant figures.

(a) 23.518 is 23.5

(b) 336.8 is 337

(c) 19.18 is 19.2

(d) 0.007526 is 0.00753

(e) 0.03573 is 0.0357

State the following to the number significant figures shown.

Number	Significant figures	Answer
24.69	3	
349.2	3	
2.481	2	
0.0369	2	
0.0193	1	

Converting decimal fractions to vulgar fractions

Examples

(a) $0.25 = \frac{25}{100} = \frac{1}{4}$ (b) $0.6 = \frac{6}{10} = \frac{3}{5}$ (c) $0.325 = \frac{325}{1000} = \frac{13}{40}$

Convert the following decimals to fractions

(a) 0.125 =   (b) 0.8 =

(c) 0.75 =   (d) 0.345 =

Converting vulgar fractions to decimal fractions

Examples

(a) $\frac{1}{4}$
```
    0.25
 4)1.00
    8
    20
    20
    ..
```
$\frac{1}{4} = 0.25$

(b) $\frac{13}{20}$
```
      0.65
 20)13.00
    12.0
     1.00
     1.00
     ...
```
$\frac{13}{20} = 0.65$

(c) $\frac{1}{16}$
```
      0.0625
 16)1.0000
    96
    40
    32
    80
    80
    ..
```
$\frac{1}{16} = 0.0625$

Convert the following fractions to decimals

(1) $\frac{1}{2}$ (2) $\frac{1}{8}$ (3) $\frac{2}{5}$

Solve the following to two decimal places

(1) 69.7 ÷ 7.6   (2) 126.2 ÷ 7.1   (3) 23.6 ÷ 0.22   (4) 528.9 ÷ 32.6

253

AVERAGES

The average (or mean value) of a set of numbers is equal to their sum divided by the number of them.

Find the average of 3, 5, 9 and 11

$$\text{Average} = \frac{3 + 5 + 9 + 11}{4} = \frac{28}{4} = 7$$

During a 4 hour journey a man did 40 km in the first hour, 48 in the second, 44 in the third and 51 in the last hour. What was his average speed for the journey.

$$\text{Average speed} = \frac{40 + 48 + 44 + 51}{4}$$

$$= \frac{183}{4} = 45\frac{3}{4}$$

$$= 45\frac{3}{4}\,\text{km/h}$$

Problems

1. A vehicle's fuel consumptions during three different journeys of identical mileages were calculated as 10 km/litre, 12.5 km/litre and 11.25 km/litre. The average fuel consumption figure for the vehicle during the three journeys of equal mileage is therefore

(a) 10 km/litres   (b) 11.25 km/litres

(c) 11.75 km/litres   (d) 15 km/litres

Answer (   )

2. During a check on four spark plugs, the gaps were found to be 0.6 mm, 0.55 mm, 0.7 mm and 0.75 mm. The average gap was

(a) 0.7 mm   (b) 0.8 mm

(c) 0.6 mm   (d) 0.65 mm

Answer (   )

3. If a car averages 62 km/h for $4\frac{1}{2}$ hours, the total distance covered will be

(a) 93 km   (b) 124 km

(c) 279 km   (d) 379 km

Answer (   )

4. In five consecutive months the number of services done by a garage was 86, 90, 79, 74 and 81. The monthly average was

(a) 88   (b) 44

(c) 80   (d) 82

Answer (   )

5. Four different oil measures have capacities of 4 litres, 2 litres, 1 litre and $\frac{1}{2}$ litre. The average capacity is

(a) $1\frac{1}{2}$ litres   (b) $2\frac{1}{2}$ litres

(c) 3 litres   (d) $1\frac{7}{8}$ litres

Answer (   )

6. After a tyre inspection on a vehicle the tread depths were found to be 3.5 mm, 2.5 mm, 0.5 mm and 2 mm. What was the average tread depth?

....
....
....
....
....

7. If the average interval between three oil changes on a vehicle is 9000 km, and the intervals between the first two are 6000 km and 10 000 km, what is the interval between the second and third oil change?

....
....
....
....

8. If a roll of copper tubing 16 m in length costs £86.40 what is the average cost per metre?

....
....
....
....

9. Six apprentices receive a wage of £40 each. If four other apprentices receive wages of £48 each, what is the average wage of all the apprentices?

....
....
....
....

10. If the times taken to fit water pumps to three cars of the same type are 2.5 hours, 2.8 hours and 2.4 hours, what is the average time for the job?

....
....
....
....

11. If the total number of crankshafts sold by the stores in one year is 276, what is the average monthly sales figure?

....
....
....
....

PERCENTAGES

Per cent or percentage (usually denoted by %) refers to a part or fraction of some quantity expressed in hundredths.

To obtain the percentage, the fraction or the decimal is multiplied by 100.

Express the following as percentages:

(a) $\frac{3}{5} \times \frac{100}{1} = 60\%$ (b) $\frac{9}{75}$ (c) $\frac{23}{32}$

(d) 0.4   (e) 0.35   (f) 0.01

When commencing a workshop exercise, 15 students share equally a bar of mild steel 2 m in length. What percentage of the bar will each student receive?

Each will receive $\frac{1}{15}$ of the bar.

∴ The percentage will be $\frac{1}{15} \times \frac{100}{1} = 6\frac{2}{3}\%$

If the repair charge for a job is £120 and 27% of this is the cost of parts, how much did the parts cost?

$$\text{Cost of parts} = \frac{27}{100} \text{ of } £120$$

$$\therefore \text{Cost of parts} = \frac{27 \times 120}{100} = \frac{162}{5} = 32\frac{2}{5}$$

$$\text{Cost of parts} = £32.40$$

1. A vehicle's cooling system capacity is 8 litres and a mixture of 25% antifreeze is required. How much antifreeze must the owner purchase?

....

....

....

....

2. If 2 litres of antifreeze are mixed with water in a 4 : 1 water/anti-freeze ratio, how many litres of mixture are available to fill a cooling system and what percentage antifreeze does this mix represent?

....

....

....

....

3. The rate for repair charges at a garage is £18.15 per hour. If 20% of this is profit, 60% is overheads and the rest is the mechanic's pay, at what hourly rate is the mechanic paid?

....

....

....

....

4. A stick of solder has a mass of 3 kg. If it is composed of 30% tin and 70% lead, what is the mass of lead?

....

....

....

....

....

5. An engine cylinder is to be rebored to give a 2% increase in diameter. If the original diameter is 60 mm, determine the diameter after reboring.

....

....

....

....

6. If the retail price for a brake master-cylinder is £30 and a mechanic is allowed 12½ % discount on this, how much would he pay for the master cylinder?

....

....

....

....

7. If a car reduces speed by 8% and is then travelling at 70 km/h, what was its former speed?

....

....

....

....

8. The cooling system capacity of a commercial vehicle is 15 litres and a 30% antifreeze mixture is to be used. How much antifreeze is required?

....

....

....

....

RATIO AND PROPORTION

A 'ratio' is a comparison of the size of two quantities. For example, if the stroke of an engine is 80 mm and the bore of the engine is 50 mm, the stroke-to-bore ratio would be:

Ratio $= \frac{80}{50} = \frac{8}{5}$ or $1\frac{3}{5}:1$

Divide a line 48 mm long into two parts in the ratio of 3 : 1 and determine their lengths.

1 part $= \frac{48}{4} = 12$

3 parts $= 12 \times 3 = 36$

Therefore the two parts would be 36 and 12 mm.

Problems

1. The ratio of petrol and oil for a certain two-stroke engine is 20 : 1. Therefore the oil added per litre of petrol would be

   (a) 0.1 litres   (b) 0.2 litres

   (c) 0.05 litres   (d) 0.02 litres

   Ans. (   )

   ....
   ....
   ....
   ....
   ....
   ....

'Proportion' is the relationship between two or more quantities, i.e. if one quantity was changed, the others would correspondingly increase or decrease to keep the relationship the same. For example, if 2 litres of oil cost 15p, how much would 6 litres cost?

2 litres cost 15p

1 litre costs $\frac{15p}{2}$

Therefore 6 litres would cost

$\frac{15}{2} \times \frac{6}{1} = 45p$ Ans.

2. 14 litres of fuel are pumped into a tank in 25 seconds. How much fuel would be pumped into it in 45 seconds?

   ....
   ....
   ....
   ....
   ....
   ....

3. Calculate the rear axle ratio of a vehicle, if the crown wheel has 30 teeth and the meshing pinion 7 teeth.

   ....
   ....
   ....
   ....

4. A mixture of antifreeze and water is in the ratio of 4 parts water to 1 part antifreeze. How much antifreeze should be added to a cooling system with a capacity of $6\frac{1}{2}$ litre?

   ....
   ....
   ....

5. A commercial vehicle chassis is 11.5 m in length. If the chassis is lengthened in the ratio of 5 : 4, what is the new length of chassis?

   ....
   ....
   ....

6. A hydraulic ramp lifts a vehicle to a height of 2 m in 30 seconds. At what height would the vehicle be after 13 seconds?

   ....
   ....
   ....
   ....

7. A mechanic, using a spanner 175 mm long, exerts a torque on a bolt of 14 N m. What torque would be produced by applying the same force on a spanner 20 mm longer?

   ....
   ....
   ....
   ....

8. Five similar cars, doing similar work, use 150 litres of fuel in three days. How long would the same quantity of fuel last two of the cars?

   ....
   ....
   ....
   ....

USE OF ROUGH CHECKS

Rough checks often provide a practical and realistic approach to problems.

They are also used as a quick method of checking the accuracy of answers.

For example, how many litres of fuel may be bought for £1 at 33p/litre?

Answer = $\frac{100}{33}$ = approx. 3 litres

How much time is needed to cover 100 km at a speed of 48 km/h.

Answer = $\frac{100}{48}$ = just over 2 h.

....
....
....
....
....
....
....
....
....
....
....
....
....

1. 1 inch = 25.4 mm, therefore 12 inches are approximately

   (a) 250 mm   (b) 300 mm
   (c) 600 mm   (d) 297 mm

   Ans. (   )

2. If each cylinder of a 4-cylinder engine has a capacity of 447 cm³, the engine capacity would be roughly

   (a) 1600 cm³   (b) 1800 cm³
   (c) 2000 cm³   (d) 1999 cm³

   Ans. (   )

3. A certain type of metal pipe has a mass of 1.9 kg/m. Therefore 50 kg of the pipe would have an approximate length of

   (a) 50 m   (b) 10 m
   (c) 25 m   (d) 30.2 m

   Ans. (   )

4. The length of round bar required to make 20 studs 0.0382 m long is approximately

   (a) 0.8 m   (b) 80 m
   (c) 0.6 m   (d) 0.06 m

   Ans. (   )

5. If a vehicle takes $6\frac{1}{4}$ h to cover 600 km, its average speed would be approximately

   (a) 48 km/h   (b) 50 km/h
   (c) 100 km/h   (d) 50.3 km/h

   Ans. (   )

6. A vehicle uses 69.3 litres of fuel to cover a distance of 697 km. Calculate the approximate fuel consumption in km/litre.

   ....
   ....
   ....
   ....

7. A vehicle requires topping up with 0.5 litre of oil every 700 km. Approximately how much oil is used over a 10 000 km period?

   ....
   ....
   ....
   ....

8. The labour charge on a job is £1.97 per hour and the cost of materials is £20.20. Give a rough estimate of the total cost of repair, if the time taken was 8 hours.

   ....
   ....
   ....
   ....
   ....
   ....

9. Show how you would quickly check the accuracy of the answer to the following problem.

   $$\frac{40 \times 3.9 \times 2.1 \times 59}{60 \times 39} = 8.26$$

   ....
   ....
   ....
   ....
   ....

10. Find the approximate answer to the following problem.

    $$\frac{51.2 \times 1980 \times 12}{997 \times 99 \times 25.25}$$

    ....
    ....
    ....
    ....

11. The overall gear ratio in first gear on a vehicle is 19.75 : 1. What would be the approx. speed of the rear wheels when the engine was running at 3980 rev/min?

    ....
    ....
    ....
    ....
    ....

Chapter 12

Vehicle Electronic Systems

ELEMENT 3   **PART OF UNIT 1**

NOTE: Pages 50 to 60 should be completed before commencing this Element.

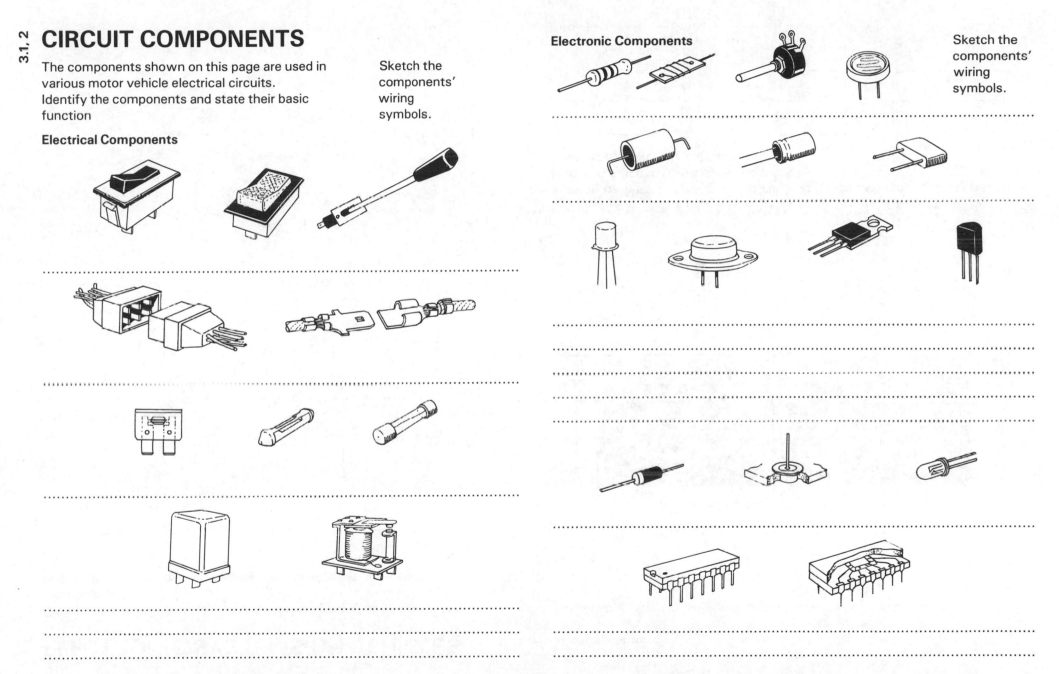

3.1.2 CIRCUIT COMPONENTS

The components shown on this page are used in various motor vehicle electrical circuits.
Identify the components and state their basic function

Sketch the components' wiring symbols.

Electrical Components

Electronic Components

Sketch the components' wiring symbols.

259

ELECTRONIC SYSTEMS ON VEHICLES

On modern vehicles most electrical signals are controlled by some form of electronic unit.
Identify the items shown on this page and state what they control.

Ignition

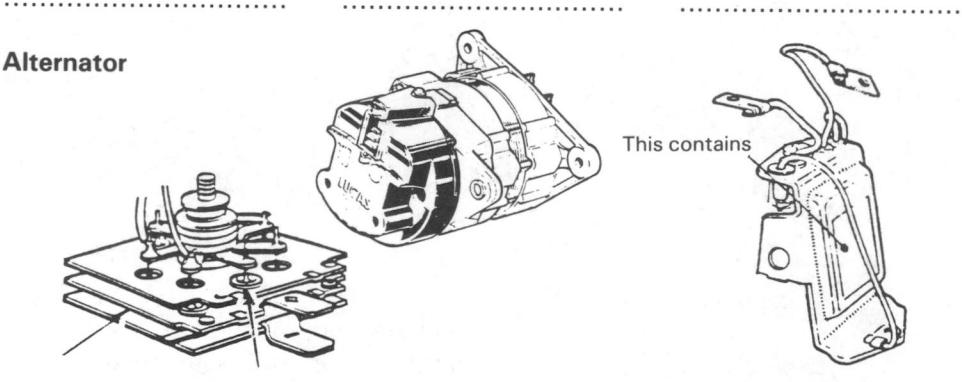

Carburation

Instrumentation

Indicate the items on the drawing that are controlled electronically.

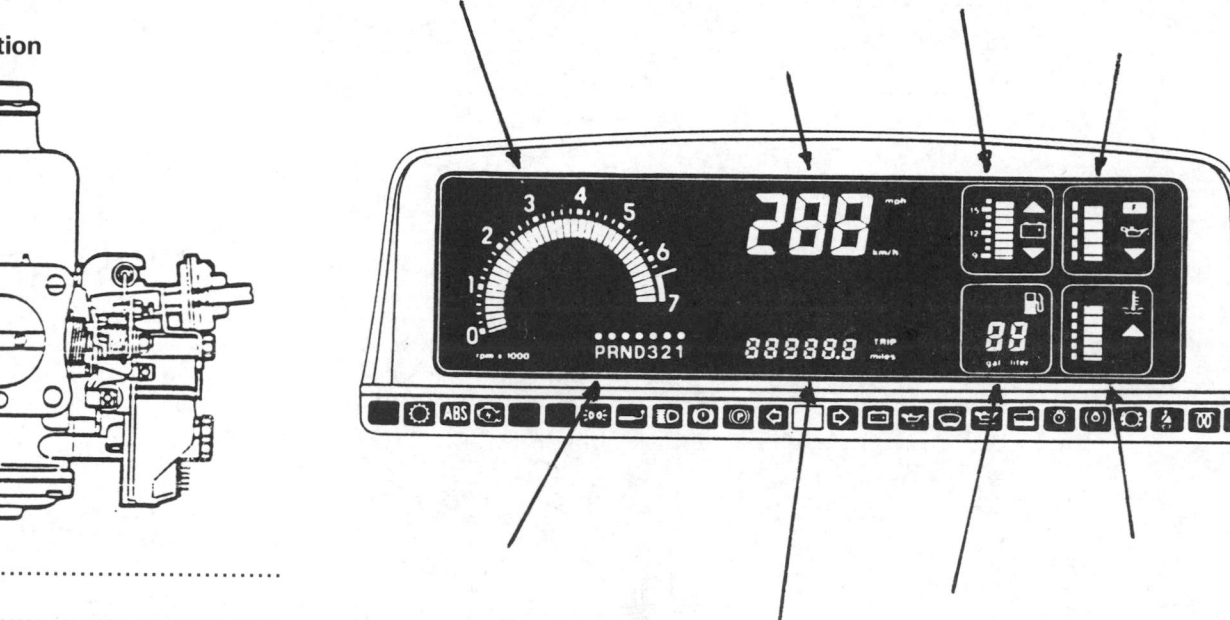

....
....

....
....

Alternator

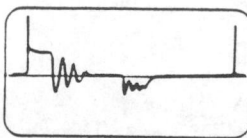

This contains

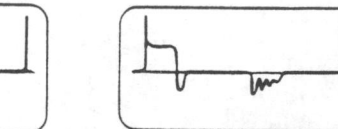

Fault finding is also carried out using electronic diagnostic equipment. One example of this is the use of an oscilloscope for checking the ignition system. Below are three different traces obtained by an oscilloscope.
State what each trace indicates.

....
....

....
....

....

ENGINE ELECTRONIC CONTROL UNIT

The diagram opposite shows an electronic control unit and the items to which it is connected.

Name the parts indicated on the drawing.

....

....

....

....

Electronic circuits operate on very low voltages, and to ensure long-term high-quality contact between their terminals special connections and plugs have been introduced.

....

....

....

....

An engine ECU module is shown below. Where are these units usually positioned in the vehilce?

....

....

....

....

....

....

....

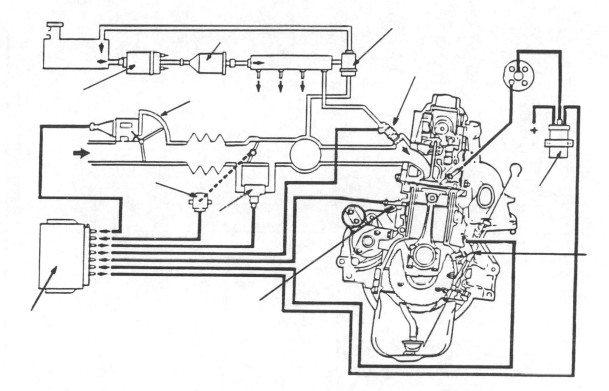

BOSCH MOTRONIC COMBINED IGNITION & PETROL INJECTION SYSTEM

Describe how the plug should be removed and replaced.

....

....

....

....

....

....

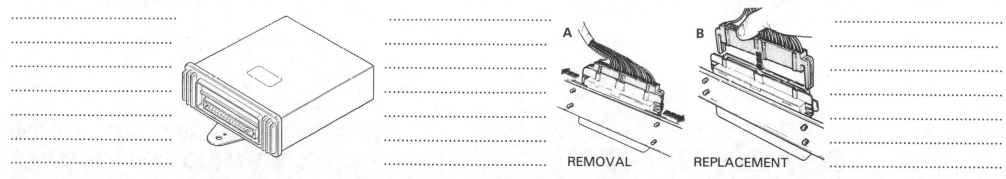

A   B

REMOVAL   REPLACEMENT

....

....

....

....

....

....

SYMBOLS FOR CONTROLS, INDICATORS AND TELL-TALES

Modern vehicles now use international standard symbols on control knobs, switches, fuse units etc. to indicate what each item does. The symbols are designed to give the driver a clear pictorial indication of the function of each item. The number of these symbols seems to be inexhaustible and it can sometimes be difficult to interpret what they all indicate. Examine the examples on this page, and use information from other sources to familiarise yourself with these types of symbols.

NOTE: If the symbol is in side view, that is, lamps, assume the vehicle is driving from right to left; and if a plan view is shown, the vehicle is driving upwards.

A fuse/relay box from a FORD vehicle is shown below. Complete the tables opposite to state what the relays operate and what main circuits the fuses protect.

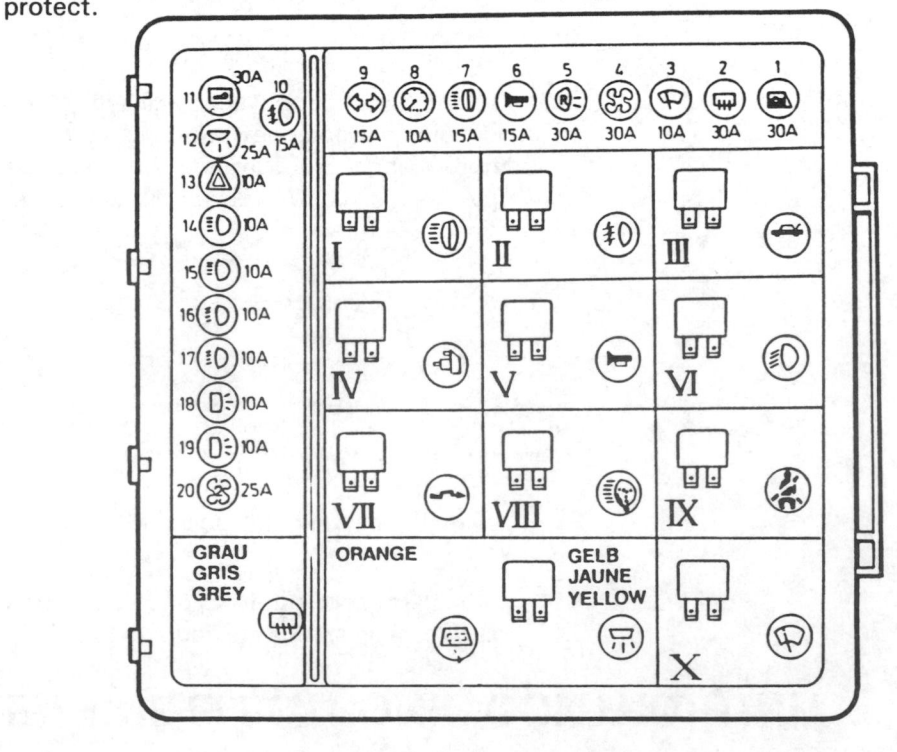

CIRCUITS OPERATED BY RELAYS	
i	viii
ii	ix
iii	x
iv	Grey
v	Yellow
vi	Orange
vii	

MAIN CIRCUITS PROTECTED BY FUSE	
1	11
2	12
3	13
4	14
5	15
6	16
7	17
8	18
9	19
10	20

State what the following symbols represent.

....

....

The diagram illustrates the instrument panel of a Ford Granada 2.0i Ghia.

Enlarged are shown 40 standard symbols which are positioned on the vehicle instruments and control knobs.

Examine the position of these items and identify their function using the similar drawings on the next page.

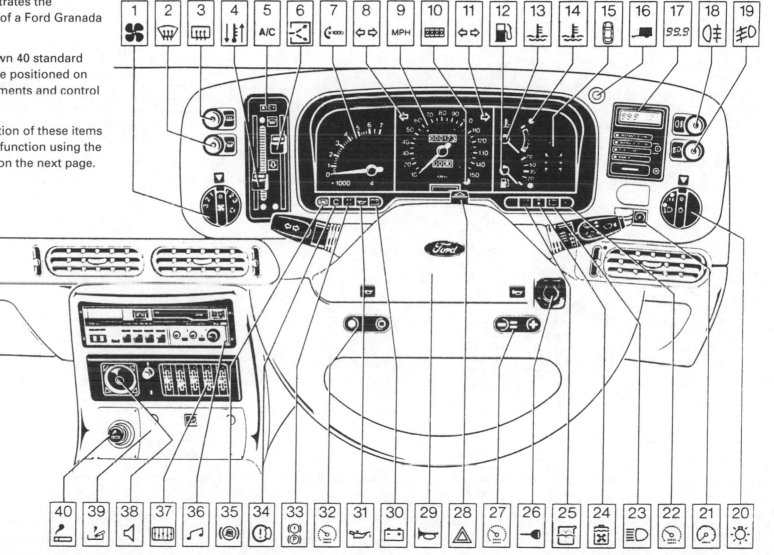

Name the instrument/control knob symbols shown below

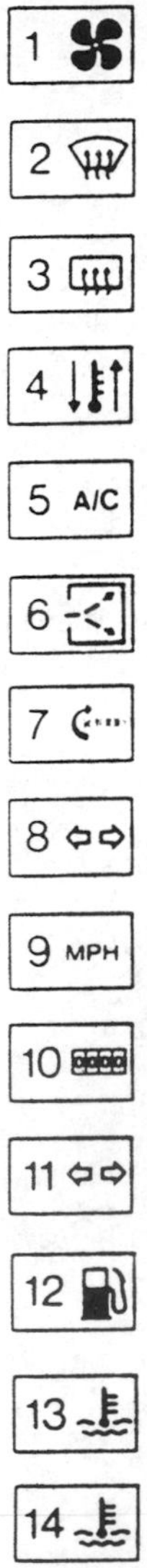

1 .... 15 .... 29 ....

2 .... 16 .... 30 ....

3 .... 17 99.9 .... 31 ....

4 .... 18 .... 32 ....

5 A/C .... 19 .... 33 ....

6 .... 20 .... 34 ....

7 .... 21 .... 35 ....

8 .... 22 .... 36 ....

9 MPH .... 23 .... 37 ....

10 .... 24 .... 38 ....

11 .... 25 .... 39 ....

12 .... 26 .... 40 ....

13 .... 27 ....

14 .... 28 ....

NOTE: Complete page 209 before commencing this page.

SERIES CIRCUITS

With the aid of diagrams state the basic laws of series circuits, and show calculations to obtain values if the battery voltage and resistances are shown.

The ammeters (diagram 2) and voltmeters (diagram 3) are shown in their relative testing positions.

1. RESISTANCE ....
....
....
....
....
....
....

2. CURRENT ....
....
....
....
....
....

3. VOLTAGE ....
....
....
....
....
....
....
....

1. Three resistors of 15, 30 and 12 Ω are connected in series. What is the total resistance in the circuit?

....
....
....

2. Five resistors of 100 Ω, 500 Ω, 1 kΩ, 1.5 kΩ and 1 MΩ are connected in series. What is the total resistance of the circuit?

....
....
....

3. Four resistors of 6, 10, 14 and 18 Ω are connected in series to a 12 V circuit. Calculate the total resistance of the circuit and the current flowing in each resistance.

....
....
....
....
....

4. Two resistances of 1.25 Ω and 3.75 Ω are connected in series. What voltage would be required to cause a current of 2.5 A to flow in the circuit?

....
....
....
....

5. Three resistors of 2, 4 and 6 kΩ are connected in series to a 12 V battery. Calculate the current flowing in the circuit.

....
....
....
....
....
....

6. Two resistors each 2 kΩ are connected in series to a 9 V supply. Calculate the current flowing and the voltage between the two resistors.

....
....
....
....
....

3.4 PARALLEL CIRCUITS

With the aid of diagrams state the basic laws of parallel circuits, and show calculations to obtain values if the battery voltage and resistances are as shown.

The ammeters (diagram 2) and voltmeters (diagram 3) are shown in their relative testing positions.

1. RESISTANCE

....
....
....
....
....
....
....
....
....
....

2. CURRENT

....
....
....
....

3. VOLTAGE

....
....
....
....

Problems

1. Two resistances of 3 and 4 Ω are connected in a 12 V parallel circuit. Calculate the total current flow.

....
....
....
....
....
....

2. Three conductors are placed in a parallel circuit, their resistances being 4, 8 and 12 Ω. Calculate the current flow in each resistance and the total current flow when connected to a 12 V system.

....
....
....
....
....
....
....

3. Two resistances of 8 and 6 Ω are connected in parallel. What voltage would be required to cause a current flow of 7 A?

....
....
....
....
....
....
....
....

4. Three resistors of 4, 8 and 16 Ω are connected to a 12 V battery. Calculate the equivalent circuit resistance.

....
....
....
....
....
....
....
....

266

SERIES AND PARALLEL CIRCUITS

Many electronic circuits have multiple resistors connected in series and parallel together.

Calculate the total resistance of the following circuits:

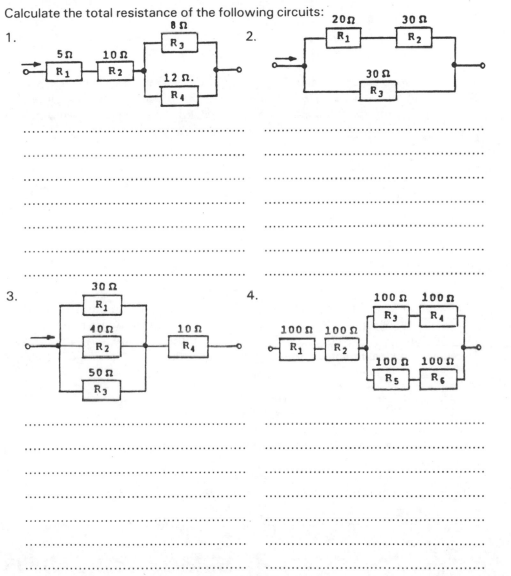

1.

2.

....

....

....

....

....

....

3.

4.

....

....

....

....

....

....

Which circuit divides its total:

current .... resistance .... voltage ....

The division of voltage is most important, particularly in electronics, since a varying voltage allows the switching on and off of components requiring control.

Potential Divider

This divides potential (voltage) in a series circuit. If a variable resistor is used, the output voltage can be varied and provide control.

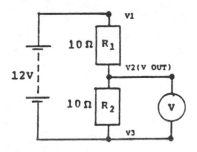

From previous work, if the resistances are equal then voltage at V = half the total voltage; this is known as the output voltage or voltage out. By altering the values of the resistors, this voltage can be very high or very low.

From diagram, Voltage out = ...

VOLTAGE OUT can be calculated using the formula

$$\text{Voltage out} = \frac{R_2}{R_1 + R_2} \times \text{supply voltage}$$

Calculate the voltage out values when:

1. $R_1 = 1\ \Omega$ and $R_2 = 59\ \Omega$

2. $R_1 = 100\ \Omega$ and $R_2 = 5\ \Omega$

....

....

....

....

....

....

3.4 ELECTRICAL POWER

Power is the rate of doing work and is measured in ....

The definition of electrical power is: ....

The power consumption in electronic circuits is very small, milliwatts (mW) or microwatts (μW), whereas the power consumed by lamps may be measured in watts (W), and by starter motors in kilowatts (kW).

1. If an alternator is generating a current of 60 A with an output voltage of 14 V, what power is required to turn the alternator?

....

....

....

....

....

2. A starter motor when cranking an engine consumes a current of 135 A. The terminal voltage is 11.5 V. Calculate the starter motor's power output.

....

....

....

....

....

3. A current of 250 flows through a starter motor when the p.d. is 11 V. Calculate the power supplied.

....

....

....

....

....

4. A starter motor develops a lock torque of 19.5 Nm with 460 A at 7 V. What power is it consuming.

....

....

....

....

....

5. Calculate the amount of current used by a 12 V 48 W headlamp bulb.

....

....

....

....

....

6. Calculate the amount of current used by two 12 V 54 W headlamp bulbs.

....

....

....

....

....

7. Calculate the total power and current flow when two 12 V 60 W headlamp bulbs, five 12 V 6 W side lamp bulbs, two 12 V 21 W flasher bulbs and three 12 V 3 W panel-light bulbs are in operation at the same time.

....

....

....

....

....

....

....

....

....

8. A motor vehicle operating on a 12 V system has the following lamps operating:
two 54 W headlamps,
five 6 W side and tail lamps,
two 48 W spotlamps.
The engine is running and the ignition system takes 6 A.
If the alternator is generating a current of 35 A, calculate the power:
(a) required to operate the components,
(b) required to turn the alternator,
(c) available to charge the battery.

....

....

....

....

....

....

....

....

3.4 VOLTAGE DROP

In all electrical systems the voltage (or pressure) across the component being operated — say the starter motor — is always less than the voltage at the generating source, in this case the battery. This is because some electrical pressure is required to force the current along the cable from the battery to the starter motor.

Define:

e.m.f. ....

....

p.d. ....

....

v.d. ....

....

The voltage drop in a circuit   v.d. =

Example

The open circuit battery voltage is 12 V. When the starter motor is operated the battery voltage is reduced to 9.5 V; determine the v.d.

v.d. = ...

Alternatively if the internal resistance of a component is known, the v.d. may be found by applying Ohm's Law.

$$V = I \times R$$

or v.d. = ...

Example

Calculate the v.d. in a starter cable when the internal resistance of the cable is 0.0012 Ω when carrying a current of 220 A.

V = ...

Problems

1. A battery has a p.d. of 9.75 V when operating a starter motor. The battery e.m.f. is 12.5 V. Determine the v.d. when the starter is in operation.

....

....

....

....

2. If the volt drop in a starter cable is 2.75 V and the e.m.f. is 12.85 V, determine the terminal voltage at the starter motor when it is in operation.

....

....

....

....

3. Calculate the v.d. in a starter cable if the internal resistance of the cable is 0.0016 Ω when carrying a current of 284 A.

....

....

....

....

....

4. A 12 V battery gave an open-circuit voltage of 12.77 V.
   When supplying a current of 18 A the terminal voltage drops to 12.05 V. Calculate the internal resistance of the battery.

....

....

....

....

....

5. The leads from a 12 V battery to a starter motor have a total resistance of 0.005 Ω. What p.d. will be required to send a current of 200 A through these leads? What would be the voltage at the starter motor terminals in this case?

....

....

....

....

....

....

....

RESISTANCE OF ELECTRICAL CABLES

If the length of cable supplying current to a component is doubled, the internal resistance of the cable will

....

that is, length is directly ....

.... to the resistance.

Problems

1. If the resistance of a wire is 0.009 Ω when it is 6 m long, what will be its resistance when it is 72 m long?

....

....

....

2. If 5 m of starter cable has a resistance of 0.025 Ω, calculate the resistance of 30 m of this cable.

....

....

....

3. Calculate the resistance of 1.5 m of cable if 60 m has a resistance of 0.05 Ω.

....

....

....

If the cable's cross-sectional area is doubled, the internal resistance will

....

that is, cross-sectional area is ....

.... to the resistance.

Problems

1. A cable has a resistance of 0.04 Ω and an area of 15 mm². If the area is increased to 90 mm², what would be the resistance?

....

....

....

2. A cable has an area of 2 mm² and a resistance of 0.03 Ω. If the area is increased to 72 mm², what would be the resistance?

....

....

....

3. A cable has a cross-sectional area of 105 mm² and a resistance of 0.005 Ω. What would be the resistance if the area was only 7 mm²?

....

....

SHORT AND OPEN CIRCUITS

Two simple light circuits are shown, one is an open circuit, the other has a short circuit.
Identify, giving reasons for choice.

The circuit ....

....

....

The circuit ....

....

What could be a probable cause and effect of the short circuit?

....

....

....

A common fault of electrical circuits is unwanted series resistance. What is meant by this term and how does the resistance occur?

....

....

....

....

....

....

....

....

ELECTRICAL TEST EQUIPMENT

Ammeter

The ammeter measures current flow in amperes. How is an ammeter connected into the circuit to measure current flow?

Voltmeter

The voltmeter measures electrical pressure in volts. How is a voltmeter connected into the circuit?

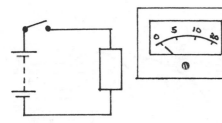

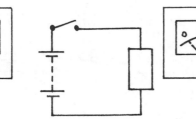

Draw an ammeter in position on the circuit shown above.

Draw a voltmeter in position on the circuit shown above.

What type of ammeter and voltmeter are shown above?

....

When testing electronic circuits meters having a very high input impedance (resistance) are preferred. These are digital meters.

Ohmmeter

The ohmmeter looks similar to the two other meters shown above, it measures electrical resistance of circuits or components in circuits. What is a feature of the ohmmeter which does not occur with the other types of meter?

....
....
....
....

What precautions must be taken before checking a component?

....
....

Multimeters

All multimeters will measure voltage (both a.c. and d.c.), current and resistance.

Examine the type of meter used in the workshop, and sketch its face in the block opposite naming the important features.

Meter   Name/number

....
....

Below is shown a multimeter connected to electronic equipment. State to which meter the settings will be connected and the type of test being carried out.

....
....

ELECTRICAL TESTING

Describe how the resistance of a component should be tested using an ohmmeter or multimeter.

1. ....

2. ....

....

3. ....

....

Select FIVE electrical/electronic components and measure their resistance.

COMPONENTS					
RESISTANCE					

How can current flow through a circuit be tested?

....

....

Describe how a voltmeter should be used to check the continuity of a circuit for high resistance.

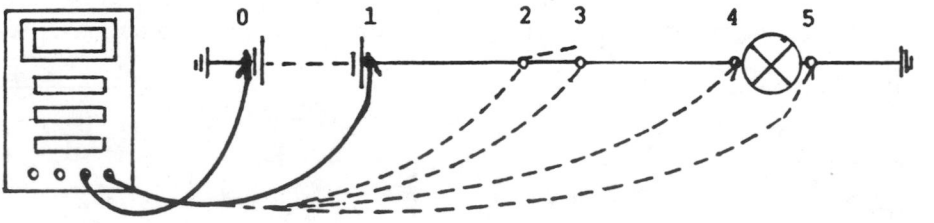

....

....

....

....

Which meter may be used to check the continuity of a non-live circuit? ....

PRECAUTIONS WHEN TESTING OR REPLACING COMPONENTS

Describe any special precautions to be observed when:

1. Disconnecting electrical components ....

....

....

....

....

....

2. Replacing components/units ....

....

....

....

....

....

....

3. Testing components ....

....

....

....

....

What faults are especially dangerous to electronic components?

1. ....

2. ....

....

GLOSSARY OF TECHNICAL
TERMS AND ABBREVIATIONS

As with any specialised subject, motor-vehicle technology has its own 'language'. This chapter has been compiled to help you understand some of the more commonly used terms and abbreviations.

COMMON ABBREVIATIONS

Since public interest in motor vehicles is so widespread, quite a lot of the abbreviations are not so precise or standardised as those used in the strictly technical sense. However, the following will often be encountered in such as manufacturers' brochures, manuals and in general conversation.

A (amp)	Ampere
ac	Alternating current
AF	American Fine (thread)
Ah (amphr)	Ampere hour
bdc	Bottom dead centre
bhp	Brake horsepower
BSF	British Standard Fine (thread)
BSW	British Standard Whitworth (thread)
cb	Contact breaker
cc	Cubic centimetre
dc	Direct current
DoT	Department of Transport
emf	Electromotive force
hp	Horsepower
HT	High tension
ifs	Independent front suspension
irs	Independent rear suspension
k/h (km/h)	Kilometres per hour
LT	Low tension
mpg	Miles per gallon
mph	Miles per hour
ohc	Overhead camshaft
ohv	Overhead valve
psi	Pounds per square inch
rpm (rev/min)	Revolutions per minute
SW	Switch
tdc	Top dead centre
UNC	Unified Course (thread)
UNF	Unified Fine (thread)

GLOSSARY

additives   Chemicals added to oil and petrol to give them special properties.

air filter   Usually found on top of the carburettor. It filters the air before it enters the engine.

air vent   Small hole in the top of a fluid reservoir, float chamber or tank to allow atmospheric pressure to act on fluid.

air-cooled engine   Engine cooled only by air which is blown over finned cylinder surfaces, usually by a fan.

alignment   Usually describes adjustment of front wheels, also the setting of headlamp beams.

alternator   Engine-driven electric generator which creates alternating current and rectifies it to direct current. It is more efficient at low engine speeds than a dynamo.

ammeter   Instrument that measures the amount of electric current passing to and from the car's battery. It is often marked with a + and − for charging or discharging.

automatic choke   Device in the carburettor which controls the choke flap according to the engine temperature, to provide a rich mixture for starting and an increasingly weak mixture as the engine warms up.

automatic transmission   Gearbox that alters the gear ratio automatically to suit car speed and load. It also eliminates the need for manual clutch and gear lever.

axle   Transverse beam which carries the wheels and supports the body via springs.

ball joint   Method of joining two components end to end so that they can pivot in any direction relative to each other.

beam axle   Rigid transverse axle carrying wheels with no independent suspension.

bearing   Device for supporting a rotating shaft or moving component with the minimum of friction and wear.

bevel gears   Conical-shaped gears which permit transmission through 90°, as in the final drive.

big end   Larger end of the connecting rod mounted on the crankpin of the crankshaft.

big-end bearing   Material between the connecting rod big end and the crankpin.

bore   Diameter of any hole, but especially used to describe internal diameter of a cylinder.

bottom dead centre Lowest point of the piston's travel in the cylinder, at the bottom of its stroke.

brake back plate Describes the plate of a drum-brake assembly which is fixed and which carries the brake shoes.

brake drums The drums are fixed to the road wheels and rotate with them. Shoes inside the drums are pressed against them, so that the friction slows and eventually stops the wheels.

brake fluid The hydraulic fluid used in the braking system in order to transfer energy from the pressing of the brake pedal to the operation of the discs or drums.

brake shoe Metal segmentally-shaped components with friction material on the outer face of the curve. Used inside the drum of a drum brake, they are forced apart to brake the wheel.

breather An opening or vent used to relieve internal pressure or to allow air to enter a space, e.g. gearboxes have breathers.

brushes Pads made of carbon that transfer the current from the rotating armature of an alternator or the rotating commutator of a dynamo.

bush A sleeve, usually of metal, rubber or plastic, which is fitted into a bore and acts as a bearing.

butterfly, or butterfly valve Used to describe the throttle valve in the main air vent of the carburettor, which is a disc of metal that can be rotated to control the air flow and so the speed of the engine.

by-pass filter A type of oil filter in the engine's lubricating system which receives some of the oil from the pump and filters it before it is pumped to the engine. (Not common on modern engines.)

cam A rounded wedge, usually on a shaft, which will push and release another component as the shaft rotates, e.g. the engine camshaft which opens and closes the valves.

cam follower Any component that transmits the motion of the cam to the next component in line,

like a push-rod or valve stem.

camber angle The angle by which wheels deviate from 90° to the road, looking from the front. Positive camber means that the wheels are further apart at the top; negative camber means they are further apart at the bottom.

camshaft The shaft which is rotated by the engine and actuates the valve gear. It may also drive the distributor and fuel pump.

capacity Usually expressed in cubic centimetres, the capacity of an engine is the volume swept by all the pistons in the engine over the length of their travel from bdc to tdc.

carburettor A device to meter the amounts of fuel and air drawn into an engine, and mix them together.

clutch A part of the transmission which enables the driver to move the vehicle away smoothly from rest; disconnects engine from gearbox during gear changing, and gives temporary neutral.

clutch drag Inefficiency of clutch disengagement usually caused by faulty adjustment or mechanical wear.

clutch lining Friction material bonded or riveted to either side of the clutch-driven plate.

clutch pressure plate Heavy metal disc which forces the clutch-driven plate against the flywheel.

clutch slip Used to describe the effect of the failure of the pressure plate to grip the driven plate properly. Usually caused by oil contamination or excessive wear.

clutch-driven plate A metal disc mounted on the shaft leading to the gearbox. It has friction linings on its face which transmit drive from the flywheel.

coil Two windings of copper wire housed together and providing the high voltage current necessary for causing a spark at the spark-plug gap. It does this by collapsing the magnetic field created by low-voltage current flowing through the outer (shorter) winding

and so inducing high voltage from the inner (longer) winding.

coil ignition Describes an ignition system which employs a coil to induce high voltage.

compression ratio The ratio of the volume of mixture above the piston at the bottom of its travel compared with the volume above it at the top. The higher the ratio, the more the power output of the engine. Average-sized car engines will have a compression ratio of 8.5 : 1 to 9.5 : 1.

compression-ignition engine An engine in which combustion is achieved by the heat generated by compressed air, i.e. the diesel engine. In this, a charge of atomised fuel is injected into the hot compressed air in the combustion chamber, so effecting ignition.

connecting rod The forged steel component that joins the piston to the crankshaft, transferring the up-and-down motion of the piston to the rotary motion of the crankshaft.

constant-mesh gears Describes gears on the gearbox which are always meshed together.

constant-velocity joint A type of universal joint which gives a smooth drive on front-wheel drive cars even when steering on full lock.

contact breaker A switch in the coil ignition system which constantly breaks and remakes the low-voltage current, so causing the current in the coil to collapse and provide high-voltage current. It is operated mechanically, usually by a cam mounted on the distributor spindle. Also referred to as 'points'.

control box Part of the electrical charging system with three functions together in a sealed box; automatic cut-out, voltage regulator and current control.

crankpins Bearing surfaces of the crankshaft which carry the big-end bearings of the connecting rods.

cylinder block   Iron or aluminium alloy cast block housing the cylinders and their water-cooling passages, or fins for air-cooled engines. On water-cooled engines it is usually one piece with the crankcase.

cylinder head   Cast iron or aluminium piece which fits on the cylinder block and which contains the combustion chambers and the valve gear, as well as the continuation of water passages or finning.

cylinder liners   Usually cast-iron sleeves which fit inside the cylinder block where the piston does not run directly in the block itself, although they can be used to replace worn cylinder walls. Dry liners are surrounded by the metal of the block, whereas wet liners are exposed directly to the coolant.

cylinder-head gasket   Thin layer, sometimes of metal with asbestos, used to prevent leakage of gas between the cylinder block and cylinder head. It also stops water from the water passages getting into the cylinders.

damper   A device used to control the movement of the piston in a variable-jet carburettor, by damping the action, thus smoothing out the response to the throttle. Also a term used to describe a shock absorber in a suspension system.

decarbonising   A process for removing the carbon deposits that can build up on piston crowns, valve ends and inside the combustion chamber.

detergent oil   Specially formulated engine oil that has an additive to hold sludge-forming material in suspension, preventing it from settling, and so keeping the engine interior clean.

differential   A set of gears (usually in a housing bolted to the crown wheel) which enables the driven wheels to rotate at different speeds (as when cornering) but still receive equal torque.

direct current   Electric current which only flows in one direction, such as that produced by a battery or supplied by the alternator or dynamo.

disc brakes   A braking system which works by heavy metal discs being pinched by friction pads mounted in calipers that surround the disc. The disc is attached to the road wheel and rotates with it.

distilled water   Purified water used for topping up the battery.

distributor cap   Hard plastic moulding with connections which accept the high-voltage current from the coil, and subsequently pass it to each spark-plug lead by way of the rotor arm.

distributor drive shaft   The shaft that rotates the rotor arm and the cams which operate the contact breaker. Driven by the engine camshaft, it is geared to rotate at half engine speed.

distributor rotor arm   Resin-based plastic with a brass strip inlaid along the top. It rotates underneath the distributor cap and passes high-voltage current from the high-voltage input connection from the coil to the connectors leading to the spark plugs.

dog clutch   As with all types of clutch, these are a means of transferring drive. Projections around the edge of one half of the clutch slide into corresponding indentations on the other. Usually found in gearboxes.

drag coefficients   A measure of the resistance to air of a moving object, such as a car body.

drag-link   The rod between the drop arm of a steering box and the linkage which controls the track rod.

drain-plug   A screw-in plug found at the bottom of a component for draining fluid. Typically found in the sump, gearbox, final drive or radiator.

drive-shafts   Especially used where the shafts are not enclosed in the axle casing. They transmit the drive from the final drive to the road wheels. Another name for *half shafts*.

drop arm   Lever mounted on the steering box which is operated by the steering wheel pinion and which in turn controls the track-rod linkage.

drum brakes   A method of braking in which drums attached to the wheels are slowed by internal convex shoes lined with friction material, forced outwards by hydraulic pressure from the brake pedal assembly.

dual-braking   Two separate hydraulic braking systems fitted to provide adequate braking if one circuit should fail. These can either duplicate the whole braking system, or one front and one rear brake, diagonally opposed.

dust excluder   *See* **gaiter.**

dynamic balance   The balance of any rotating part, such as the wheels or crankshaft, while the component is revolving.

earth   The connection from any electrical component which attaches to the chassis or body to effect a completed circuit.

east – west mounting   Also known as *transverse*, this describes an engine mounted across the car instead of the more usual mounting in which the engine is in line with the car.

electrolyte   A solution of distilled water and sulphuric acid in the battery.

electronic ignition   A system of ignition in which an electronic unit triggers pulses of high-tension electrical energy to the spark plugs, so replacing the contact-breaker assembly. More efficient than the mechanical method, especially in high-performance engines.

ethylene glycol   A chemical which prevents water from freezing at the usual temperature, and is thus used in most antifreeze compounds. It is mixed with corrosion-inhibiting chemicals so that it will not attack the metal of the coolant system.

exhaust gases   The gases given off by the combustion of petrol and air. They include carbon monoxide, carbon dioxide, oxides of nitrogen, unburnt hydrocarbons and water vapour.

exhaust manifold   Cast-iron pipework of various

configurations which is bolted to the engine and which takes away the exhaust gases forced out of the cylinders.

feeler gauges   A set of hardened metal strips of varying thickness used to measure clearances in components, e.g. the gap in a spark plug.

final drive   The last phase of the transmission system. On a rear-wheel drive car this would be the crown wheel and pinion.

firing order   The order in which the cylinders of an engine reach the 'firing' or 'power' stroke.

fluid reservoir   This usually refers to a container which stores hydraulic fluid for the brake or clutch systems. (May also describe such components as a container storing windscreen-washer fluid.)

flywheel   Heavy metal disc bolted to the engine crankshaft. It smooths out the individual bursts of energy from the cylinders; forms a convenient mounting point for the clutch; and has the starter ring gear around its outer edge.

four-stroke cycle (Otto cycle)   The basic sequence of operations of the internal combustion engine. i.e.　　Induction
　　　　　　Compression
　　　　　　Power
　　　　　　Exhaust

Also known somewhat picturesquely as: 'suck', 'squeeze', 'bang', 'blow'.

free travel (free play)   The amount of 'play' or free movement in, for example, a control lever or foot pedal before it begins to take effect.

friction pads   Segments of friction material in a disc brake that are pressed on to the disc to effect braking.

front-wheel drive   A transmission system in which the engine drives the front wheels of the car.

fuel pump (petrol pump)   A pump which draws fuel from the tank and delivers it to the engine.

full-flow filter   A type of oil filter through which all the engine oil must pass before it reaches the engine bearings.

fuse   A thin piece of wire of known electrical-carrying capacity which is incorporated in a circuit in order to protect it. It should be the first part of the circuit to break in the event of an overload.

gaiter (dust excluder)   A synthetic rubber flexible shroud or cover used to keep out dust and grit from such components as a steering ball joint.

gap   This usually refers to such a gap as the distance between the contact-breaker points, or between the spark-plug electrodes.

gasket   A thin sheet of material, such as copper, cork, rubber or paper, which is sandwiched between two close-fitting components so as to prevent leakage of any kind.

gear ratio   Relative speeds at which two gears revolve. If the input gear rotates twice as fast as the output one, the gear ratio is 2 : 1.

gearbox   Can be applied to almost any housing (or box) containing gears. Usually it refers to the transmission gears which are controlled by the driver in accordance with conditions of load, speed and gradient. It then also provides a means of reverse and a permanent position of neutral.

generator (dynamo)   A device which converts mechanical energy into electrical energy. One of its prime functions is to charge the battery. An alternator performs the same function.

glass-reinforced plastic (glass-fibre)   Often known simply as GRP, this is a laminated material used in the manufacture and repair of some car bodies.

independent suspension   Each wheel has its own spring and linkage with the car body, allowing it to move without influencing another wheel.

inlet manifold   Pipework (often aluminium) which conducts petrol/air mixture from the carburettor to the engine.

jets   Generally carburettor components with small-diameter holes drilled in them. They are used to control the amount of fuel that can pass through them. Windscreen washers also have jets to control fluid flow.

king pin   A hardened steel pin about which a front wheel pivots. On most modern cars it has been replaced by two ball joints which give the same steering effect but also allow for movement of the independent front suspension.

leaf spring   A long, fairly narrow spring consisting of one, or more, flat blades (or leaves). Common on commercial vehicles and the rear suspension of many cars.

manifold   *See* **inlet manifold** and **exhaust manifold**.

master cylinder   The main pressure pump of a hydraulic brake (or clutch) system.

oil seal   A component used to prevent oil (or grease) leaking out along a shaft protruding from a housing, e.g. a crankshaft where it passes through its crankcase. Usually made of synthetic rubber.

overall gear ratio   Number of engine revolutions per single revolution of the driving wheels. (Gearbox ratio × final drive ratio.)

piston   Forms a movable gas and oil-tight seal in the engine cylinder. It transmits, via the gudgeon (or piston) pin, the force of the expanding gases to the small end of the connecting rod. Most pistons are made of aluminium. Pistons of different design are used in hydraulic braking systems.

points   *See* contact breaker and spark plug.

pressure cap   This is usually the radiator filler-cap. It also maintains the liquid in the cooling system under pressure and so raises the temperature at which it boils.

propellor shaft (prop-shaft)   The tubular shaft which in a front-engined, rear-drive vehicle transmits torque from the gearbox to the rear axle. It is usually fitted with two universal joints and a sliding joint.

radiator   The device used for lowering the temperature of the coolant which has absorbed heat from the engine.

rocker cover   A deeply-domed cover (or lid) which encloses the valve mechanism on top of an overhead valve engine.

seal   *See* **oil seal.** 'Seal' is sometimes used instead of the word 'gasket'.

servo (brake)   A form of auxiliary power used to assist the driver when applying the brakes. In most cars the auxiliary power is provided via vacuum existing in the inlet manifold.

shock absorber   Damper to control body movement in relation to the suspension, preventing continuous bouncing on the springs.

silencer   The part of an exhaust system designed to reduce exhaust noise. It has a larger volume than the exhaust pipe and contains baffle plates and sound-deadening materials which reduce resonance. A faulty system, allowing carbon monoxide fumes into the car, can be lethal.

slave cylinder   A cylinder at the end of the hydraulic brake or clutch system which converts the hydraulic pressure back into mechanical effort, and operates the brakes or clutch.

slow running   Also called either 'tick-over' or 'idling', it is the low speed at which the engine runs when the vehicle is not moving and the accelerator is not depressed.

small end   The smaller end of the connecting rod which is connected to the piston by the gudgeon pin (piston pin).

solenoid   A tightly wound coil of wire with a central, movable iron core. When current is passed through the winding, the magnetic field produced causes the core to be pulled into the winding. The moving core can close large-area contacts (as in a starter solenoid).

spark plug   The component providing the insulated spark gap within the combustion chamber. It has a metal body, which screws into the engine cylinder head, and a central electrode insulated by ceramic material, which carries the high-tension current to the gap. The gap between the spark plug's two electrodes is usually in the region of 0.025 in. (twenty-five 'thou') or 0.6 mm and this is where the high-tension current from the ignition coil must jump across, creating a spark and igniting the fuel/air mixture.

starter motor   A small, but powerful, electric motor used to start the engine. When activated, it engages a small pinion gear with a toothed ring on the engine flywheel.

starter ring (ring-gear)   The toothed ring fitted to the outer edge of the flywheel with which the pinion of the starter motor engages.

stub axle   A short fixed shaft on which the non-driven hub of a car wheel revolves on bearings.

synchromesh   A component which causes two gears to revolve at the same speed before they are meshed together, in order to prevent clashing. The effect is achieved by using a cone clutch to synchronise the speed of rotation of one gear with the other.

tappet   A colloquial term for a follower which bears on the engine camshaft. It is usually a short, bucket-shaped cylinder, the flat end of which bears against the cam. The open end holds a push-rod or a valve stem (if an overhead camshaft system is fitted).

thermostat   A temperature-sensitive valve placed in the cooling system between the top of the engine and the radiator. The thermostat is closed when the engine is cold, allowing the coolant in the engine to warm up quickly. As an operating temperature of about 85° is reached, it opens to allow the passage of coolant through the radiator.

torque   A twisting or turning force. It can be applied in very many ways. For example, the firing strokes exert (via the pistons and connecting rods) a force to turn the engine camshaft so as to drive the car. Equally, torque is applied when a nut is released (or tightened) by means of a spanner.

torsion bar   Steel bar used in suspension system of some models instead of coil spring. The bar is fixed at one end and twisted at the other by means of a lever attached to the wheel.

universal joint   A coupling between two shafts which provides a positive drive, while permitting some angular deflection between the shafts.

valves (engine)   Flat-topped, mushroom-shaped devices which open and close the inlet and exhaust ports in the combustion chamber. They work in special bearings called valve guides.

wheel cylinder   *See* **slave cylinder.**

The Editor's thanks are extended to:

    Automobile Association
    Burmah–Castrol (UK) Ltd
    Renault UK Ltd
    Royal Automobile Club

for help in compiling the Glossary.